ABSTRACT SET THEORY

STUDIES IN LOGIC

AND

THE FOUNDATIONS OF MATHEMATICS

Editors

L. E. J. BROUWER, *Laren (N.H.)*

A. HEYTING, *Amsterdam*

A. ROBINSON, *Los Angeles*

P. SUPPES, *Stanford*

NORTH-HOLLAND PUBLISHING COMPANY

AMSTERDAM

ABSTRACT SET THEORY

THIRD, REVISED EDITION

ABRAHAM A. FRAENKEL

Late Professor of Mathematics
Hebrew University, Jerusalem

1966

NORTH-HOLLAND PUBLISHING COMPANY
AMSTERDAM

First edition 1953
Second, revised edition 1961
Third, revised edition 1966

PRINTED IN THE NETHERLANDS

FROM THE PREFACE TO THE SECOND EDITION

The book is chiefly intended for undergraduate students of mathematics, for graduates in philosophy, and for highschool teachers. Regarding the method of exposition, a middle course has been steered between Cantor's naive attitude prevailing in most current textbooks and a formal axiomatic development. Zermelo's axioms in a slightly improved form are introduced at suitable junctures, accompanied with appropriate arguments justifying them; the axiom of choice appears relatively late for obvious didactic reasons. Yet the derivation of the material from the axioms is explicitly carried out in those cases only where it seemed desirable as a matter of principle. The antinomies are merely touched.

Even freshmen will understand the book, provided they take pains to advance from the easy arguments of the first sections to the more abstract concepts and proofs of the later ones. Before entering a rather difficult proof the student should realize what is its aim, why a proof is necessary, and which is the nature of the difficulties to be overcome. The method of exposition in the book is intended to facilitate this approach.

The text should be completely comprehensible without the footnotes. Their task is to supply further details and literature regarding special problems, to furnish historical information, and to provide advanced readers with stimuli and bibliographical material for research problems.

Jerusalem, December 1959 (40 years after the first publication of *Einleitung in die Mengenlehre*)

ABRAHAM A. FRAENKEL

PREFACE TO THE THIRD EDITION

The second edition, published in 1961, was out of print in 1965. In this new edition changes have been limited to modifications in some 30 pages.

The principal changes are: first, Paul J. Cohen's discoveries regarding the continuum problem (1963) are mentioned in short, especially on p. 229; second, two remarks of A. Church, regarding the equality between sets and the Cartesian product, were taken into account. Furthermore, a supplementary bibliography was added, containing mostly literature which appeared during the last few years, and the Index of Authors was renewed.

The references to the book *Foundations of Set Theory* relate to the edition of 1958 (in the Bibliography, Fraenkel and Bar-Hillel). However, late in 1966 a completely revised edition of this book, with A. Lévy as co-author, will appear; then the references to the *chapters* will still hold but not to the *pages*.

Jerusalem, summer 1965   ABRAHAM A. FRAENKEL

CONTENTS

PREFACE V

INTRODUCTION 1

CHAPTER I

FOUNDATIONS. THE CONCEPT OF CARDINAL NUMBER

§ 1. EXAMPLES. CANTOR'S SET CONCEPT 4

§ 2. FUNDAMENTAL CONCEPTS. FINITE AND INFINITE SETS 12
1. The membership relation. Equality 12. — 2. Subsets 13. — 3. Union,
Intersection, Difference 18. — Mapping and Equivalence 23. — Finite
and Infinite Sets 27. — Exercises 32.

§ 3. DENUMERABLE SETS 33
1. Denumerability 33. — 2. Simplest Examples and Theorems 34. — 3. The
Set of all Rationals 36. — 4. The Set of all Algebraic Numbers 39. — 5.
Applications to Infinite Sets in General 43. — Exercises 46.

§ 4. THE CONTINUUM. TRANSFINITE CARDINALS 47
1. Further Examples of Equivalent Sets 47. — 2. Proof that the Continuum
is not Denumerable 50. — 3. Remarks and Supplements to the Proof 53. —
4. Extensions of Theorem 1. The Transcendental Numbers 56. — 5. The
Concept of Cardinal Number. The Cardinals $\aleph_0$ and $\aleph$ 58. — 6. Further
Analysis of the Concept of Cardinal 61. — 7. The Set of all Functions and
its Cardinal 63. — Exercises 64.

CHAPTER II

EQUIVALENCE AND CARDINALS

§ 5. ARRANGEMENT OF CARDINALS BY MAGNITUDE 66
1. Definition of Order 66. — 2. Immediate Consequences 68. — 3. Cantor's
Theorem. The Power-Set 69. — 4. The Equivalence Theorem 72. — 5. The
Problem of Comparability 78. — Exercises 78.

§ 6. ADDITION AND MULTIPLICATION OF CARDINALS 79
1. Introduction 79. — 2. Union of Sets 81. — 3. Addition of Cardinals 82.
— 4. Formal Laws. Examples 84. — 5. Cartesian Product. The Axiom of
Choice 87. — 6. Multiplication of Cardinals and its Formal Laws 91. —
7. Inverse Operations. Inequalities 96. — 8. Examples of the Multiplication
of Cardinals. The Cardinal of a Two-Dimensional Continuum 100. —
9. Intersection of Sets. Boolean Algebra 105. — Exercises 108.

§ 7. EXPONENTIATION OF CARDINALS. TRANSFINITE NUMBERS AND INFINITES-
IMALS 109
1. Exponentation as Repeated Multiplication 109. — 2. The Insertion-Set
110. — 3. The Power-Set 112. — 4. Formal Laws of Exponentiation 113. —
5. The Power-Set of a Denumerable Set 115. — 6. Further Examples of
Exponentiation 116. — 7. The Problem of Infinitesimals 120. — 8. Non-
Archimedean Domains 122. — Exercises 124.

CHAPTER III

ORDER AND SIMILARITY. ORDER-TYPES AND ORDINALS

§ 8. ORDERED SETS. SIMILARITY AND ORDER-TYPES 126
1. Introduction 126. — 2. Order-Relation and Ordered Sets 128. — 3.
Similarity 134. — 4. Order-Types 138. — 5. Addition of Two Order-
Types 141. — 6. General Addition of Order-Types 144. — 7. On the
Multiplication of Order-Types 149. — Exercises 154.

§ 9. LINEAR SETS OF POINTS 155
1. Dense or Continuous Ordered Sets 155. — 2. Examples 157. — 3. The
Type η of the Set of Rationals 160. — 4. The Type λ of the Linear Continuum 163. — 5. Accumulation Point and Related Concepts 167. — 6.
Examples 170. — Exercises 173.

§ 10. GENERAL THEORY OF WELL-ORDERED SETS. FINITE SETS 174
1. The Concept of Well-Ordered Set 174. — 2. Transfinite Induction 178.
— 3. Comparability of Well-Ordered Sets 183. — 4. Addition and Multiplication. Ordinals 186. — 5. Elementary Properties of Well-Ordered Sets
189. — 6. On Finite Sets and their Ordinals 192. — Exercises 194.

§ 11. ORDINALS AND ALEPHS. WELL-ORDERING AND COMPARABILITY . . . 195
1. Arrangement of Ordinals by Magnitude 195. — 2. The Comparability
of Ordinals 197. — 3. Exponentiation. The Series of Ordinals 202. — 4.
Arithmetic of Ordinals 208. — 5. Alephs, Number-Classes, Initial Numbers 215. — 6. The Well-Ordering Theorem 222. — 7. The Comparability
of Plain Sets and Cardinals 227. — Exercises 233.

§ 12. THE ORIGIN AND THE SIGNIFICANCE OF SET THEORY 236

BIBLIOGRAPHY 241

SUPPLEMENTARY INDEX FOR THE BIBLIOGRAPHY 268

SUPPLEMENTARY BIBLIOGRAPHY 270

LIST OF LITERATURE FOR READERS OF *Foundations of Set Theory* 272

INDEX OF AUTHORS 289

INDEX OF TERMS 293

SYMBOLS 297

INTRODUCTION

"I protest ... against the use of infinite magnitude as if it were something finished; this use is not admissible in mathematics. The infinite is only a *façon de parler*: one has in mind limits approached by certain ratios as closely as desirable while other ratios may increase indefinitely." [1] C. F. Gauss, presumably the foremost mathematician of the 19th century, expressed this view in 1831 in reply to an idea of Schumacher's and hereby uttered a *horror infiniti* which up to almost the end of the century was the common attitude of mathematicians and seemed unassailable considering the authority of Gauss. Mathematics should deal with finite magnitudes and finite numbers only while the treatment of actual infinity, whether infinitely great or small, might be left to philosophy.

It was the mathematician Georg Cantor (1845–1918) [2] who dared to fight this attitude and, in the opinion of the majority of 20th century mathematicians, has succeeded in the task of bestowing legitimacy upon infinitely great magnitude. Besides the creative intuition and the artistic power of production [3] which guided Cantor in his work, an enormous amount of energy and perseverance was required to carry through the new ideas, which for two decades were rejected by his contemporaries [4] with the arguments that they were obscure or meaningless or false or

---

[1] *Briefwechsel Gauss–Schumacher*, vol. II (1860), p. 269; *Gauss' Werke*, vol. VIII (1900), p. 216.

[2] Cf. the biography Fraenkel 30 and the edition of Cantor's Collected Papers (including notes of E. Zermelo and a shorter biography) Cantor 32; cf. also Schoenflies 22 and 28, Ternus 29, Cantor-Dedekind 37.

All literature references in this book, composed of the author's name and the year of publication, apply to the Bibliography at the end of the book. In the dates of the 20th century the initial digits 19 are suppressed. — The literature references are given for the benefit of readers interested in the sources or in additional details; the text is self-contained without them.

[3] Cf. the motto annexed to the (Latin) *Habilitationsschrift* of 1869 by which he won the admission as a lecturer at the University of Halle: *Eodem modo literis atque arte animos delectari posse.* (Cantor 32, p. 62.)

[4] Especially by Kronecker. However, two others of the leading mathematicians of that time, Weierstrass and (contrary to an erroneous tradition) Hermite, turned their initial distrust soon into appreciation and even admiration. Still before, Mittag-Leffler had given Cantor active support by inducing Poincaré and others to translate Cantor's papers into French (cf. Mittag-Leffler 28); these translations, published in

1

"brought into the world a hundred years too early" [1]). Not only Gauss and other outstanding mathematicians were quoted in evidence against actual infinity but also leading philosophical authorities such as Aristotle, Decartes, Spinoza and modern logicians [2]). Set theory was even charged with violating the principles of religion, an accusation rejected by Cantor with particular vigor and minuteness [3]). Only in the last years of the 19th century, when Cantor had just ceased engaging in mathematical research, did set theory begin to infiltrate many branches of mathematics [4]).

A chief purpose of the present book is to show how definite and distinct infinitely great magnitudes can be introduced and handled in mathematics — another evidence of the *free creation* which is characteristic of mathematics to a higher extent than of other sciences. It is no mere accident that at the birth of set theory (1883) the slogan was coined: the very essence of mathematics is its freedom [5]).

---

volume 2 of *Acta Mathematica*, contributed much to propagate Cantor's ideas.

The first applications (cf. also below, § 12) to the theory of functions and to geometry are found in Hurwitz 1883, Poincaré 1883, Mittag-Leffler 1884, Scheeffer 1884 and 1884a. Bendixson's papers of the same years (1883, 1883a, 1884, 1884a) took a course parallel to Cantor's work.

[1]) According to Cantor–Stäckel 1897, this was the argument with which the *Acta Mathematica*, previously so appreciative of Cantor's ideas, rejected the final exposition, which later (as Cantor 1895–97) appeared in the *Mathematische Annalen*. Even the papers 1874 and 1878 had only been published after much hesitation and delay by Kronecker (cf. Schoenflies 22, p. 99). As late as 1908 Cantor complained, in a letter to W. H. Young, of the lack of appreciation given to his work in Germany, as in contrast to Great Britain (Young 26, p. 422).

[2]) A few important philosophers who *affirmed* actual infinity were overlooked by Cantor, in particular Lucretius (cf. Keyser 18) and Chasdai Crescas (cf. Wolfson 29).

[3]) Cf. Cantor 1879–84 (particularly V), 1886, 1887–88; Gutberlet 1886 and 1919; Ternus 26. It goes without saying that the concept of infinity has its origin in *religious* thought; it was, at least within the occidental civilization, introduced into *science* only by the Greeks. In medieval scholastic theology and philosophy on the whole (not only in the treatment of infinity) one finds trains of thought which, in their subtlety and in the preference given to logical analysis over existential questions, are kindred with set-theoretical methods. In fact Cantor (and still more Bolzano, somehow his predecessor) had a good scholastic training. Cf. Isenkrahe 20, Klein 26 (pp. 52 and 56), Bodewig 32, Bocheński 34, 38, and 56.

For the history of the problem of actual infinity in general the reader is referred, also for literature, to Cohn 1896, Russell 14/26, Keyser 16, Weyl 26/49, 31, 32; for the prehistory and early history of set theory to Jourdain 05–14, Schoenflies 00–07, 13, Young–Young 06, Hessenberg 06, Cavaillès 38.

[4]) First in France, where the appendix of Couturat 1896 and the classical works Borel 1898 and Baire 1899 spread the knowledge of set theory in wide circles.

[5]) Cantor 1879–84V, p. 564; cf. the preceding paragraphs of this paper. The book edition of this paper has a foreword touching by its humility.

How distinctly the revolutionary character of his research was realized by Cantor at an early period and how confident he then was of the ultimate victory of his ideas over all objections may be gathered from the following passage which opens his decisive paper 1879–84V:

> The previous exposition (namely I–IV) of my investigations in the theory of manifolds [1]) has arrived at a spot where the continuation becomes dependent upon a generalization of the concept of real integer beyond the usual limits; a generalization which takes a direction that, as far as I know, nobody has as yet looked for.
>
> I depend upon that generalization of the number concept to such an extent that without it I should hardly be able freely to take even the least step forward in the theory of sets; may this serve as a justification or, if necessary, an apology for my introducing seemingly strange ideas into my considerations. In point of fact the venture is to generalize or to continue the series of real integers beyond the infinite. Daring as this might appear, I do express not only the hope but the firm conviction that in due time this generalization will be received as a quite simple, suitable, and natural step. Still I am well aware that by taking this step I put myself in a certain opposition to wide-spread views of the infinite in mathematics and to current opinions regarding the nature of number.

It will be up to the reader to form his own judgment, on account of the systematic development given from § 2 on, whether this generalization of the number concept is legitimate and has been sufficiently restricted to secure consistency.

---

[1]) This term *(Mannichfaltigkeit)* was earlier used by Cantor for what he later, even in the same paper, called *Menge* (set; *ensemble* in French). In English, earlier the term *aggregate* was used synonymously with *set*.

CHAPTER I

FOUNDATIONS. THE CONCEPT OF CARDINAL NUMBER

§ 1. EXAMPLES. CANTOR'S SET CONCEPT

Cantor's attempt to *define* the concept of set shall be analyzed in view of the following simple examples of sets. These informal examples do not form part of the system we are going to develop from § 2 on.

a) Consider a collection of concrete objects, for instance of the apples, oranges, etc. in a fruit shop. We may call it a set of fruit, the individual apples etc. being the members (or elements) of the set. Conceiving the collection as a new single concept is an elementary intellectual act.

We may attach to each piece of fruit a label with a number, using the positive integers 1, 2, 3, etc., in an arbitrary way, but attaching different integers to different pieces of fruit. By contemplating the set whose members are the integers used in this process we obtain a set of numbers instead of the set of fruit. Hereby a set of abstract members has been obtained; there is a definite (one-to-one) correspondence between the members of both sets by which to each piece of fruit a single number is related and conversely — up to the last integer used for labelling the fruit. Hereby, using the natural order of integers according to magnitude, we may also introduce a certain succession of the pieces of fruit whereas originally no definite succession was defined in either set.

Taking into consideration the succession thus defined or any other succession, while disregarding the nature of the members, i.e. their being pieces of fruit or integers, we obtain a scheme of order: first, second, third, etc., i.e. an ordered set of units; moreover, in both cases *the same* ordered set. If we disregard the succession also, a plain collection (set) of units evolves which determines a certain (cardinal) number, namely the number of the members contained in the collection. This number evidently is independent of whether the original members are fruit or integers.

Nothing essential is changed if in the shop there is one piece of fruit only, say one apple. We may attach the integer 1 to this apple. The set containing the apple, being an abstract concept, should be distinguished from the apple itself and the same applies to the set whose only member is the integer 1.

b) While the number of members contained in the sets just considered is finite however large our shop may be, the situation fundamentally changes if the set contains as its members *all* integers 1, 2, 3, 4, ... That is to say, every member of the set is a positive integer and each such integer is contained in the set. *This set of all positive integers* (or natural numbers) has infinitely many members and is therefore called an "infinite set", in contrast with the "finite sets" of example a) — whatever the logical meaning of the notions "finite" and "infinite" may be: cf. § 2, 5.

If in example a) we take integers as the members of the set we may designate the set by writing down all its members. While this way of completely designating a set by its members becomes impracticable if the finite set contains very many members, for an infinite set it is impossible in principle; one then uses the word "etc." or dots as above. Thus the set of all positive integers may be denoted by

$$\{1, 2, 3, 4, \ldots\} \text{ or } \{\ldots, 4, 2, 3, 1\}, \text{ etc.}$$

It is not accidental that for an example of an infinite set we have used members of a *mathematical character* (integers). In fact recent developments of science, particularly of physics and astronomy, suggest that any set whose members are drawn from nature will be finite, owing to the atomic structure of matter and energy and to the limitation of matter in nature (and possibly to the nature of the physical space itself). On the other hand, it may seem as if collecting *all* integers to a set were psychologically simpler than, say, collecting just a billion numbers — though the latter collection is finite; for in this case we contemplate a huge number of distinct individuals while the set of all integers only involves an initial number (1) and the general law of proceeding from any integer n to its successor $n + 1$.

In almost all branches of mathematics, especially in analysis (for instance, in the theory of series and in calculus, also called "infinitesimal calculus"), the term "infinite" occurs frequently. However, mostly this infinite is but a *façon de parler* (see above p. 1); the statement

$$\lim_{n \to \infty} \frac{1}{n} = 0$$

asserts nothing about infinity (as the ominous sign ∞ seems to suggest) but is just an abbreviation for the sentence: $\frac{1}{n}$ can be made to approach zero as closely as desired by sufficiently increasing the positive integer n. In contrast herewith the set of all integers is infinite (infinitely comprehensive) in a sense which is "actual" (proper) and not only "potential". (It would, however, be a fundamental mistake to deem this set infinite because the integers 1, 2, 3, ..., n, ... increase infinitely, or better, indefinitely.)

To illustrate the abyss between finiteness and actual infinity as appearing in an infinite set we may use the following utopian but would-be intuitive idea which goes back at least to E. E. Kummer. 1000 different types for consonants, vowels, digits, punctuations-marks etc. as well as for the empty space may serve as the raw material for printing books. Considering that "short" books can be extended by adding spaces and "long" books decomposed into several volumes, we may define as a *book* any distribution (with repetitions) of the types among, say, a million available spots on paper. Though most of such books are just meaningless accumulations of types and spaces, also all real books, poems, advertisements, menus, etc. published in the past or to be published in any future — among them the Bible, Euclid, Shakespeare's dramas, logarithm tables, reports on the first manned flight to the Moon — constitute each a "book".

The "Universal Library" of all such books, even if printed on the thinnest paper available, would fill the universe beyond the farthest visible stars; nevertheless the Library constitutes a finite set of books, containing exactly $1000^{1,000,000}$ volumes.

Hence, adding the utopian assumption that there were infinitely many celestial bodies (say, corresponding to all positive integers) where intelligent beings lived and wrote books on mathematics, we should conclude that upon infinitely many different stars identical mathematical books with the same author, publishing firm, even the same misprints ought to appear; for all books — at least one mathematical book for each star — are contained in the Universal Library which contains a finite number only of *different books*.

c) Draw an arbitrary segment (see fig. 1) and denote its middle by P_1.

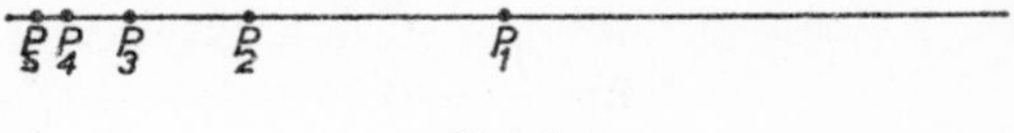

Fig. 1

Bisect one of the halves (say, the left-hand half as in fig. 1), calling its middle P_2, and proceed so indefinitely, denoting the middles of the left halves by $P_3, P_4, \ldots$; the nth step, where n denotes any positive integer, will then produce a point P_n and on its left a segment whose length is $\frac{1}{2^n}$ of the original segment.

The plain (un-ordered) set of all points P_n differs from the set of all positive integers (example b)) only by the nature of the members, as we see by relating the point P_n to the integer n. Even conceived as ordered sets, both sets yield the same scheme of order if the succession of integers is taken from smaller to greater numbers and the succession of points in fig. 1 from the right to the left.

We may also interpret fig. 1 as a possible scheme for the *race between Achilles and the Tortoise*, which has proven stimulating in mathematics, physics, and philosophy from its invention by Zenon's Eleatic School in the fifth century B.C. to our days [1]).

For this purpose we may conceive the right-hand end of the original segment as the starting-post of Achilles, P_1 as the starting-post of the Tortoise, and the segment from P_n to P_{n+1} as the nth step in the Tortoise's race. Also the set whose members are all these *segments* is an infinite set of the same kind as the set of all positive integers or of all points P_n.

d) The set considered in b) is certainly included in the *set of all real numbers*. Postponing further treatment of the concept of real number to §§ 4 and 9, we here only remark that a real number is either *rational*, i.e. of the form $\frac{m}{n}$ (where n is a positive integer and m any integer), or else an *irrational* real number. The integers are the rationals of the form $m = \frac{m}{1}$ where m is positive, negative, or 0.

A set of geometrical nature which is closely related to the set of all

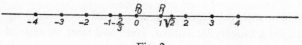

Fig. 2

---

[1]) There exists a multitude of literature dealing with this race. A few of the more recent treatments are: Russell 03 (pp. 346 ff.) and Hasse–Scholz 28 for the mathematical, Morris 29, Weiss 38 (pp. 232 ff.), Shiraishi 54, Grünbaum 55 for the philosophical viewpoint.

real numbers is obtained as follows. On a given straight line (fig. 2) we choose first an arbitrary *point* P_0 of the line to be also denoted by 0, secondly one of the two possible directions on the line to be called the *positive direction* (in fig. 2 the direction rightwards), thirdly an arbitrary *unit of length*. Proceeding from 0 in the positive direction by the unit we reach a point P_1 which shall be denoted by 1; through laying off further units we obtain points 2, 3, ... corresponding to the positive integers, while by proceeding from 0 in the negative direction, i.e. opposite to the positive, we reach points to be denoted by $-1, -2, -3, \ldots$. Furthermore we divide the unit-segment $(0,1)$ into two, three, four, ... equal parts, thus obtaining points which are denoted by $\dfrac{k}{n}$ $(0 < k < n)$; by transferring the same division to all other segments $(m-1, m)$ we arrive at all *rational points* $\dfrac{m}{n}$. However, for a rather "natural" conception of the notion *point of a line* (see § 9, 1) the rational points are not sufficient; by adding others, the so-called *irrational points* (among them, for instance, the point $\sqrt{2}$), the *set of all points* of the line is established.

The concept "point of a line" is hereby extended just so as to relate a single point to each real number and conversely. This allows us alternatively to use the set of all real numbers and the set of all points of a line *(line of numbers)*. Our correspondence includes a corresponding *order* if the real numbers are arranged according to magnitude and the points in fig. 2 in the direction from the left to the right. Cf. § 9, 1.

e) A last example serves the double purpose of illustrating certain complications of the set concept and of preparing an important application of set theory to mathematical analysis.

Every root x of the algebraic equation

$$a_0 x^n + a_1 x^{n-1} + \ldots + a_{n-1} x + a_n = 0 \quad (a_0 \neq 0)$$

with a positive integral degree n and integral coefficients a_k ($k = 0, 1, \ldots, n$) is called an *algebraic number*. Here and later we restrict ourselves, for the mere sake of simplicity, to *real* algebraic numbers, though there are also others, e.g. the roots of the equation $x^2 + 1 = 0$: imaginary and complex algebraic numbers. Certainly every rational number $\dfrac{m}{l}$ is algebraic, viz. the (only) root of $lx - m = 0$; the equation $x^2 - 2 = 0$, for instance, shows that there are also irrational algebraic numbers, in our case $\sqrt{2}$ and $-\sqrt{2}$ (see § 9). Finally, every (real) number which is not algebraic is called *transcendental*. (Here again the restriction to real numbers is not essential.)

These definitions do not reveal anything about the *existence* of transcendental numbers, a question which had remained open until the middle of the nineteenth century and which shall be answered in the affirmative in § 4. Yet even independently of the answer we may contemplate *the set of all (real) transcendental numbers;* if there existed none at all then the set in question would be empty, a case with which we shall deal in § 2. A real difficulty, however, lies in the fact that there is *no general method* of deciding, with respect to each "given" real number r (given, e.g., as a decimal or as a regular continued fraction with a law yielding the successive digits or denominators), whether r is algebraic or transcendental. While the algebraic nature of a number r can be confirmed by producing an algebraic equation satisfied by r, the proof of its transcendency is in principle an "impossibility proof", showing that r is not a root of *any* such equation; this accounts for the difficulty of the problem. In fact, only in the last decades of the nineteenth century were such well-known numbers as e and π proven to be transcendental.

Nevertheless, the notion of the set of all real transcendental numbers should be admissible and logically clear. Any given real number is either algebraic or transcendental, no matter whether we can find out which one, and in the second case it is a member of our set.

In the light of these examples we are able to appraise *Cantor's definition of the concept of set*.[1]) It runs (translated from the German): A set is a collection into a whole of definite, distinct objects of our intuition or of our thought. The objects are called the elements (members) of the set.

One can hardly regard this reference to the primitive process of collecting individual objects to a new unit as a definition proper; it rather is a paraphrase of the notion "set". Still less can the reference to our intuition and thought be considered part of a definition; it just means that *anything* may serve as a member of a set. (It might be preferable to restrict the members to mathematical objects or even to sets

---

[1]) Given in Cantor 1895, p. 481, at the start of the final exposition of his life-work in set theory. For earlier attempts to define the concept see Cantor 1879–84III, pp. 114 ff. and V, p. 587.

alone.[1])) The significant ingredients of Cantor's definition are the restrictions contained in the attributes *definite* and *distinct*.

The meaning of the latter is simple. It states that any two objects which appear as members of the same set are *different*; in other words, that an object may belong, or not belong, to a set but cannot "more than belong", for instance belong repeatedly, as may be the case in a *sequence* such as the sequence $(\frac{1}{2}, 1, \frac{2}{3}, 1, \frac{3}{4}, 1, \ldots)$ which contains the member 1 infinitely many times. (The concept of sequence is essential to analysis but far less to set theory; see p. 19.)

The meaning of "definite" is more involved. It expresses that, given a set s, it should be intrinsically settled for any possible object x whether x is a member of s or not. Here the addition "intrinsically" stresses that the intention is not to actual decidability with the present (or with any future) resources of experience or science; a definition which intrinsically settles the matter, such as the definition of "transcendental" in the case of the set of all transcendental numbers, is sufficient. To be sure, we thus essentially use the Aristotelian *principle of the excluded middle* which guarantees that for a given object there is no third case additional to those of its belonging, or not belonging, to the set in question.[2])

Yet the main question connected with the above definition is whether the reference to the logical act of collecting individuals with the purpose of forming a "higher" unit which comprehends the individuals is admissible without further ado. The philosophers and mathematicians of the nineteenth century were inclined to answer in the affirmative without even thinking it worth while to enter into a serious investigation; they would have added that this logical act was familiar to primitive, pre-scientific thinking and not given to a further analysis.[3]) Therefore it was one of the worst shocks in the history of logic and mathematics — somewhat comparable to the shock caused in the Pythagorean school of the fifth pre-Christian century by the discovery of incommensurable (irrational) magnitude, yet apparently far more resistent to possible remedies — when about the turn of the nineteenth century *contradictions and anti-*

---

[1])   See § 2, 1 and *Foundations*, pp. 28–31. Throughout the present book, *Foundations* always refers to the book *Foundations of Set Theory* (Fraenkel–Bar Hillel 58 in the Bibliography; a completely revised edition appears 1966).

[2])   Chapter IV of *Foundations* deals with *neo-intuitionism*, a mathematical doctrine which rejects the principle of the excluded middle.

[3])   For an interesting remark of Dedekind's regarding his and Cantor's conceptions of set, cf. Dedekind 30–32 III, pp. 447–449. (The remark dates from 1887.)

nomies of various kinds were discovered which directly or indirectly *originate from the notion of set*, i.e. from collecting individuals to a unit.

In the course of the present book we shall occasionally touch upon some of those contradictions; a more comprehensive discussion with a full bibliography is contained in Chapter One of *Foundations*.

During many decades the attempts to "improve" Cantor's definition have remained utterly unsuccessful, and it has become inevitable *to renounce a definition of the general concept of set*. The possible remedies for this situation are mainly three, namely: to conceive and define the concept of set in so narrow a sense that most of "classical" mathematics (analysis, geometry, set theory) will become meaningless or inadmissible; or to adopt a penetrating reform of logic as the basis of mathematics, a way involving difficulties which have not been overcome so far; or to take recourse to the *axiomatic method*, which in other branches of mathematics serves as an alternative to a definitory approach but here would constitute the only way out.

These three attitudes are exhibited in detail in Chapters Four, Three, and Two of *Foundations*, yet they seem too complicated for the present elementary book. Most textbooks of set theory [1] content themselves with explicitly or implicitly starting from Cantor's definition, yet using it with caution, viz. only to an extent which seems to escape the antinomies known to us.

In the present book we shall steer a middle course between formal axiomatics and the intuitive way of other expositions. At appropriate junctures certain Principles or *Axioms* will be introduced which chiefly correspond to the "general" axioms of the system Z developed in Chapter Two of *Foundations*. As a rule we shall restrict ourselves to sets which can be proven to exist on account of these axioms and occasionally sketch this connection explicitly. When exceptionally a collection of objects in the naive intuitive sense is mentioned we shall use the logical term "class" instead of "set". Hence, if the *existence of a set* is mentioned, e.g. in Axioms II–VII, this will stress that we have in mind a set in the stricter sense and not merely a class. However, lest the exposition become too involved or pedantic, in general we shall proceed more freely without

---

[1]) Comprehensive books are Hausdorff 14(49) and 27(62), Sierpiński 28 and 58, Quine 63, Klaua 64. — Kamke 28(50), Halmos 60, Suppes 60 are shorter good textbooks. Cf. Beth 59(ch. 14), Keene 61, Skolem 62, and in particular Bourbaki 51–56. — Schoenflies–Baire 09, Kamke 39, H. Bachmann 55 have encyclopedic character. Haalmeijer–Schogt is a Dutch, Cuesta 59 a Spanish, Kuratowski–Mostowski 52 an outstanding Polish textbook. (Axiomatic or logical monographs are not mentioned here.)

reference to the axioms while strictly avoiding the spots of danger that derive from exploiting Cantor's definition in an unrestricted manner.

We shall not enter into a discussion of the logical character of the objects called "sets" or "classes"[1]); the particular attitude taken has no effect on the mathematical theory of sets, just as arithmetic is independent of the various logical (and psychological) theories dealing with the nature of number.

Fundamental mathematical concepts such as group, ring, field are obtained by specializations from the concept of set. For an extension of this remark, regarding concepts such as number, function, mapping, see § 12; cf. § 4, **6**; § 7, **2**; § 2, **4**; etc.

Whenever one does not care about what the nature of the members of the set may be one speaks of an *abstract set*. Throughout this book, except for parts of § 9 and incidental examples not properly belonging to the subject-matter, *we shall deal with abstract sets only*. While abstract set theory [2]) is, of course, the substratum of every theory where particular assumptions about the nature of the members are made, such theories deviate early from the theory of abstract sets owing to the problems originating from the specific nature of the members. The most important specialization deals with *sets of points* or of (real, complex) numbers; cf. § 9.

§ 2. FUNDAMENTAL CONCEPTS. FINITE AND INFINITE SETS

1. The Membership Relation. Equality. Set theory as developed in this and the following sections is based on a single primitive relation, the *membership relation*, to be denoted by ϵ. It is a dyadic (binary) relation, i.e. it has two arguments x and y; $x \epsilon y$ may be read "x is a *member* (or element) of y" or "x is contained in y" or "x belongs to y", or "y contains x (as a member)". The negation of $x \epsilon y$ is denoted by $x \notin y$ ("x is not a member of y"). In the light of Cantor's definition (p. 9) the membership relation would appear to be defined; yet since we abandon this definition

---

[1]) The reader interested herein is referred to Chapter 17 of Russell 19 where sets are considered to be "logical fictions" rather than proper "objects"; cf. Stebbing 30, p. 453. This attitude is partly influenced by Occam's razor *("entia non sunt multiplicanda praeter necessitatem")*. For a comprehensive survey with references to literature see *Foundations*, Chapter V, § 8. — The term "fiction" used by Russell has nothing to do with its use in Vaihinger's *Philosophy of the Als-ob.*

[2]) "Theory of abstract sets" would be more logical.

ϵ should be rather considered to be an undefined (primitive) relation and used only as far as justified by the axioms.

We shall in general also contemplate one sort only of objects which are admissible as arguments of the membership relation; these objects shall be called *sets* and can, save for one exception which will be stated in Theorem 2, be characterized as those s for which there is an x such that $x \epsilon s$ is true. We assume that at least one object exists, i.e. that our theory is not void.

To be sure, we shall frequently deal with numbers, functions, points etc. as members of a set. Yet integers can easily be conceived as sets, hence all kinds of numbers and also functions etc., as will be seen later (in particular in §§ 7 and 11). Besides, such objects are mostly used as mere illustrations and not as integral parts of the systematic development.

The relation of *equality* (identity) between sets (objects), $a = b$, shall be conceived in the sense which at least since Leibniz has been generally adopted, namely as *identitas indiscernibilium*; that is to say, a and b are equal if they cannot be distinguished within the system. Since the membership relation is the only primitive relation of the system this means that $a = b$ *holds if and only if, for every set x, $a \epsilon x$ implies $b \epsilon x$ and vice versa*. Accordingly the equality relation is, as usual, *reflexive* $(a = a)$, *symmetrical* $(a = b$ implies $b = a)$, and *transitive* $(a = b$ and $b = c$ imply $a = c)$; left-hand substitutivity (i.e., $a \epsilon x$ and $a = b$ imply $b \epsilon x$) is part of the very definition; for right-hand substitutivity see exercise 6) on p. 33.

As usual, we denote the negation of $a = b$ by $a \neq b$, read "a is different from b".

2. **Subsets.** We start with two simple definitions.

> DEFINITION I. If every member of S is also a member of T (i.e. if, for every x, $x \epsilon S$ implies $x \epsilon T$) S is called a *subset* of T, or *included in* T. If, in addition, T has at least one member that is not a member of S then S is also called a *proper subset* of T.

The subset (inclusion) relation is expressed by $S \subseteq T$; if we wish to emphasize that S is a proper subset we write $S \subset T$.

It is essential to distinguish between the relations of membership and of inclusion (part-whole relation) which formerly were frequently confused, owing to equivocal use in everyday language. (T "contains" S, or "comprehends" S [1]), seems to mean both $S \epsilon T$ and $S \subset T$, and the use of the copula "is", e.g. in "man is an animal", has further contributed to confusion.) Frege and Peano have succeeded in making the distinction between both relations recognized and accepted.

From our definition we immediately conclude

THEOREM 1. *Every set is a subset of itself, and a subset of a subset of T is also a subset of T.* In symbols: $S \subseteq S$; $R \subseteq S$ and $S \subseteq T$ imply [2]) $R \subseteq T$.

Hence the relation $\subseteq$ is reflexive and transitive (but not symmetrical) while the relation $\subset$ evidently is irreflexive, asymmetrical (i.e., if $S \subset T$ is true, $T \subset S$ is false), and transitive.

DEFINITION II. If the sets S and T have no common member they are called *disjoint sets* [3]). A set such that every two of its members are disjoint is called a *disjointed set*. (Hence any set with no more than one member may be considered disjointed.)

In order to develop set theory we start with three axioms [4]).

Axiom (or Principle) of Extensionality (I). Two sets which contain the same members are equal.

Using symbols we express this in the form: if, for every x, $x \epsilon S$ implies $x \epsilon T$ and vice versa, then $S = T$; or on account of Definition I, $S \subseteq T$ and $T \subseteq S$ together imply $S = T$.

Hereby an additional characteristic of equality, not contained in the definition of p. 13, is postulated. In fact, the axiom states that *a set S is*

---

[1]) Still more ambiguous is the term "consists of". A train, while consisting of carriages, does certainly not contain carriages as members; whether its carriages may be regarded as subsets is a matter of convention. The question of a unit-set, i.e. of a set containing a single member, will be raised presently.

[2]) Throughout this book the term "implies" is used in the sense of "if — then —".

[3]) For a generalization to "almost disjoint sets" see Sierpiński 28a; also exercise 8) on p. 125.

[4]) The axioms stated in the present book, called *principles* in the first edition, are roughly Axioms I–VII introduced in Chapter II, §§ 2-5, of *Foundations*. However, they appear here in a different succession, motivated by didactic (and not, as in *Foundations*, by systematic) reasons; only the axiom of extensionality is the first in both cases.

determined by the totality of its members a, b, c, ...; hence we shall denote S also by

$$\{a, b, c, ...\} \ ^1)$$

where the brackets $\{\ \}$ hint at the membership relation. Within these brackets either all members of S are written or, if this is not possible or practical, dots are used to hint at all members in an unmistakable way.

Axiom I has the effect — which may be considered desirable or regrettable, according to the purpose in mind — that *no more than one set can exist that is empty*, i.e. has no member at all. In fact, each of two empty sets is a subset of the other by Definition I.

For purposes where several different "individuals", i.e. objects which have no member, are required one may weaken Axiom I so as to apply only to "proper sets", namely sets with members. For our exposition, which in its systematic parts does not use individuals except that of Theorem 2 below, no such modification of the axiom is required [2]).

Apart from the special problem of individuals, Axiom I has a general significance. It ensures that, no matter how a set is defined, it is determined by the totality of its members. Certainly "the set of all even prime numbers" and "the unit-set containing 2" are logically different designations, yet since either set has 2 as its only member they are equal [3]). This feature of equality is more striking when a less trivial or even an unsolved mathematical problem is involved; for instance, the question whether the set of all positive integers n for which the Diophantic equation with the unknowns x, y, z

$$x^n + y^n = z^n$$

has integral solutions x, y, z, equals the set $\{1, 2\}$ or not, depends on the question (unanswered as yet) whether Fermat's Last Theorem is true [4]).

---

[1])   It is true that here the members appear in a certain succession while the concept of set does not include order. But this is only caused by man's inability to name or write things *simultaneously*. Since no order of the members is intended by the above notation, $\{c, a, b, ...\}$ etc. will do as well.

[2])   For a comprehensive discussion of the possible attitudes towards the equality relation and the admission of individuals cf. *Foundations*, pp 28–33.

[3])   Cf. Specker 54, pp. 235 f.

[4])   The formulation "$a = b$ if a and b denote the same object" is not helpful in this context. Cf. the discussion between Alice and the Pigeon about girls being serpents, owing to the Pigeon's definition of serpents as animals having long necks and eating eggs.

Returning to the theme of subsets, it should be stressed that Definition I, while enabling us to ascertain whether one of two given sets is a subset of the other, is of course no instrument for *producing subsets*; for instance, for producing from the set of all integers the subset of all odd integers. True, the naive attitude, going back to Cantor and still prevailing in textbooks of set theory, fancies that by taking some of the members of a set one obtains a subset. However, already more than fifty years ago this attitude led to antinomies of the semantical type (*Foundations*, Chapter I). Therefore a stricter method has to be adopted, as expressed in

Axiom (or Principle) of Subsets (II). For any set S and any predicate P (in other words, any condition on x, $P(x)$) which is meaningful (,,definite") for all members x of S there exists the set $\overline{S}$ that contains just those members x of S which satisfy the predicate P (the condition $P(x)$).

The set $\overline{S}$ — like the sets introduced in the following axioms — is uniquely defined in view of extensionality (Axiom I) and is a subset of S. *It shall be denoted by* $\overline{S} = S_P$.

The concept of "definite predicate" requires some precisifying. Obviously predicates such as "odd", "greater than —", "prime", "transcendental" are meaningful if S is a set of numbers [1]), but not "green", "eternal", "quadrilateral". Since 1921 lively discussions around this concept have arisen which we need not go into here [2]). $x \epsilon t$ and $x = u$ as well as their negations are certainly meaningful conditions on x, whatever the fixed sets t and u may be.

If we take for $P(x)$ the condition "x is a member of S", or any other condition satisfied by *each* member of S, we obtain S itself as the subset $\overline{S}$ of S. But what happens if *no* member of S satisfies the condition? (This case is realized most simply by taking the predicate "is not a member of S"; if S is the set of all integers we may also, for instance, use the predicate "is irrational".) In this case the set $\overline{S}$, which certainly exists on account of Axiom II, contains no member whatsoever. Moreover, this set is, according to extensionality, the *only* set without members; by

---

[1]) Naturally, "meaningful" does not involve that for every x it can actually be *decided* whether x satisfies the predicate; cf. the remark on p. 10 regarding the set of transcendental numbers.

[2]) A historical and logical survey with references to the literature is given in *Foundations*, pp. 38–42. The concept "condition on x" is, for instance, defined in Rosser 53, p. 200. In the above formulation the condition is assumed to be monadic, i.e. to have a single argument x; however, the axiom may also be extended so as to allow additional arguments (parameters) z, t etc. to enter P.

Definition I it is a subset of *every* set, for the definition is fulfilled "vacuously". Hence we have

THEOREM 2. *There exists one and only one set which has no member. It is a subset of every set.*

We call this set the *null-set* or the empty set and denote it by O [1]).

Theorem 2 derives from stating Axiom II without exception; exceptions which are so familiar in grammar are abhorred by the mathematician and can as a rule be avoided by defining in an appropriate, if sometimes unaccustomed or even paradoxical way. A few philosophers have raised objections against subsuming under the concept of set a set which contains no member (and even against calling a set a subset of itself, which corresponds to calling an integer a divisor of itself) [2]). Such objections derive from misunderstanding the *nature of a definition*, which is not a statement (true or false) but an abbreviating convention (useful or not). Only the advantage brought about by the definition can justify it, and in the case of the null-set the advantage is obvious, as seen above (with respect to Axiom II) and frequently later (for instance, in the following paragraph and in Definitions III and IV below). Asking whether it is true that the empty set constitutes a set is as absurd as discussing whether man is an animal or not.

According to Definition I, Axiom II, and Theorem 2 the set $\{1, 2, 3\}$ has $8 = 2^3$ subsets, namely

$$\{1, 2, 3\}, \{1, 2\}, \{2, 3\}, \{3, 1\}, \{1\}, \{2\}, \{3\}, O.$$

We shall see in §§ 5 and 7 that this statement about the number of subsets is a special case not only of a well-known theorem of combinatorial analysis but of a far-reaching theorem of set theory which equally holds for finite and infinite sets.

Our example suggests two general remarks. First, clearly the set $\{1\}$ differs from the number 1, and "in general" one has to distinguish between an object a and its unit-set $\{a\}$. The question remains open whether there exist "extraordinary" objects (sets) a such that $\{a\} = a$. In the present book such sets do not occur; the question in principle is raised in *Foundations*, Chapter II, § 5.

More pressing for our system is the question whether each of the eight sets named above *exist* (independently of Cantor's definition of set), i.e. whether they constitute sets and not just "classes". With regard to O

---

[1])   The null-class was first used in symbolic logic; cf. the historical sketch Cipolla 37. In set theory the null-set was introduced only at the beginning of the present century by Russell, Zermelo, and others. Besides O, other symbols (e.g., $\varnothing$ or $\wedge$) are in use.

[2])   Some of these objections originate from confusion between the membership and the inclusion relations; e.g., Carmichael 43.

the answer is in the affirmative. Assuming the existence of the starting-set $\{1, 2, 3\}$, the other six sets are easily obtained by means of the axiom of subsets through predicates of the form "equal to — or —" for the sets with two members, and of the form "equal to —" for the unit-sets. However, given the objects 1, 2, 3, Axioms I and II do not yield the set $\{1, 2, 3\}$ nor similar sets if two or more objects are given. A partial instrument, which (in conjunction with Axiom IV, below) will prove sufficient with respect to finitely many given objects, is

Axiom (or Principle) of Pairing (III). For any two different objects a and b there exists the set that contains just a and b.

It is called the *pair* of a and b and denoted, according to p. 15, by $\{a, b\}$ or by $\{b, a\}$.

Axiom III is formulated for the case $a \neq b$ only. If $a = b$, i.e. if the existence of the unit-set $\{a\}$ of one object a is concerned, we can *prove* the statement. For according to Theorem 2 and Axiom III [1]) there exists the pair $\{a, O\}$, from which by means of the predicate "equals a" (or "is different from O") the set $\{a\}$ emerges. Hence

THEOREM 3. *For any given object a there exists the unit-set $\{a\}$ which contains a and no other member.*

In the example of p. 17 a set with three members was used in an informal way only, for even if three different objects a, b, c are given we cannot assert the existence of the set $\{a, b, c\}$ with the resources (axioms) at our disposal. (It will be ensured in 3.) On the other hand, *assuming* that a comprehensive enough set is given, any finite subset containing $a, b, c, \ldots$ exists by Axiom II, through predicates of the form "equals a or b or $c \ldots$".

3. Union, Intersection, Difference. If S and T are sets we may ask for the sets which contain either the members that belong to *any one* of them or those that belong to *each* of them. The first operation corresponds to logical *disjunction* ("or" [2]), the second to logical *conjunction* ("and":

---

[1]) This proof fails if $a = O$. But in this case the axiom of power-set (§ 5, **3**), which yields the set containing all subsets of a given set, produces the set $\{O\}$, since the empty set has no subset but itself.

[2]) The intention is to "alternation", i.e. to "at least one of both", and not to the exclusive disjunction which means "just one of both". Confusion has been created by the defectiveness of many languages which use the same word (or, *ou*, *oder*, etc.) for both kinds of disjunction; in Latin, however, alternative disjunction is denoted by *vel*, exclusive by *aut*. For the use in logic, the alternative disjunction is more suitable.
Compare the use of "or" in the sentences "in this or the next block you will find a cab" and "the child just born is male or female".

Fig. 3

members belonging to both S and T). If in fig. 3 the set of all points belonging to the horizontal rectangle is denoted by S and the set of those of the vertical rectangle by T then the first operation yields the set of all points contained in the cross-shaped figure, the second the set of those in the inner square alone.

We shall now generalize these operations, first from two sets to any finite number of sets, secondly to any (infinite) sequence of sets. (As usual in mathematics, a *sequence* means an ordered collection which contains, for each positive integer n, an nth member, while conversely every member of the collection is the nth for a certain n. This definition of sequence allows a repeated occurence of the same member, in contrast with sets as remarked on pp. 10 and 14.) A generalization to any infinite *set* of sets will be given in § 6, **2**.

DEFINITION III. Let be given finitely many sets $S_1, S_2, \ldots, S_n$ or a sequence [1]) of sets $(S_1, S_2, \ldots, S_n, \ldots)$. The set U of all members contained in *at least one* S_k is called the *union* of the given sets, the set I of all members contained in *each* S_k is called the *intersection* of the given sets.

We write [2])
$$U = S_1 \cup S_2 \cup \ldots, \quad I = S_1 \cap S_2 \cap \ldots.$$

According to this definition, each term S_k is a subset of the union while the intersection is a subset of each term S_k.

Examples.

1) $S_1 = \{1, 2, 3, \ldots\}, S_2 = \{2, 3, 4, \ldots\}, S_k = \{k, k+1, k+2, \ldots\}$ for every positive integer k. The union of all S_k is S_1, the intersection is the null-set; for, n denoting *any* member of S_1, there are sets in which n is not contained, namely all S_k with $k > n$.

---

[1])   A sequence is, as usual, denoted by round parentheses ( ), in contrast with a set which is denoted by curly brackets { }. Though the notion of sequence fundamentally differs from that of set we shall in § 6 (Definitions III and VI) use a method of incorporating sequences in the terminology of sets; therefore it is unnecessary to mention sequences in Axiom IV below.

[2])   Many (in particular, French and Polish) authors use the symbols + and · respectively for our $\cup$ and $\cap$; so does also Kleene 52. This notation has its origin in a partial analogy mentioned later in this subsection; for + also in Definitions II and III of § 6.

2) $S_1 = \{1, 2, 3, \ldots\}$, $S_2 = \{\frac{1}{2}, 1, \frac{3}{2}, 2, \frac{5}{2}, \ldots\}$ (all positive multiples of $\frac{1}{2}$), $S_3 = \{\frac{1}{3}, \frac{2}{3}, 1, \frac{4}{3}, \ldots\}, \ldots, S_k = \{\frac{1}{k}, \frac{2}{k}, \frac{3}{k}, \ldots\}$. The union of all S_k is the set of all positive rational numbers, the intersection is S_1.

3) Let S_1 be the set of all real numbers except the integers, S_2 the set S_1 except the rationals with the denominators 1 and 2, and S_k, for any k, the set S_1 except the rationals with the denominators $1, 2, 3, \ldots, k$. The union is S_1, the intersection the set of all irrational numbers.

The examples 1) and 3) show that the intersection of a sequence of infinite sets, each of which is a proper subset of its predecessor, may be either empty or contain members (even infinitely many). This remark will prove useful in § 5, **4**. Incidentally, example 1) again shows the expediency of having an empty set (the null-set) at our disposal; otherwise the intersection of given (not-empty) sets would not necessarily be a set.

However, we have not yet ensured the *existence* of the sets (union and intersection) defined above. To achieve this in an even wider sense (as required in § 6) we introduce

Axiom (or Principle) of Sum-Set (IV). For any set A of sets [1]**) there exists the set that contains just the members of the members of A.**

This set is called the *sum-set of A* or the *union of the members of A*, and denoted by $\bigcup A$ or, if $a, a', \ldots$ are the members of A, by $a \cup a' \cup \ldots$.

Axiom IV guarantees not only the existence of the union but also of the *intersection* of the members of A which, in addition to the notation of Definition III, *shall also be denoted by* $\bigcap A$. In fact, let a be an arbitrary member [2]) of A, and $P(x)$ be the condition "x is a member of *each* member of A". Then we obtain, according to the axiom of subsets, a subset a_P of a which is the intersection of the members of A, according to Definition III (even for any *set A* of sets).

Given finitely many different sets $s_1, s_2, \ldots, s_n$, we are now in a position to form the set which contains them. The method will become sufficiently clear by taking $n = 4$ and $n = 3$.

By the axiom of pairing the sets

$$\{s_1, s_2\} = S, \quad \{s_3, s_4\} = S', \quad \{S, S'\} \quad [3])$$

---

[1]) The words "of sets" are essentially superfluous; they only serve the purpose of easier understanding. Besides, as pointed out in **1**, systematically we use no other objects than sets.

[2]) It is evident that the set a_P is independent of the particular member a chosen. We may as well avoid the arbitrariness of a and, instead of a, start from the sum-set $\bigcup A$; our condition $P(x)$ then yields the same subset, namely the intersection.

[3]) Since the s_k were assumed to be different we have $S \neq S'$.

exist, hence by the axiom of sum-set also

$$\cup \{S, S'\} = S \cup S' = \{s_1, s_2, s_3, s_4\}.$$

To obtain the set $\{s_1, s_2, s_3\}$ we use, instead of S', the set $\{s_3\}$ which exists by Theorem 3.

Though the formal laws valid for the operations of Definition III are formulated only in § 6 in full generality, it is preferable to anticipate their simplest cases at this juncture.

The *commutative laws*

$$S_1 \cup S_2 = S_2 \cup S_1, \quad S_1 \cap S_2 = S_2 \cap S_1$$

which state that the result of the operations is independent of the order of the terms (and which also hold for any number of terms) need not be proven since no order of the terms occurs in Definition III ("at least one S_k", "each S_k"). This situation differs fundamentally from that in arithmetic where, for instance, the addition of two numbers is defined in an inductive way which distinguishes between the first and the second term (cf. § 10, 2); hence in arithmetic the commutative law is a theorem requiring a proof.

The *associative laws*

$$(S_1 \cup S_2) \cup S_3 = S_1 \cup (S_2 \cup S_3) = S_1 \cup S_2 \cup S_3,$$
$$(S_1 \cap S_2) \cap S_3 = S_1 \cap (S_2 \cap S_3) = S_1 \cap S_2 \cap S_3$$

require proofs also in the present case — even proofs additional to those of arithmetic, where $a + b + c$ is just an abbreviation for the common value of $(a+b)+c$ and $a+(b+c)$, while here, for instance, $S_1 \cup S_2 \cup S_3$ is independently defined by Definition III. It will be sufficient to prove two of the above statements as the proofs of the two others are almost verbatim the same.

To prove $(S_1 \cup S_2) \cup S_3 = S_1 \cup S_2 \cup S_3$ we have to show, according to extensionality, that the left-hand and the right-hand sets contain the same members. If x belongs to $(S_1 \cup S_2) \cup S_3$ it belongs either to $S_1 \cup S_2$ or to S_3 (or to both): hence x belongs to $S_1 \cup S_2 \cup S_3$. If the latter is the case then x belongs to at least one of the sets S_1, S_2, S_3, hence to $S_1 \cup S_2$ or else to S_3, hence to $(S_1 \cup S_2) \cup S_3$.

The proof of $(S_1 \cap S_2) \cap S_3 = S_1 \cap S_2 \cap S_3$ is quite similar. x belonging to the left-hand set means that x belongs to both $S_1 \cap S_2$ and S_3, hence to both S_1 and S_2, hence to $S_1 \cap S_2 \cap S_3$. Conversely, if x belongs to the latter set, i.e. to each of the sets S_1, S_2, S_3, then x belongs to $S_1 \cap S_2$ as well as to S_3, hence to $(S_1 \cap S_2) \cap S_3$. Herewith the proof is completed.

Finally, the operations of Definition III are connected with each other by the following two *distributive laws*

$$S_1 \cap (S_2 \cup S_3) = S_1 \cap S_2 \cup S_1 \cap S_3, \quad ^1)$$
$$S_1 \cup S_2 \cap S_3 = (S_1 \cup S_2) \cap (S_1 \cup S_3).$$

In fact, if x belongs to $S_1 \cap (S_2 \cup S_3)$, i.e. to both S_1 and $S_2 \cup S_3$, x belongs to both S_1 and S_2 or to both S_1 and S_3, hence to $S_1 \cap S_2 \cup S_1 \cap S_3$; the converse direction is confirmed as easily.

For the second law we show that any x belonging to S_1 or to both S_2 and S_3 also belongs to the right-hand expression; in fact, in either case x belongs to both $S_1 \cup S_2$ and $S_1 \cup S_3$. The proof in the direction from the right to the left is analogous.

All these formal laws, with one exception, correspond to the formal laws of arithmetic — if, for instance, we take addition instead of union and multiplication instead of intersection. The corresponding arithmetical laws are written in the forms

$$a_1 + a_2 = a_2 + a_1, \ a_1 a_2 = a_2 a_1, \ (a_1 + a_2) + a_3 = a_1 + (a_2 + a_3),$$
$$(a_1 a_2)a_3 = a_1(a_2 a_3), \ a_1(a_2 + a_3) = a_1 a_2 + a_1 a_3.$$

The exception is the second distributive law whose counterpart $a_1 + a_2 a_3 = (a_1 + a_2)(a_1 + a_3)$ is not valid in arithmetic. (Had we replaced union by multiplication and intersection by addition then the first distributive law would be the exception.)

There is an intrinsic reason for the exception. In contradistinction to the operations of union and intersection, which are parallel to each other and even *dual* (see § 6, 9), arithmetical multiplication is *based* on addition — in the simplest cases just defined as repeated addition, and not vice versa.

We conclude with a notion of limited importance only.

DEFINITION IV. If S_0 is a subset of the set S $^2)$, the set of those members of S which do *not* belong to S_0 is called the *difference* of S and S_0 and denoted by $S - S_0$.

$^1)$ Here, as in the arithmetical notation $ab + ac$, parentheses for $S_1 \cap S_2$ etc. are omitted.
$^2)$ Some authors drop this condition. However, for our purposes a more general definition is not required.

The difference exists by the axiom of subsets through the predicate "is not a member of S_0". If $S_0 = S$ we have $S - S_0 = O$.

4. Mapping and Equivalence. In the first example of § 1 we dealt with a certain correspondence between a set of fruit and a set of numbers. Such correspondences may be regarded as the basis of the concept of finite number and we shall see in § 4 that by their means also the concept of infinite number can be introduced.

The notion of *unique* (single-valued) *correspondence* or *function* is well-known inside and outside mathematics. A thermograph is an instrument which notes the temperature T for every moment (at a given place, during a given week). The function $T = f(t)$ marked by the thermograph is single-valued, for to every moment t corresponds a uniquely defined temperature. If, however, we ask at what time a certain temperature (say, within the temperature-range in question) has been reached then the answer is given by a function — the inverse of the function $T = f(t)$ — which in general is not single-valued because the same temperature may be reached at different moments. The concept of a single-valued but not uniquely invertible function is much used in mathematical analysis; cf. § 7.

However, in practical life as well as in science one also uses correspondences with an additional property. Anthropologists tell us of primitive tribes where only three numerals are known, viz. one, two, many. To compare nevertheless heaps of apples the notion of "proper subset" may prove sufficient. Yet a decisive step towards the creation of the *number-concept* is taken when, for the purpose of barter, a heap of apples is compared with a multitude of eggs. To attach (relate) a single egg to each apple is not enough because then to different apples the same egg might correspond. It is necessary to use *one-to-one* (biunique, that is to say single-valued and uniquely invertible) *correspondences*, i.e. such as attach a single egg to each apple and different eggs to different apples; hereby also a single apple is attached to each egg [1]). If two heaps have the property that such a correspondence between them exists then there exist various correspondences, save for the trivial case where the "heap" contains a single object only.

---

[1]) In a polygamic society husbands are uniquely related to their wives, in a monogamic society even biuniquely; in the latter, therefore, the set of married women is "equivalent" to the set of married men in the sense of Definition V.

Correspondences of this kind belong not only to the simplest material of mathematical processes but to the most primitive and fundamental activities of human mind in general. They yield the notion of *number* as positive integer or "cardinal number" which answers the question "how many?"; for multitudes of arbitrary objects between which a one-to-one correspondence exists may be defined to possess "the same cardinal number", hence cardinal number can be introduced as the common characteristic of such multitudes [1]).

A well-known example of achieving such a process for multitudes which are not finite is given in example d) of § 1. Further examples will appear in this and the following sections.

The very concept of finite cardinal number as developed in this way — a way whose importance for the beginnings of civilization in general can hardly be over-estimated — also provides us with a universal and inexhaustible kind of objects to be used as general mediators, thus sparing us the direct comparison of multitudes of different objects. These mediators are the integers 1, 2, 3, ... They have the advantage of not possessing accidental properties, as they are just qualified for the process of counting and yield "normal" sets to which multitudes of any objects can be compared.

Without introducing a (superfluous) limitation to finite multitudes (sets) we therefore define:

DEFINITION V. If the members of a set T can be related to the members of a set S in a *one-to-one* (biunique) *correspondence*, i.e. so that a single member of T corresponds to each member of S and vice versa, we speak of a (one-to-one) *mapping* [2]) *of S onto T*. In this case the set T is called *equivalent* [3]) to the set S, written $T \sim S$.

---

[1]) For a non-technical exposition of this subject for finite sets and numbers cf., for instance, Russell 19 or Dantzig 30. A stricter treatment that includes infinite sets is given below in § 4.

[2]) In the present book no other mappings are used, hence the attribute "one-to-one" will usually be dropped. Some authors say "representation" instead of "mapping".

We shall distinguish between *correspondence* (between the members of the sets) and *mapping* (between the sets).

[3]) True, the term "equivalent", introduced by Cantor in this sense, is overladen by its various meanings in logic and mathematics. We shall avoid misunderstandings by using *"equipollent"* (instead of "equivalent") for logical equivalence.

Some authors use "similar" for set-theoretical equivalence. Yet we shall need "similar" for a different purpose (§ 8).

Mappings are usually denoted by Greek letters such as φ, ψ, Φ etc.

To prove that given sets are equivalent it is sufficient to define a certain mapping (among various, even infinitely many, mappings which may exist). However, for the proof that T is *not* equivalent to S we cannot rely upon the failure of an attempt to construct a mapping but have to show that every such attempt is bound to fail. Cf. § 4, 3.

When finite sets are concerned a mapping can be defined by listing, for each member of the one set, the *image* in the other to which it shall be related. This is impossible with respect to infinitely many members; then the correspondence can only be defined by a law (function), i.e. by a rule which, though formulated in a finite way, defines to each of the infinitely many members of the one set its image in the other. Also for finite sets which contain a considerable number of members a law is, as a rule, preferable to a complete list.

Equivalence as defined above is not a property but a *relation*[1]), more strictly, a dyadic [2]) (binary, two-place) relation $X \sim Y$ with two arguments, i.e. free variables, X and Y for which sets can be inserted. A relation may have certain properties; we shall now prove that the equivalence relation has the properties of *reflexivity*, *symmetry*, and *transitivity*.

Equivalence is reflexive, i.e. for every set S holds $S \sim S$. This is proven, for instance, by the *identical mapping* which relates each member of S to itself. (The null-set is also called equivalent to itself.)

Equivalence is symmetrical, i.e. from $T \sim S$ follows $S \sim T$. This is an immediate consequence of the fact that our correspondences are biunique (one-to-one); for if $t \in T$ corresponds to $s \in S$ then vice versa $s \in S$ corresponds to $t \in T$, whereby a mapping of T onto S is produced.

---

[1]) Greek philosophy, and even medieval and modern philosophy until the later part of the nineteenth century, have not become aware of the distinction between properties and relations, owing to the similarity in the grammatical structure of sentences expressing property or relation statements. Only with the development of Symbolic Logic (cf. *Foundations*, Chapters II and III) was the fundamental importance of relations recognized. An unforgettable device for stressing the distinction between a property and a dyadic relation is provided by the following joke. A woman calls on her friend who has born twins and says, your children are so beautiful, particularly the one on the left. Then another friend calls and remarks, your children are so alike, particularly the one on the left. Grammatically the sentences are equally shaped, but "beautiful" expresses a property, "alike" a relation.

[2]) Cf. the beginning of § 2. There are also triadic relations and such with more places. Triadic is, for instance, "the point y lies between the points x and z" or "the number z is the sum of x and y", i.e. $z = x + y$. Properties (predicates) may be regarded as monadic (one-place) relations.

The symmetry of the equivalence relation allows us to treat S and T homogeneously, that is to say, to speak of the equivalence, and of a mapping, *between* the sets S and T (and of a one-to-one correspondence between their members) or to state that S *and* T are equivalent.

Finally, equivalence is transitive, i.e. from $S \sim T$ and $T \sim U$ follows $S \sim U$. In view of the symmetry we may formulate transitivity also in the form: if two sets S and U are equivalent to the same set T, they are equivalent to each other; for $U \sim T$ implies $T \sim U$.

To prove transitivity let φ be an arbitrary mapping between S and T, ψ an arbitrary mapping between T and U. In the following we shall stick to these mappings and refer to them in speaking of "the image". Now if $t \in T$ is the image of an arbitrary $s \in S$ and $u \in U$ the image of $t \in T$ then a one-to-one correspondence χ between the members of S and of U is produced by relating $u \in U$ to $s \in S$. From the assumption it follows that the correspondence defined is unique; that it is even bi-unique results from $t \in T$ being the image of $u \in U$ and $s \in S$ the image of $t \in T$. Hence χ is a mapping, i.e. $S \sim U$. This proof contrives to eliminate the mediating set T by a direct transition from S to U (hence the term *transitive*). Thus we have proven

THEOREM 4. *The equivalence between sets is a reflexive, symmetrical, and transitive relation. Hence in a collection of sets such that each set is equivalent to a definite set, each is also equivalent to any other.*

The various meanings in which the term "equivalent" is used in different branches of mathematics and of logic have the common feature that the respective relations have the three properties expressed in Theorem 4. (Naturally any equality relation, for instance the equality of sets, is also an equivalence relation.) These properties are *not independent*; for $S \sim T$ implies $T \sim S$, hence (by transitivity) $S \sim S$. Accordingly, if for every S there exists a T such that $S \sim T$, reflexivity is a consequence of symmetry and transitivity.[1])

Later (in §§ 5 and 8) we shall deal with relations which have other properties, e.g. such as are irreflexive, non-symmetrical, or even asymmetrical; also the membership relation ϵ has none of the above properties.

Prior to a more general treatment in § 6, we here state the following properties of equivalence in connection with concepts introduced earlier in this section.

---

[1]) Cf., however, exercise 5) at the end of this section.

1) A given mapping between S and T *maps every proper subset of S onto a proper subset of T.*

2) If S_1 and S_2 are disjoint sets and if the mappings φ_1 and φ_2 respectively map S_1 and S_2 onto the *disjoint* sets T_1 and T_2 then $S_1 \cup S_2$ *is mapped onto $T_1 \cup T_2$ by the "union" of the mappings φ_1 and φ_2, which* union is also a mapping. Hence $S_1 \cup S_2 \sim T_1 \cup T_2$.

The proofs follow from the very definition of mapping.

Finally, a question of principle with respect to the equivalence relation shall be raised. In subsection 1 we stated that our system of set theory is based on a single primitive relation, the membership relation ϵ. However, in Definition V a new relation, that of mapping or equivalence, has been introduced. Is this compatible with the earlier statement?

The answer is that *the equivalence relation can be reduced to the membership relation.*[1]) Restricting ourselves to the case where the given sets S and T are disjoint [2]), we can easily prove (cf. § 6, 5) the existence of the set P of all pairs $\{s, t\}$ with $s \in S$ and $t \in T$. Possibly P has subsets $\overline{P}$ of the following property π: each member of $S \cup T$ appears in *one and only one* member of $\overline{P}$. Any such subset $\overline{P}$ can be regarded as a mapping between S and T. In fact, for a given $s \in S$ there is a single member (a pair $\{s, t\}$ of $\overline{P}$) which contains s, and the other member t of the pair may be considered to be related to s by the mapping $\overline{P}$; moreover, according to the property π every $t \in T$ is related in this way to a single $s \in S$. We therefore have $S \sim T$. If no such subset $\overline{P}$ exists then the sets S and T are not equivalent. Hereby equivalence is defined through the membership relation.

By means of Axiom VI and the axiom of subsets it can easily be shown (*Foundations*, p. 126) that the set of *all* subsets $\overline{P}$ of P with the property π exists. If it contains members then each is a mapping between S and T; if it is empty S and T are not equivalent.

5. Finite and Infinite Sets.

Up to now we have used the terms „finite" and "infinite" sets or "finitely" and "infinitely" many objects in a naive way, as they are presupposed in other branches of mathematics. Set theory, however, is connected with the notion of infinity [3]) to such an extent that a stricter discussion cannot be further delayed, and the concept of equivalence proves helpful for this discussion. To be sure, throughout the present book we shall not cease discussing the notion of infinity, which discussion is also the intrinsic subject of the book *Foundations*.

---

[1]) To be sure, for this purpose an axiom is required which is introduced in § 5, 3 for a more general purpose, viz. Axiom VI (the axiom of power-set).

[2]) If they are not disjoint a more complicated device has to be used; see *Foundations*, pp. 126 f.

[3]) H. Weyl, one of the foremost mathematicians of the last generation, begins his paper 25 with the slogan: mathematics is the science of infinity. This may suggest that mathematics in its entirety should be based upon set theory, which in fact is the opinion of most mathematicians (though it was not Weyl's own opinion); cf. § 12.

The most obvious way is to refer to the concept of integer and to define as follows:

> DEFINITION VI. A set I is called *finite* and more strictly, *inductive* if there exists a positive integer n such that I contains just n members. The null-set O is also called finite. — A set which is not inductive is called *infinite (non-inductive)*.

Objections to using the concept of integer may be of two kinds. Either the objection is based on the conviction that a main purpose of set theory is to base the concept of integer, hence this concept must not appear in basing set theory, whether explicit or implicit; yet it seems difficult to see how any abstract doctrine can be developed without some (possibly intuitive) use of the notion of number (cf. § 10, 6). On the other hand, the objection may mean that the concept of integer should not be presupposed but derived from (actually or seemingly) more general concepts. Though on the whole this attitude is not taken in the present book in view of its elementary character, the explicit reference to the number concept in Definition VI can easily be eliminated, for instance in the following way due to Bertrand Russell:

a) A set of (cardinal) numbers is called *hereditary* if its containing a number n implies that it contains $n + 1$. ($+ 1$ has to be conceived by using the concept of union; cf. § 6, Definition II.)

b) A number (cardinal) is called *inductive* if it belongs to every hereditary set that contains 0.

c) A *set* is called inductive if its cardinal is inductive.

Simpler definitions were given later, for instance the following definition due to Tarski:[1] I is inductive if every non-empty set K of subsets of I has at least one maximal member, i.e. a member which is not a subset of any other member of K.

While we shall occasionally use well-known statements of finite arithmetic without proving them, an explicit proof of the following theorem will be given in view of its great importance in the present context.

THEOREM 5. *An inductive set I is not equivalent to any proper subset of I.*

Proof. The theorem is clearly true if I contains no member ($I = O$) or a single member; in the first case because O has no proper subset, in the second because its only proper subset is O, and a set containing one member is not equivalent to the empty set.

To prove the theorem generally we use the method characteristic of arithmetic of finite numbers (positive integers), namely *mathematical induction*. While this method will be treated in detail in § 10, 2 where it

---

[1] Tarski 25; cf. also A. Lévy 58 and 58a. Tarski proves in an "elementary" way, i.e. without the axiom of choice (§ 6, 5), that this definition is equipollent to Russell's, see § 10, 6.

appears as a particular case of a far more general method peculiar to set theory, we here only use the elementary statement of arithmetic that a theorem on finite (inductive) numbers is true if it is true for a least number, usually 0 or 1, and if its truth for any number n implies its truth for $n + 1$.

Let us, therefore, assume the statement of Theorem 5 to be true for all inductive sets containing n members, n denoting any given positive integer, and let S be any set of $n + 1$ members,. We shall show the truth for S of the statement of Theorem 5 by indirect proof, i.e. by presupposing the contrary and then deriving a contradiction.

The presupposition is that S is equivalent to a proper subset $S_0 \subset S$; a certain mapping between S and S_0 shall be denoted by φ.

Let a be a member of S which is not contained in the proper subset S_0 of S, and let b be the image in S_0 which is related to the member a of S by the mapping φ. If the member a is dropped from S and the member b from S_0 then the remaining part of φ constitutes a mapping $\bar{\varphi}$ between the set $S - \{a\}$ and a proper subset of this set. But the set $S - \{a\}$ contains only n members; hence the existence of the mapping $\bar{\varphi}$ would contradict our assumption that the statement of Theorem 5 is true for all sets which contain n members.

The contradiction thus obtained shows that the statement is also true for all sets which contain $n + 1$ members, and since it is true for every unit-set the theorem has been proved.

While Definition VI is one of the possible ways of characterizing infinite sets, namely as non-inductive sets, in medieval philosophy [1]) and more strictly by Galileo (*Discorsi* I, *Opere Complete* XIII) another characteristic of infinity was pointed out which much later, by Peirce and Dedekind (independently) [2]), was proposed for *defining* infinity, viz.

DEFINITION VII. A set R is called *infinite* and more strictly, *reflexive* if R has a proper subset that is equivalent to R. A set which is not reflexive is called *finite (non-reflexive)*; in other words, a non-empty set is non-reflexive if every mapping *into* itself is a mapping *onto* itself.

---

[1])   Cf. Thomas 58.
[2])   Peirce 33, pp. 210–249 (published in 1885), also p. 360 (cf. Keyser 41); Dedekind 1888. Cf. also Bolzano 1851 (§ 20) and Cantor 1878.

That there exist sets which are reflexive is shown by the very first example of an infinite set considered in § 1, b), namely the set N of all positive integers. If N_0 is the set of all integers greater than 1 we have $N_0 \subset N$ and $N_0 \sim N$, as is shown by the mapping that relates every $n \in N_0$ to $(n - 1) \in N$, hence every $n \in N$ to $(n + 1) \in N_0$. This mapping is illustrated by the scheme

$$N: \quad 1 \quad 2 \quad 3 \quad \ldots \quad n - 1 \quad n \quad \ldots$$
$$\downarrow \quad \downarrow \quad \downarrow \qquad \qquad \downarrow \qquad \downarrow$$
$$N_0: \quad 2 \quad 3 \quad 4 \quad \ldots \quad n \quad n + 1 \quad \ldots$$

The reluctance of many a beginner to accept the possibility of such mappings has its origin in a rather nebulous conception as if each member of the one set should be related *to itself* in the other. Obviously no mapping onto a proper subset can be managed in this way; it is therefore important to thoroughly comprehend the above example, which will be followed in the next sections by many other mappings between a set and a proper subset.

That also some trained philosophers have taken the same reluctant attitude may be explained by their adherence to the classical principle *totum parte maius* (the whole is greater than a part). This principle in its proper meaning is, however, limited to the domain of finite sets (Theorem 5); its invalidity in the domain of infinity [1]) is just characteristic of the latter. Unfortunately, dogmatic adherence to that principle has seriously hampered the growth of set theory, even in the hands of a pioneer as daring as Bolzano (cf. § 12).

An immediate consequence of Definitions VI and VII is

THEOREM 6. *A set which is equivalent to a finite (infinite) set is also finite (infinite).*

Leaving the proof to the reader as far as Definition VI is concerned, we show that a set S which is equivalent to a reflexive set R is reflexive as well.

---

[1]) The paradoxical impression deepens when the phenomenon of equivalence between sets of obviously different sizes is transferred, as it were, to real life. Of course such would-be reality is fictitious; for instance the story of *Tristram Shandy* who writes his autobiography so pedantically that the description of each day takes him a year. If he is mortal he can never terminate; but did he live forever then no part of his biography would remain unwritten, for to each day of his life a year devoted to that day's description would correspond.

R, being reflexive, has a proper subset $R_0 \subset R$ such that $R \sim R_0$. According to our assumption there is a mapping φ between S and R and φ maps R_0 onto a proper subset S_0 of S (see 1) on p. 27). But the relations

$$S \sim R, \quad R \sim R_0, \quad R_0 \sim S_0$$

yield $S \sim S_0$ by the transitivity of equivalence; hence S is equivalent to its proper subset S_0, i.e. S is reflexive.

Therefore, by logical inversion, a set which is equivalent to a non-reflexive set is non-reflexive.

We shall now examine the connection between Definitions VI and VII, which, besides the material difference, are also formally heterogeneous inasmuch as VI starts with finiteness and conceives infinity as its negation while in VII infinity is the primary concept and finiteness secondary. The equipollence between both definitions, to be shown below, is dependent on a rather profound theorem whose natural place is in the following section (Theorem 4 of § 3); of course, in the proof of that theorem no use will be made of the present results.

According to Theorem 5 above, every inductive set is non-reflexive, hence every reflexive set non-inductive. The remaining question is, therefore, whether there are sets which are neither inductive nor reflexive ("mediate" sets). To exclude their existence we prove that *every non-inductive set S is reflexive.*

In short the proof runs as follows. A subset S^* of S which is equivalent to the set of positive integers has a proper subset equivalent to S^*, as shown on p. 30. By separating S into S^* and $S - S^*$ one also obtains a proper subset of S which is equivalent to S.

We now describe this in detail. According to Theorem 4 of § 3, S has a subset S^* which is equivalent to the set N of all positive integers. Taking a definite mapping between S^* and N and marking the members of S^* by the corresponding indices we may write

$$S^* = \{s_1, s_2, \ldots, s_k, \ldots\}.$$

If $S - S^* = S'$ (hence $S' = O$ in the case $S^* = S$) we have $S = S^* \cup S'$, where S^* and S' are disjoint.

By dropping s_1 from the set S^* we obtain a proper subset $S^* - \{s_1\} = S_0^*$ which proves equivalent to S^* in view of the mapping that relates $s_{k+1} \epsilon S_0^*$ to $s_k \epsilon S^*$, just as on p. 30. Moreover, $S_0^* \cup S' = S_0$ is a proper subset of S since $s_1 \epsilon S$ but $s_1 \notin S_0$. Finally, we have $S^* \cup S' \sim S_0^* \cup S'$, i.e. $S \sim S_0$, in view of the above mapping between S^* and S_0^* on the one hand, of the identical mapping between S' and S' on the other; according to 2) on p. 27 we thus obtain a mapping between S and its proper subset S_0, which proves our statement.

Pending the proof of Theorem 4 of § 3, "inductive" and "non-reflexive", as well as "non-inductive" and "reflexive", have been shown to be equipollent concepts. Accordingly, we shall henceforth speak plainly of *finite sets* and of *infinite sets*, without distinguishing between Definitions VI and VII. For more subtle distinctions regarding the concepts "finite" and "infinite" (sets and numbers) the reader is referred to § 10, 6 and to *Foundations* (especially Chapter II, § 4).

We conclude this section with a remark of principle regarding *the existence of infinite sets*. By means of the axioms introduced hitherto we are not able to prove that there exists an infinite set. While Axiom I is certainly of no avail for this problem Axiom II yields only subsets of sets previously secured and Axiom III sets with two members; Axiom IV starts with a given set A of sets, and if A as well as its members are finite the same holds for the sum-set $\cup A$. We therefore introduce

Axiom (or Principle) of Infinity (V). There exists an infinite (reflexive) set; for instance, the set N of all positive integers $\{1, 2, 3, \ldots\}$.

That N is reflexive was shown above.

The explicit use of the concept of integer in the axiom of infinity can be avoided (cf. p. 28) by postulating the existence of at least one set Z that satisfies the following two conditions:
   a) $O \epsilon Z$
   b) if $a \epsilon Z$ then also $\{a\} \epsilon Z$.[1])
Though Z is not uniquely determined by a) and b) one can prove (by also using Axiom VI in § 5, 3) the existence of a uniquely defined *least* set Z_0 satisfying a) and b). Z_0 contains just the members

$$O, \{O\}, \{\{O\}\}, \{\{\{O\}\}\}, \ldots$$

which prove different from each other.

By writing 1 for O, 2 for $\{O\}$, etc., generally $k + 1$ for $\{k\}$, one perceives that Z_0 is, save for the notation, the set of all positive integers. For the proof of these remarks see *Foundations*, p. 83. Cf. below § 11, 2.

Exercises

1) Prove that the following relations between sets are equipollent:
a) $S \subseteq T, S = S \cap T, S \cup T = T$;
b) $S = T$ and $S \cap T = S \cup T$;
c) $S \subseteq T \subseteq U$ and $S \cup T = T \cap U$.

---

[1]) This is the procedure of Zermelo 08a (his Axiom VII). Somewhat different is von Neumann's procedure (cf. below, § 11, 2).

2) Given a mapping between two equivalent sets, are there any other mappings? (Give some examples.) Are there any exceptions to the answer? Specialize to the case of mapping a set onto itself.

3) Is it possible to use, respectively, the functions

$$y = 3x + 5, \quad y = x^2, \quad y = \sqrt{x}, \quad y = \sin x$$

to map the set of the argument-values x onto the set of the function-values y, in the sense of a one-to-one mapping? When this is impossible, can the purpose be effected by suitably restricting the variability of x, say to an interval etc.?

4) Note that to define a relation one has to fix the domains of variability for the arguments of the relation. For instance, the symmetry of the relation "x is a brother of y" depends on the domain taken for y, as shown by the examples: $x =$ Moses, y either $=$ Aaron or $=$ Miriam.

5) The relation $x \cdot y \neq 0$ between real numbers x, y is symmetrical and transitive yet (contrary to the remark on p. 26) not plainly reflexive, namely not "totally reflexive", as shown by $x = 0$.[1])

6) Prove that the equality between sets is substitutive to the right (p. 13), i.e. that $z \in a$ and $a = b$ imply $z \in b$ [2]), by means of the axiom of subsets in its extended form (footnote [2]) on p. 16). Hint: let c be the unit-set $\{a\}$, and $d \subseteq c$ be determined by the condition on x: $z \in x (\epsilon c)$; then $a \in d$, hence $b \in d$ by the definition of equality. Therefore $z \in b$.

7) Why is it suitable to start the proof that non-reflexive and reflexive sets cannot be equivalent (p. 30/1), with a *reflexive* set?

§ 3. DENUMERABLE SETS

1. Denumerability. In this section we shall deal with the simplest type of infinite sets, viz. the denumerable sets.

> DEFINITION I. A set which is equivalent to the set of all positive integers is called *denumerable* (or countable). If its members are *ordered* according to the magnitude of the integers related to them one speaks of an *enumerated* (ordered) set.

---

[1]) See the profound investigations in Scholz–Schweitzer 35, § 5, and in Aubert 49 and 52. In these papers not only dyadic but also n-adic or $2n$-adic relations are contemplated. A comprehensive treatment of n-adic relations, including their classification, is given in Fraïssé 55. Of earlier investigations cf. Peano 24, Padoa 30, Itô 33–35.

[2]) Cf. A. Robinson 39 (in the Supplementary Bibliography).

With respect to the totality of the members of a denumerable set it is often convenient to say "denumerably many", just as with respect to the members of a finite set one says "finitely many".

If N is the set of all positive integers and D any denumerable set there exist, according to the definition, mappings between N and D. Of these (incidentally, infinitely many) mappings let an arbitrary one be denoted by φ and let d_n be the member of D that is related by φ to the integer n ($n = 1, 2, 3, \ldots$); the index n of d_n is, then, the image in N (by φ) of d_n, which for short is also called "the nth member of D". Thus every positive integer occurs as the index of a single member d_n of D and only these members d_n belong to D.

Hence we can write D in the form

$$\{d_1, d_2, d_3, \ldots, d_n, \ldots\}$$

without hereby expressing an order in D, in accordance with the concept of set which involves no notion of order. If, however, the d_n shall be arranged according to increasing values of n we obtain the sequence [1]) or the enumerated set

$$(d_1, d_2, d_3, \ldots, d_n, \ldots).$$

Though we shall deal with ordered sets in general only in § 8, the notion of enumerated set will prove useful before.

An immediate consequence of Definition I is that *a set equivalent to a denumerable set is itself denumerable*. A denumerable set is infinite both in the sense of Definition VI and of Definition VII of § 2. The axiom of infinity ensures that *there exist denumerable sets*.

2. Simplest Examples and Theorems. Any set M that originates from N, or from any denumerable set, by dropping finitely many members *is also denumerable*; to form a mapping onto N we have only to relate the first remaining member to 1, the second to 2, etc. The particular case of dropping a single member was described on p. 30.

The result is not restricted to the case where finitely many members of a denumerable set are removed but remains valid if this is done for infinitely many members, provided the remainder is still infinite. Thus the set E

---

[1]) Yet not every sequence is an enumerated set because in a sequence, in contrast with a set, the same member may occur repeatedly. An (infinite) sequence may, then, contain finitely many *different* members only.

of all even positive integers is obtained from N by dropping all (infinitely many) odd integers. A mapping is marked by the scheme

$$N: \quad 1 \quad 2 \quad 3 \quad \ldots \quad n \quad \ldots$$
$$\updownarrow \quad \updownarrow \quad \updownarrow \qquad \updownarrow$$
$$E: \quad 2 \quad 4 \quad 6 \quad \ldots \quad 2n \quad \ldots$$

In other words, every $n \in N$ is related to $(2n) \in E$ and every $e \in E$ to $\frac{e}{2} \in N$. Generally we have

THEOREM 1. *Any subset of a denumerable set D is either finite or denumerable.*

Proof. Let again $D = \{d_1,\ d_2,\ d_3,\ \ldots,\ d_n,\ \ldots\}$ and let D_0 be any subset of D. If D_0 is empty it is finite; otherwise let n_1 be the least integer [1]) for which $d_{n_1} \in D_0$, n_2 the least integer for which $d_{n_2} \in (D_0 - \{d_{n_1}\})$, and so forth, according to mathematical induction. We distinguish between two cases.

a) A certain step of the procedure, say the kth, is the last because the set $D_0 - \{d_{n_1}, d_{n_2}, \ldots, d_{n_k}\}$ is empty. Then $D_0 = \{d_{n_1}, d_{n_2}, \ldots, d_{n_k}\}$, i.e. D_0 is a finite set.

b) The procedure can be continued indefinitely, i.e. to *each* positive integer k corresponds a member $d_{n_k} \in D_0$. Then by the above definition D_0 is denumerable, which completes the proof.

However, also a set which is more comprehensive than N may be denumerable. We again start with an example, namely the set I of *all integers* which also contains 0 and the negative integers. Arranged according to the magnitude of the numbers this set is not enumerated since every integer is preceded by infinitely many smaller negative (and possibly some positive) integers. Yet we obtain an enumeration, i.e. a proof that I is denumerable, by placing every negative integer $-n$ immediately after the corresponding positive n and by letting 0 precede all other integers. Thus a mapping between I and N emerges according to the following scheme

$$I: \quad 0 \quad 1 \quad -1 \quad 2 \quad -2 \quad \ldots \quad n \quad -n \quad \ldots$$
$$\updownarrow \ \updownarrow \quad \updownarrow \ \updownarrow \quad \updownarrow \qquad \updownarrow \quad \updownarrow$$
$$N: \quad 1 \quad 2 \quad 3 \quad 4 \quad 5 \quad \ldots \quad 2n \quad 2n+1 \quad \ldots$$

where n ranges over the positive integers.

---

[1]) Here we use the arithmetical fact that in every non-empty set of positive integers there is a *least* integer.

By this example, in which no other property of integers is used than the denumerability of N and $I - N$, we perceive that the addition of denumerably many (all the more, of finitely many) members to those of a denumerable set produces a denumerable set.

Since this procedure may be repeated any finite number of times we have

THEOREM 2. *The union of finitely many sets each of which is finite or denumerable, and one at least denumerable, is a denumerable set.*

Theorem 2 is a counterpart of Theorem 1; the latter deals with "reductions", Theorem 2 with certain "extensions" of a denumerable set.

3. The Set of all Rationals.

To obtain an essentially stronger result we again start with an example, namely with the set R of all *rational numbers* (or common fractions) $\frac{m}{n}$ where $n \neq 0$. It is preferable to consider the rationals in the *reduced form* only where the denominator n is a *positive* integer and the positive or negative numerator m is *prime to n*; the number 0 is then represented in the form $\frac{0}{1}$. The reduced rationals $\frac{m_1}{n_1}$ and $\frac{m_2}{n_2}$ are, therefore, equal only if $m_1 = m_2$ and $n_1 = n_2$.

Arranging the rationals according to their magnitude we observe that between any two different rationals $\frac{m_1}{n_1}$ and $\frac{m_2}{n_2}$ there are infinitely many different others; for if $\frac{m_1}{n_1} < \frac{m_2}{n_2}$ we may divide the positive difference $\frac{m_2}{n_2} - \frac{m_1}{n_1}$ into two, three, ..., k, ... equal parts which are also rational, and by adding them to $\frac{m_1}{n_1}$ we obtain rationals greater than $\frac{m_1}{n_1}$ and less than $\frac{m_2}{n_2}$. Thus the set of all rationals is in a definite sense infinitely more comprehensive than the examples contemplated above.

Nevertheless R *turns out to be also denumerable.* One of many ways to show this is the following. In a plane we draw denumerably many horizontal straight lines and denumerably many vertical lines, either system corresponding to all integers. (See fig. 4.) Denote an arbitrary horizontal and an arbitrary vertical line respectively by 0, the lines upwards and

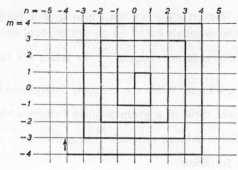

Fig. 4

rightwards of 0 successively by 1, 2, 3, ..., the lines downwards and leftwards of 0 by — 1, — 2, — 3, ... Every intersection between a horizontal and a vertical line is called a *lattice point*. Each lattice point is determined by the respective horizontal and vertical lines m and n, and to every ordered pair of integers m and n belongs a uniquely determined lattice point, to be denoted by (m, n).

To enumerate, first, the lattice points we follow the broken bold line drawn in fig. 4 from its starting-point $(0, 0)$ via $(1, 0)$, $(1, 1)$, $(0, 1)$ etc. We arrange the points in this order, thus obtaining all lattice points as the members of a sequence. (Usually the procedure of rearranging a sequence of sequences to a single sequence is called the *diagonal method of Cauchy*, cf. § 6, **8**.) From this sequence we drop all those lattice points (m, n) for which the corresponding $\dfrac{m}{n}$ is not a *reduced* rational, in particular those for which n is 0 or a negative integer. Finally we conceive the infinitely many remaining points (m, n) as the corresponding rationals $\dfrac{m}{n}$; they also form a sequence (Theorem 1), *the denumerable set of all (reduced) rationals*. Its numeration according to the procedure just used begins with

$$\frac{1}{1}, \frac{0}{1}, -\frac{1}{1}, \frac{2}{1}, \frac{1}{2}, -\frac{1}{2}, -\frac{2}{1}, \frac{3}{1}, \frac{3}{2}, \ldots$$

This arrangement fundamentally differs from that according to magnitude, as illustrated by the line of numbers (fig. 2, § 1); had we taken the rationals in the latter arrangement then no enumeration would have emerged.

No geometrical argument was essential in forming our enumeration of the rationals. Nevertheless we shall also give a (slightly different) enumeration of the rationals based on an arithmetical description.

To every *positive* reduced rational $\frac{m}{n}$ we relate the sum $a = m + n$ which is a positive integer. While a is uniquely determined by $\frac{m}{n}$ the converse does not hold. Still to a given positive integer a there exist only finitely many positive reduced rationals $\frac{m}{n}$ such that $m + n = a$, namely those among the fractions

$$\frac{a-1}{1}, \frac{a-2}{2}, \ldots, \frac{2}{a-2}, \frac{1}{a-1}$$

which are reduced, and the same rational cannot occur more than once, namely related to a single a only.

Hence we may enumerate all positive rationals according to increasing values of $a = 2, 3, 4, \ldots$; for a definite a we use, say, the above arrangement according to increasing denominators. If we begin with $0 = \frac{0}{1}$ and let every positive rational $\frac{m}{n}$ be succeeded by the negative $-\frac{m}{n}$ then an enumeration of all rationals emerges which slightly differs from the previous one; it begins with

$$\frac{0}{1}; \frac{1}{1}, -\frac{1}{1}; \frac{2}{1}, -\frac{2}{1}; \frac{1}{2}, -\frac{1}{2}; \frac{3}{1}, -\frac{3}{1}; \frac{1}{3}, -\frac{1}{3}; \frac{4}{1}, -\frac{4}{1}; \frac{3}{2}, \ldots.$$

The mapping of the set of all rationals $r = \frac{m}{n}$ onto the set of all positive integers n, in either way, is conspicuous enough, yet for large r it is not easy to calculate the integer n to which r is related. For this purpose single-valued and uniquely invertible functions $n = f(r)$ have been constructed in various ways.[1]

Finally, what has been achieved in this subsection is an enumeration not just of the rationals but more generally of any sequence of sequences. In fact, we have used no special properties of the positive rationals

---

[1] Faber 05, Oglobin 29 (cf. Boehm 29), Godfrey 38, Johnston 48, Hanani 55.

but only their property of forming a sequence (for $n = 1, 2, 3, \ldots$) of sequences $\left(\dfrac{m}{n}\right)$ where, for each n, m ranges over a sequence of positive integers. We may, therefore, express our result in the following form which extends the result of Theorem 2:

THEOREM 3. *The union of denumerably many different sets each of which is finite* [1]) *or denumerable, is a denumerable set.*

4. The Set of all Algebraic Numbers. We saw in 3 that between any two different rationals there are infinitely many others. In view of a one-to-one mapping between the real numbers and the points of a line (§ 1, fig. 2) this means that the subset of those points of the line which are related to rational numbers — in short, the subset of all *rational points* — is (infinitely) *dense*, a term to be defined in § 9, 1 for ordered sets of points in general. Yet it was pointed out in § 1 that in spite of their density the rational points do not exhaust the notion "point of the line". We shall now, through an example which was Cantor's first discovery in set theory, enlarge the set of all rationals to a still more comprehensive (and dense) set of numbers which will also prove denumerable. The question whether the corresponding set of points constitutes the *totality* of the points of the line (or at least whether this totality is denumerable) will then assume an additional urgency. In fact, during his earliest study of the problem Cantor took the result of the present subsection as suggesting the denumerability of the set of all points of the line. Therefore the (contrary) answer which is given in § 4 will constitute the corner-stone of set theory as a new branch of mathematics and at the same time the first important application of this theory to other, classical domains of mathematics.

As defined in § 1, every root of the algebraic equation of the degree $n > 0$

(1) $$a_0 x^n + a_1 x^{n-1} + \ldots + a_{n-1} x + a_n = 0 \quad (a_0 \neq 0)$$

with *integral* coefficients a_k is called an *algebraic number*. Such a root need not be real; however, since the inclusion of imaginary and complex

---

[1])   This extension of our result is clearly admissible in view of Theorem 1, without the condition (stated in Theorem 2) that at least one of the sets be denumerable. In fact, infinitely many different finite sets yield an infinite union.

roots would not contribute anything important to our arguments (while transcending the geometric-intuitive frame of the points of a line), we shall for the sake of simplicity restrict ourselves to *real* algebraic numbers and always conceive the term *algebraic number* with this (somewhat artificial) restriction.

The rationals are the algebraic numbers which are roots of linear equations ($n = 1$); the totality of all algebraic numbers contains, in addition, the roots of equations with the infinitely many degrees 2, 3, 4, ...[1]). Cf. § 9, **2**.

In the proof of this subsection we shall not use the so-called fundamental theorem of algebra which is rather profound and states that every algebraic equation of a positive degree has a (real or complex) root, but only the following quite elementary theorem: *an algebraic equation of the degree n has not more than n real roots.*

In fact, if we denote the polynomial on the left-hand side of (1) by $p(x)$ and if r_1 is a real root of (1), the division of $p(x)$ by $x - r_1$ yields

$$(2) \qquad p(x) = (x - r_1) \, p_1(x) + s_1.$$

Inserting r_1 for x in (2) gives $0 = 0 + s_1$, i.e. $s_1 = 0$. Repeating this procedure with regard to a real root r_2 (if any) of the equation $p_1(x) = 0$ and proceeding further in the same way, we finally arrive at an identity of the form

$$(3) \qquad p(x) = (x - r_1) (x - r_2) \ldots (x - r_k) \, p_k(x)$$

where $p_k(x) = 0$ has no real root and $k \leqslant n$. (If the polynomial $p_k(x)$ is a constant we have $k = n$ and $p_n(x) = a_0$.)

(1) has no real root in addition to $r_1, r_2, \ldots, r_k$; in fact, for any other real $x = r_{k+1}$ each factor of the right-hand side of (3) is different from 0, hence also $p(r_{k+1}) \neq 0$.

To prove that the set of the algebraic numbers is denumerable [2]) we start with enumerating the algebraic *equations*. This can certainly not be achieved by arranging the equations, as usual in algebra, according to their degrees, for then the linear equations, i.e. the rational numbers, would already exhaust the enumeration. To accomplish our task we attach to the equation (1) not its degree but the positive integer

$$(4) \qquad h = (n - 1) + \mid a_0 \mid + \mid a_1 \mid + \ldots + \mid a_n \mid$$

---

[1]) To be sure, m/l is also a root of (infinitely many) equations with degrees > 1, e.g. of the equation $l^2 x^2 - m^2 = 0$. Yet to each degree there exist algebraic numbers which are not roots of equations with a lower degree — a fact not required for our argumentation here.

[2]) The proof is essentially that of Cantor 1874, § 1. For an explicit enumerating function cf. Vandiver 36.

where $|a_k|$ denotes the absolute value of a_k (i.e. the non-negative integer equaling $\pm a_k$); h will be called the *amount* of the equation (1). For instance, $2x^2 - 3x + 1 = 0$ has the amount $1 + 2 + 3 + 1 = 7$, $x^3 = 0$ the amount $2 + 1 + 0 + 0 + 0 = 3$.

While every algebraic equation has a definite positive integer for its amount we shall now prove that to a given positive integer h there belong only *finitely many* algebraic equations with the amount h. First, the degree n of such an equation cannot exceed h because of (4) and of $|a_0| \geqslant 1$. Hence there are no more than $h + 2$ terms, at most, on the right-hand side of (4). But obviously the positive integer h can be decomposed into the sum of at most $h + 2$ non-negative terms in a finite number of ways only. These decompositions may be arranged in a definite order by giving n successively the values $h, h - 1, \ldots, 2, 1$ and by taking, for each single value of n, for $|a_k|$ always the respective maximal positive integer still admissible, including 0 if $k > 0$. Finally, when all non-negative integral solutions A_k of the diophantine equation

$$h = (n - 1) + A_0 + A_1 + \ldots + A_n \quad (h \text{ and } n \ (\leqslant h) \text{ given}, A_0 \neq 0)$$

have been obtained in this way, then the respective solutions a_k of (4) emerge by taking independently

$$a_0 = \pm A_0, a_1 = \pm A_1, \ldots, a_n = \pm A_n;$$

this yields at most 2^{n+1} different solution systems (just 2^{n+1} if all A_k are different from 0). Thus all equations (1) with the amount h have been arranged.

Example. $h = 3$; the degrees $n = 3, 2, 1$ only come into consideration. We have, then, to consider the diophantine equations

$$3 = (n - 1) + |a_0| + \ldots + |a_n|$$

for each of the values $n = 3, 2, 1$ and with the restriction $a_0 \neq 0$. The following seven solutions are obtained:

$$
\begin{aligned}
3 &= 2 + 1 + 0 + 0 + 0 & (n = 3) \\
&= 1 + 2 + 0 + 0 = 1 + 1 + 1 + 0 = 1 + 1 + 0 + 1 & (n = 2) \\
&= 0 + 3 + 0 = 0 + 2 + 1 = 0 + 1 + 2. & (n = 1)
\end{aligned}
$$

Finally, for each of these solutions we have to distribute independently the signs $+$ and $-$ on all terms $\neq 0$, except for the first term which refers to the degree. For instance, the first solution yields the two decompositions corresponding to (4)

$$3 = 2 + |\ 1\ | + 0 + 0 + 0 = 2 + |-1\ | + 0 + 0 + 0$$

and the third solution yields the $2^2 = 4$ decompositions

$$3 = 1 + |\ 1\ | + |\ 1\ | + 0 = 1 + |-1\ | + |\ 1\ | + 0$$
$$= 1 + |\ 1\ | + |-1\ | + 0 = 1 + |-1\ | + |-1\ | + 0.$$

The corresponding algebraic equations are respectively

$$x^3 = 0,\ -x^3 = 0,\ x^2 + x = 0,\ -x^2 + x = 0,\ x^2 - x = 0,\ -x^2 - x = 0.$$

Evidently the seven solutions obtained above yield a total of $2 + 2 + 4 + 4 + 2 + 4 + 4 = 22$ formally different algebraic equations, and these are all equations with the amount 3.

Hereby *all algebraic equations* are enumerated in a definite way, namely by taking the equations corresponding to the infinitely many amounts $h = 1, 2, 3, \ldots$ in this order and by arranging, for each h, the finitely many equations with the amount h in the way shown above. Hence, by Theorem 3, we obtain a *sequence* which contains all algebraic equations.

The last step is the transition from the equations to their (real) roots, i.e. to the algebraic numbers. Since each equation has finitely many roots only (namely an equation of the degree n at most n different roots) we may conceive these roots to be arranged anyway; for instance, according to magnitude. Thus a sequence is obtained which contains all real algebraic numbers. True, hereby the same number is listed several (even infinitely many) times; for instance, the number 2 as a root of the equations with different amounts

$$x - 2 = 0\ (h = 3),\ x^2 - 4 = 0\ (h = 6),\ x^4 - 16 = 0\ (h = 20),\ \text{etc.}$$

and also as the root of equations with equal amounts, e.g. $x - 2 = 0$ and $-x + 2 = 0$. To obtain a sequence that contains different numbers only, we drop from the above sequence every number which has occurred before; then each algebraic number appears among the roots of one equation with a minimal amount. Hereby we have proved:

The set of all (real) algebraic numbers is denumerable.

In a way similar to the enumerations of rationals defined above, this enumeration of the algebraic numbers thoroughly destroys the "natural" order of numbers according to their magnitude. For instance, the numbers $-\frac{1}{8} = -0.125$ and $\sqrt{7} = 2.645\ldots$ as roots of the equations with the amount 9

$$8x + 1 = 0 \quad \text{and} \quad x^2 - 7 = 0$$

appear near each other in our numeration whereas $-\frac{1001}{8000}$ (though differing but little from $-\frac{1}{8}$) occurs much later among the roots of the equations with the amount 9001.

5. Applications to Infinite Sets in General. While so far we have dealt with denumerable sets for themselves we shall now use denumerability as a tool for the investigation of infinite sets in general. The spring-board from which we may leap is the following theorem which has a fundamental character and will attract our attention also later.

THEOREM 4. *Every infinite set has a denumerable subset.*

We used this theorem already for proving the equipollence between two definitions (VI and VII) of infinity and finiteness in § 2, 5. Hence we must not use this equipollence in proving Theorem 4; in fact, we have to produce separate proofs according as "infinite" in Theorem 4 is considered to mean "non-inductive" or "reflexive". The proofs have thoroughly different character and, as the reader will verify, it is proof A (and not proof B) which shows the equipollence between our definitions of infinity.

Proof A. Let S be a non-inductive set; that is to say, a non-empty set which cannot be exhausted by dropping k members where k denotes any positive integer.

First, we shall show by mathematical induction that, for every positive integer n, there *exists a subset of S containing just n members.* For $n = 1$ this is clear since by assumption S is not empty and, for any $s_1 \epsilon S$, $S_1 = \{s_1\}$ is a suitable subset. If k is any positive integer we assume the statement to be true for $n = k$; this means that $S_k = \{s_1, s_2, \ldots, s_k\}$ is a subset of S. By assumption this subset does not exhaust S, hence $S - S_k \neq O$. Let s_{k+1} be an arbitrary member of $S - S_k$; then $S_{k+1} = \{s_1, s_2, \ldots, s_k, s_{k+1}\}$ is also a subset of S and contains $k + 1$ members. Thus the above statement has been shown to be true for $n = 1$ and, if true for $n = k$, also for $n = k + 1$; by mathematical induction, then, it is true for *every* n. Moreover, the finite subsets S_k of S produced successively have the property that S_{k+1} includes S_k as a proper subset.

Secondly, the sets S_k for $k = 1, 2, 3, \ldots$ form a sequence of subsets of S, and their union which contains *all* members s_k, for $k = 1, 2, 3, \ldots$, constitutes a denumerable subset $\overline{S}$ of S. ($\overline{S} = S$ is not excluded.) Hereby the proof *A* of Theorem 4 is completed.

This proof, seemingly quite simple, relies upon a procedure not ordinarily used in mathematics and certainly not included in our above axioms, namely upon an *infinity* of choices of arbitrary members of S. In fact, for every k we have chosen an arbitrary s_k to produce the sets S_k. We shall return to this point in § 6, **5** and § 11, **6**.

Proof B. Let S be a reflexive set, i.e. $S \sim \overline{S} \subset S$, and let φ be an arbitrary mapping of S onto its proper subset $\overline{S}$; φ will be retained throughout the proof. The member of $\overline{S}$ which by φ corresponds to an $s \in S$ shall be denoted by $\varphi(s)$.

Let t_1 be an arbitrary member of the non-empty set $S - \overline{S}$. We successively define the members

$$t_1, \quad \varphi(t_1) = t_2, \quad \varphi(t_2) = t_3, \quad \ldots, \quad \varphi(t_k) = t_{k+1}, \quad \ldots.$$

After t_1 has been chosen these members are uniquely determined; they all belong to $\overline{S}$, except for t_1 which belongs to $S - \overline{S}$, hence not to $\overline{S}$.

Thus we obtain a denumerable subset $\{t_1, t_2, t_3, \ldots\}$ of S *provided these members are different*. We shall, therefore, show by an indirect proof that $t_i \neq t_k$ if $i \neq k$.

If the t_k were not all different, let t_m be the first t_k which equals a preceding t_l:

(1) $$t_m = t_l. \quad (l < m, \text{ hence } m > 1)$$

t_m, then, belongs to $\overline{S}$ and is therefore *different from* t_1; hence also $t_l \neq t_1$, i.e. $l > 1$. In view of the definition of the members t_k we have $t_l = \varphi(t_{l-1})$ and $t_m = \varphi(t_{m-1})$.

Writing (1) in the form $\varphi(t_{m-1}) = \varphi(t_{l-1})$ and utilizing the biuniqueness of the mapping φ we conclude $t_{m-1} = t_{l-1}$. But this contradicts our assumption by which t_m is the *first* t_k which equals a preceding one. The contradiction shows that no t_k equals a preceding one; that is to say, all members t_k ($k = 1, 2, 3, \ldots$) are different.

Hence $\{t_1, t_2, t_3, \ldots\}$ is a denumerable set and a subset of S, which completes the proof.

In contrast with the proof *A*, in the present proof only a single member of the set desired has been chosen arbitrarily, namely t_1. It is not difficult to show (cf. *Foundations*, Ch. II, § 8) that the axioms introduced hitherto, when supplemented with Axiom VI (§ 5, **3**), are sufficient for proof B — but not for proof A in which the axiom of choice (§ 6, **5**) is utilized.

Theorem 4 enables us to prove for *any infinite* [1]) *sets* certain properties which are analogous to those expressed for *denumerable* sets by Theorems 1 and 2.

Let S be any infinite set and S_0 a finite or denumerable subset of S such that $\overline{S} = S - S_0$ still is an infinite set [2]). We shall show that $\overline{S} \sim S$.

Let $\overline{S}'$ be a *denumerable* subset of $\overline{S}$ (Theorem 4) and $\overline{S} - \overline{S}' = \overline{S}''$. ($\overline{S}''$ may be infinite, finite, or empty.) This means

$$\overline{S} = \overline{S}' \cup \overline{S}''. \quad (\overline{S}' \text{ and } \overline{S}'' \text{ disjoint sets})$$

Hence any member of S belongs to a single of the pairwise disjoint sets $S_0, \overline{S}', \overline{S}''$.

Now we construct a mapping of the set $S = S_0 \cup \overline{S}' \cup \overline{S}'' = (S_0 \cup \overline{S}') \cup \overline{S}''$ onto its subset $\overline{S} = \overline{S}' \cup \overline{S}''$ by relating every member of $\overline{S}''$ (if any) to itself [3]) and by mapping $S_0 \cup \overline{S}'$ onto $\overline{S}'$ in view of Theorem 2. Hence:

THEOREM 5. *By dropping from an infinite set S finitely many members, or denumerably many members such that still infinitely many members are left, one obtains a set which is equivalent to S.*

From Theorem 5 we immediately conclude:

THEOREM 6. *By adding to an infinite set finitely many or denumerably many members one obtains a set which is equivalent to the original set.*

This follows by taking the new (more comprehensive) set as the set S of Theorem 5.

Theorems 5 and 6 contain nothing new (cf. Theorems 1 and 2) if the

---

[1])   After having completed the equipollence proof of pp. 31–32 by Theorem 4, we shall no more distinguish between inductive and non-reflexive, or non-inductive and reflexive, sets but simply speak of *finite* and *infinite* sets.

[2])   If S_0 is finite this condition is superfluous. For denumerable S_0, however, it may be required; if S is the set of all positive integers and S_0 the set of the integers $> 10^{10}$ then the condition is not satisfied.

[3])   We have to use this identical mapping since we know nothing about the nature of $\overline{S}''$.

infinite set in question is denumerable. Their importance will show when, in § 4, the existence of non-denumerable infinite sets is ensured; for these sets S the condition of Theorem 5 ("such that...") becomes superfluous.

Exercises

1) Prove that the set of all terminating decimal fractions, or the set of all algebraic numbers between 0 and 1, is denumerable.

2) Illustrate the arithmetical way of enumerating the rationals (in 3) with regard to the lattice points of fig. 4.

3) Prove that the set of those points of the plane whose Cartesian coordinates, with respect to a given pair of axes, are rational, is denumerable.

4) Represent any given denumerable set as the union of denumerably many pairwise disjoint denumerable sets.

5) Enumerate the set of all algebraic equations by means of the following method (which essentially differs from Cantor's). Assign to the polynomial $f(x) = a_0 + a_1x + \ldots + a_nx^n$ with integral coefficients a_k the positive integer $N(f) = p_1{}^{A_0} p_2{}^{A_1} \ldots p_{n+1}^{A_n}$ where p_k denotes the kth prime number (i.e. $p_1 = 2$, $p_2 = 3$, $p_3 = 5$, etc.) and where the non-negative integers A_k are obtained from the a_k by mapping the set of all integers onto the set of the non-negative integers. Examine whether this correspondence between polynomials and positive integers yields a one-to-one mapping.

6) What denumerable subset of S evolves if proof A of Theorem 4 is used subject to each of the following rules:

a) S is the set of all positive integers; the arbitrary member to be chosen in S and its subsets shall be the *least integer* of the respective set.

b) S is the set of all positive integers; the arbitrary member shall be the *least integer divisible by 5*.

c) S is the set of all positive integers; the arbitrary member shall be the *least prime number*.

d) S is the set of all positive rationals written as reduced fractions $\dfrac{m}{n}$; the arbitrary member shall be the fraction with the *least sum $m + n$*, and if this sum corresponds to various fractions then the least (according to magnitude) among those fractions.

7) What denumerable subset of S evolves if proof B of Theorem 4 is used subject to this rule: S is the set of all positive integers, $\overline{S}$ the subset

of all even integers, φ the mapping that relates $x \in S$ to $(2x) \in \overline{S}$, and $t_1 = 5$.

8) (Cf. Theorem 5) Show that from every given infinite set one can drop denumerably many members such that still infinitely many members are left.

9) Prove Theorem 6, without referring to Theorem 5, in a way analogous to the proof of Theorem 5.

10) Assuming that there exist infinitely many (real) transcendental numbers, show that the set of all transcendental numbers is equivalent to the set of all real numbers.

Exercises 11) — 13) are for advanced readers

11) We call two closed intervals, say on the line of numbers (§ 1), *non-overlapping* if they have no common point, except possibly for end points. Prove that any set of non-overlapping closed intervals on the line is at most denumerable (i.e., finite or denumerable). (Hint: given the closed interval $a \leqslant x \leqslant b$, let k be the least integer greater than $\dfrac{1}{b-a}$, and $l = [k \cdot a]$[1]); relate $\dfrac{l+1}{k}$ to the given interval.)

It is easy to generalize the theorem from the line to the plane (using two-dimensional intervals, i.e. rectangles) or to spaces of three and more dimensions.

12) Prove that an infinite set of points (say, of a line or a plane) which has a finite number only of accumulation points (§ 9, 5) is denumerable, and show by an example that this statement cannot be inverted.

13) Prove that a *monotonic* function has at most denumerably many points of discontinuity. (Hint: for a positive integer n there are, in any closed interval, only finitely many jumps with an amount greater than $\dfrac{1}{n}$.)

§ 4. The Continuum. Transfinite Cardinals

1. Further Examples of Equivalent Sets. In the subsections 1–4 of § 3 we contemplated several sets of apparently very different sizes which, by means of various devices with increasing artfulness, proved to be *equivalent*, namely denumerable. By comparing this situation to the properties

---

[1]) As usual, [c] denotes the integer $\leqslant c$ and next to c.

of finite sets, where dropping or adding members produces sets which are *not equivalent* to the original set, the suspicion is raised that *any two infinite sets might be equivalent.* This would mean that there is only one infinite cardinal number "infinity (∞)". Every gifted schoolboy of fifteen has arrived at this notion and has contemplated relations such as $\infty + \infty = \infty$ and $\infty \cdot \infty = \infty$ which seem to correspond to Theorems 2 and 3 of § 3. If so, infinite sets would be trivial with respect to their equivalence (extent, cardinal number) and could certainly not be the subject of a new branch of mathematics.

We shall now even strengthen this suspicion by presenting further essentially different examples of sets which in spite of their obviously unlike extent prove to be equivalent. These examples, however, will be followed in subsection **2** by an exposition of Cantor's discovery (of 1874) that *there exist infinite sets which are not equivalent.* This surprising and dramatic discovery, which is at the bottom of Theory of Sets, is rendered more prominent by the following examples.

We are contemplating sets the members of which are *points.* Given two segments [1]) of different length, $\overline{AB}$ and $\overline{CD}$ (fig. 5), let M denote the set of all points of $\overline{AB}$, N the set of all points of $\overline{CD}$, including the endpoints. We prove that $M \sim N$.

A mapping can, for instance, be established in the following way. Drawing the segments parallel to each other as in fig. 5 we connect C and A, as well as D and B, by straight lines which, on account of the different length of the segments, will intersect in a point P. Any ray drawn from P intersects either both segments or neither; in the former case the inter-section point with $\overline{AB}$ shall be related to the intersection point with $\overline{CD}$, where-by clearly a one-to-one correspondence between the points of both segments evolves. Hence $M \sim N$.

This proof illustrates two earlier re-marks. First, by laying off $\overline{AB}$ on $\overline{CD}$ we may consider M to be a proper subset of N and thus obtain a new example of equivalence between the whole and a part (§ 2, **5**). Secondly,

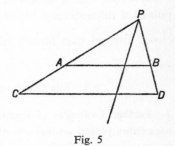

Fig. 5

---

[1]) For the sake of simplicity we take straight segments, but arcs of a circle or of another curve would do as well.

objections to our proof of $M \sim N$ have been raised, claiming that one
"ought" to establish a correspondence between the points of M and N by
drawing *parallels* (for instance, parallels to the line AC) instead of rays
with the center P. True, hereby we would *not* obtain a one-to-one
correspondence, for there will remain points on $\overline{CD}$ to which no image on
$\overline{AB}$ corresponds. This supposed failure, however, has no significance
with regard to our proof. As every highschool student knows there is
always a large variety of ways by which one will *not succeed* in proving a
given (true or false) mathematical theorem; they are insignificant, for
what counts is either *the one way* (or several ways) that leads to success,
or else a general proof showing that *no way* can lead to success (as the
proof of Theorem 1 given below in **2**).

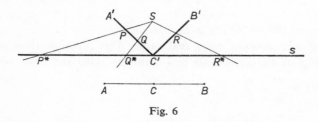

Fig. 6

A fact still more surprising than $M \sim N$ is the equivalence between an
(open) segment to be regarded as the set K of its points or of the corresponding numbers, and the set L of all points of an unlimited (infinite)
line or of all real numbers. A mapping which shows the equivalence may
be constructed as follows (see fig. 6). Denoting the straight line with s,
the segment with $\overline{AB}$, and its center with C, we bend the segment (as
though it were a thin wire) in C and lay it upon s so that C becomes a
point C' of s and that A and B — in the new position, A' and B' — lie on
the same side of s (in fig. 6, above s) in equal distance from s. Finally,
the middle of $\overline{A'B'}$ (which segment does not appear in the figure) shall be
denoted by S.

A simple one-to-one correspondence between the points of the open
segment $\overline{A'C'B'}$ and the points of the line s can be established by drawing
rays from S. Any such ray will either intersect both the open segment and
s, or intersect neither. In the first case, the points of the segment and of
the line belonging to the same ray shall be related to each other; in fig. 6,
for instance, P and P^*, Q and Q^*, R and R^* (while C' corresponds to
itself). Thus a mapping is constructed which shows the equivalence be-

tween the sets K and L, though the latter is so to speak infinitely more comprehensive than the former.

Our particular method of mapping is suitable for the open segment (without its ends A and B) and not for the closed segment [1]). Yet according to Theorem 6 of § 3, **5**, the equivalence also holds after the addition of the ends or of one of them.

Instead of the geometrical definition we may use an analytic method, for instance the trigonometric function $y = \tan x$ (fig. 7). If x is restricted to the open interval

$$-\frac{\pi}{2} < x < \frac{\pi}{2}$$

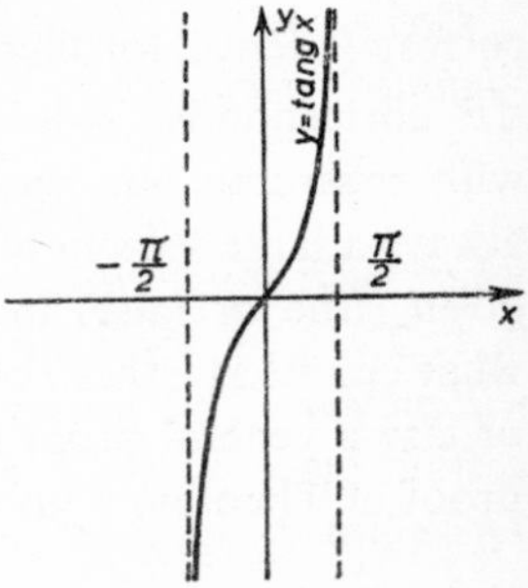

Fig. 7

(i.e. from -90^0 to 90^0), y is monotonically increasing and assumes every real value. This function, then, produces a mapping of the set of all real numbers onto the finite open segment from $-\frac{\pi}{2}$ to $\frac{\pi}{2}$.

2. Proof that the Continuum is not Denumerable. We have repeatedly dealt with the set N of all positive integers and the set *(continuum)* C of all points of a segment or interval and with many sets which proved equivalent to N or to C. We may also conceive C as a set of numbers, viz. of all real numbers of an interval. The suspicion expressed in subsection **1** would include that N might be equivalent to C.

We shall now refute this conjecture by proving that N and C are not equivalent, hence that *there are non-equivalent infinite sets*. As mentioned before, this is the fundamental result from which the theory of (infinite) sets is starting.

It makes no difference *what* interval we use as the continuum (cf. **1**) and whether we include the ends or one of them. For practical reasons which will show presently we choose for C the "semi-closed" interval $0 < x \leqslant 1$ of the positive real numbers up to, and including, 1. It is convenient to conceive the members of C as numbers t rather than as points; we shall write the numbers as *decimal fractions* (decimals) — not because this representation of the real numbers is superior to other

---

[1])   In fact, the rays from S through A' and B', being parallel to s, do not intersect s.

representations, e.g. as continued fractions, but because this is the one that every reader is familiar with.

Here and later we shall use the following *auxiliary theorem* from the theory of decimals:

Every positive [1]) *real number A has one and only one expansion into an "infinite" decimal*

$$A = m . c_1 c_2 c_3 \ldots c_k \ldots$$

where m is a non-negative integer and the digits c_k can assume the values 0, 1, 2, ..., 9, *with the proviso that after every c_k digits different from 0 will appear.* (This proviso is expressed by *infinite*; otherwise, i.e. if from a certain place on only zeros appear, we speak of a *terminating* decimal.) *Therefore, two infinite decimals which are not identical represent different real numbers.*

A positive real number that can be expanded into a terminating decimal [2])

$$m . c_1 c_2 c_3 \ldots c_n \quad (c_n \neq 0)$$

is equal to the infinite decimal

$$m . c_1 c_2 c_3 \ldots (c_n - 1) 999 \ldots$$

(*or, if it is the positive integer m, to* $(m - 1) . 999 \ldots$) [3]).

While these facts are well known from their use in school, their rigorous proof cannot be given without an analysis of the concept of *real* number. For this proof, therefore, the reader is referred to introductory textbooks (cf. also § 9, **1**). — The existence of real numbers with two non-identical decimal expansions (one infinite and one terminating) is an inconvenience which renders continued fractions superior to decimals for various purposes.

According to this theorem, our interval C may also be defined as the set of all infinite decimals of the form $0 . c_1 c_2 c_3 \ldots c_k \ldots$ (which includes the number $1 = 0.999\ldots$).

---

[1]) The number 0, to be sure, has no infinite expansion. This is why we have not included 0 in our interval.

[2]) As is well known, this holds for the rationals $\frac{m}{n}$ whose denominator in the reduced form is divisible by no other prime than 2 and 5.

[3]) The reader who should find this surprising may, for instance, comprehend the equality $1 = 0.999\ldots$ through multiplying by 9 the equality $\frac{1}{9} = 0.111\ldots$.

To show that C is not equivalent to the set N of all positive integers we prove the following

LEMMA. *Given any d e n u m e r a b l e subset C_0 of C, there exist members of C which are not contained in C_0; that is to say, C_0 is a p r o p e r subset of C.* In other words, there is no denumerable set that contains *all* members of C.

(To be sure, there exist denumerable proper subsets of C; for instance, the set of all positive *periodic* decimals between 0 and 1, whose members are rational numbers.)

Proof of the lemma [1]). C_0 being denumerable means that there exist mappings between C_0 and the set N of all positive integers. We choose such a mapping φ and express it by the following scheme:

$$
\begin{array}{ll}
\text{members of } N & \text{members of } C_0 \\
1 \longleftrightarrow 0 \,.\, a_{11} \quad a_{12} \quad a_{13} \quad a_{14} \quad \cdots \\
\qquad\qquad\qquad\quad \searrow \\
2 \longleftrightarrow 0 \,.\, a_{21} \quad a_{22} \quad a_{23} \quad a_{24} \quad \cdots \\
\qquad\qquad\qquad\qquad\quad \searrow \\
3 \longleftrightarrow 0 \,.\, a_{31} \quad a_{32} \quad a_{33} \quad a_{34} \quad \cdots \\
\qquad\qquad\qquad\qquad\qquad\quad \searrow \\
4 \longleftrightarrow 0 \,.\, a_{41} \quad a_{42} \quad a_{43} \quad a_{44} \quad \cdots \\
\qquad\qquad\qquad\qquad\qquad\qquad\quad \searrow \\
\;\cdot \qquad\qquad\qquad \cdot \qquad \cdot \qquad \cdot \qquad \cdot \qquad \cdots \\
\qquad\qquad\qquad\qquad\qquad\qquad\qquad\qquad \searrow \\
n \longleftrightarrow 0 \,.\, a_{n1} \quad a_{n2} \quad \cdot \quad \cdot \quad \cdot \quad \cdot \quad \cdot \quad a_{nn} \quad \cdots \\
\;\cdot \qquad\qquad\qquad\qquad \cdot \\
\;\cdot \qquad\qquad\qquad\qquad \cdot \\
\;\cdot \qquad\qquad\qquad\qquad \cdot
\end{array}
$$

The decimal related by φ to the integer n is here denoted by $0 \,.\, a_{n1} \, a_{n2} \, a_{n3} \, \ldots .$ Generally the first index i of a digit a_{ik} refers to the "number" of the decimal considered, i.e. to the integer to which the decimal is related, while the second index k marks the place after the decimal point

---

[1])   We follow essentially the method of Cantor 1892, which is the simplest demonstration of Theorem 1 and most convenient for generalization (cf. subsection 7). The earliest demonstration is given in Cantor 1874, simplified in 1879–84 I; cf. the ingenious method of Poincaré 10. All these proofs are *in nuce* similar, namely based on the diagonal method (see below).

where the digit a_{ik} appears in the ith decimal. The right-hand side of the scheme may be described as an "infinite square" extending rightwards and downwards from the vertex a_{11}.

The "diagonal" digits $a_{11}, a_{22}, \ldots, a_{ii}, \ldots$ (i.e. the a_{ik} for which $k = i$), marked in our scheme by arrows, shall serve to define a decimal

$$d = 0 \,.\, d_1 \, d_2 \, d_3 \ldots d_i \ldots$$

in the following way: in general d_i shall equal 1; only if $a_{ii} = 1$, d_i shall equal 2. In other words, for every $n = 1, 2, \ldots, d_n = 1$ or $= 2$ according as $a_{nn} \neq 1$ or $= 1$. Then *d is a member of C not contained in C_0*. First, d is an infinite decimal between 0 and 1. Furthermore, d is different from *all* members of C_0, i.e. from the nth member (the member related to n by φ) for all $n = 1, 2, \ldots$; in fact, the nth digit of the nth member is a_{nn} while the nth digit of d is $d_n \neq a_{nn}$, and since both the nth member and d are infinite decimals they also represent different real numbers.

Hence C_0 is a *proper* subset of C, which completes the proof of the lemma.

Finally, the lemma expresses the following property of the set C of all real numbers x with $0 < x \leqslant 1$:

THEOREM 1. *C is not denumerable, i.e. not equivalent to the set N of all positive integers.*

Thus we have confirmed the existence of two infinite sets which are not equivalent.

3. Remarks and Supplements to the Proof.

Certain features of the proof require additional remarks.

Beginners are often inclined to maintain: well, a real number d not contained in C_0 has been constructed but its addition to the members of C_0 will not impair its property of being denumerable, in accordance with Theorem 2 of § 3. This is a gross misunderstanding of the logical character of the proof. Even if only a single member of C not belonging to C_0 were produced our aim would have been attained. For the mapping φ refers to N and *any* denumerable subset of C, including more comprehensive ones than C_0. The meaning of the proof, then, is that *no* denumerable set exhausts C.

The reader will rightly ask, what is the special rôle of the digits 1 and 2 in the proof and why has 1 been favored versus 2? The answer is, no special rôle at all! (The purpose of our particular procedure will be explained presently.) d might as well have been defined by the rule: *let, for every i, d_i be any digit different from the diagonal digit a_{ii}*, which rule produces infinitely many numbers d. Proceeding in this way we should only exert caution regarding the digit 0, either by excluding $d_i = 0$ altogether or by ensuring that not finally all d_i (i.e., all from a certain $i = k$ on) equal 0; for otherwise d might be a terminating decimal, which would render the ultimate argument of the proof illusory because d might then *equal* one of the infinite decimals of C_0.

Why, then, the restriction to the digits 1 and 2 in our proof? Just to kill the prejudice, found in some treatments of the proof, as if the method were purely *existential*, i.e. as if the proof, while showing that there *exist* decimals belonging to C but not to C_0, did not allow to *construct* such decimals. The arbitrary way of singling out the digits 1 and 2 enables us to form a uniquely defined such decimal, though it has no preference over others; in 4 we shall give a quasi-practical application of this constructivity.

In our proof *decimals* have been used. It is clear that the choice of the base 10 cannot have a mathematical reason. The use of the decadic (decimal) scale of notation, including decimal fractions, in our civilization (in contrast to the old peoples of Mesopotamia and other civilizations who used 6 or 8 etc. as bases) relies on the fact that man has ten fingers with which he used to count and reckon. Any positive integer, with the exception of 1 the powers of which do not increase, is as well fit to serve as base: the mathematician gives preference to the least possible base, namely 2 (cf. § 7), which is also favored in many applications from the Morse system to electronic computers [1]). The use of system fractions with any base $\geqslant 3$, instead of decimals, would not change our proof even in its details; only the base 2 requires a slight modification since then for the a_{ik} and d_i only the values 0 and 1 are available, which affects our rule about excluding zeros. (Cf. exercise 2) at the end of this section.)

Because of the part played by the diagonal digits a_{ii} in our proof, its method is called (Cantor's) *diagonal method*. It is one of the strongest and most famous methods in modern mathematics and we shall use it at various junctures in the present exposition of set theory [2]). Objections

---

[1]) For practical arithmetic, 2 proves too small; in the dyadic system already 27 would be written with five digits, namely as 11011.

[2]) Also outside abstract set theory the method is used, for instance in the theory of sets of points and of orders of infinity.

to the diagonal method have been raised on a lower [1]) and a higher [2])
level, but its use for proving our lemma is legitimate even from intuitionistic points of view [3]) (which object to Theorem 1 because they would
not admit the continuum C as a mathematical object).

Judged in the light of mathematical technique, the proof of our result
by means of the diagonal method is surprisingly simple in comparison
with its far-reaching consequences within and without set theory (cf.
subsection 4). The simplicity and lucidity of many of Cantor's fundamental proofs constitute a particular charm of set theory and contrast
favorably with more difficult and technical proofs of important theorems
in other branches of mathematics, including the branch which in many
ways is congenial with theory of sets, namely theory of numbers.

Finally, the character of our result as an *impossibility statement* should
be pointed out. In § 3 and subsection 1 of § 4 many results showing the
equivalence of different sets were obtained by the construction of suitable
mappings. In contrast herewith, Theorem 1 asserts that it is *impossible* to
produce a mapping between the sets N and C.

In many branches of mathematics problems of impossibility have been
raised and partly been solved — the oldest among them being problems
of Greek geometry such as duplicating the cube, trisecting the angle,
squaring the circle (these three with restriction to the use of ruler and
compasses), proving Euclid's postulate of parallels; all these were solved
(in the negative) in the nineteenth century only. The difficulty (and the
charm) of most impossibility proofs has its root in the need of, as it were,
scrutinizing all possible ways of solution and of showing their futility.
By this feature the proof of Theorem 1 is distinguished from the earlier
equivalence proofs.

This difference in principle between proofs of equivalence and of non-
equivalence is missing in the comparison between *finite* sets. Here, as
even children know from experience in playing, a single failure in attempting to form a mapping is sufficient for stating the non-equivalence, just
as one success shows the equivalence. Does this contradict what was just
pointed out?

Not at all. The difference in principle remains. That it does not become
visible in dealing with finite sets is due to a particular property of these

---

[1]) For instance, by Bentley 32 and Bridgman 34. These objections are refuted in
Rust 34 and Fraenkel 35.
[2]) See in particular Kreisel 50.
[3]) See *Foundations*, chapter IV.

sets which has an arithmetical character and is proved by the method characteristic of arithmetic, viz. mathematical induction. In the beginning of § 8 we shall express this property as follows: to a given finite cardinal number there belongs only a single corresponding ordinal number; in other words, in whatever different ways the members of a finite set may be arranged, there always emerges the same scheme of order: a first, second, ..., nth member with the same concluding n. On account of this property, one failure in mapping shows that every attempt is bound to end in failure.

To show the completely different behaviour of *infinite* sets it is sufficient to refer to our experience with the *rational numbers* (§ 3, 3). If they are ordered according to magnitude there is no least rational and between any two given rationals there are infinitely many others. But if we enumerate them there is a first, and every rational is immediately succeeded by a uniquely defined other. These are just two of infinitely many *essentially different* ways of ordering the set of rationals (see § 8, **6**); for more comprehensive infinite sets the variety is increasing. Accordingly there are many ways of attempting to form a mapping between infinite sets and one failure proves nothing. On the contrary, as we saw in § 2, **5**, every infinite set is equivalent to a *proper subset*; hence besides the one-to-one correspondences between the members of two equivalent sets there are others which exhaust the members of one set but not of the other. A proof of non-equivalence, therefore, is intrinsically an impossibility proof.

4. Extension of Theorem 1. The Transcendental Numbers. In **1** we saw that intervals of different length, when considered as the sets of all real numbers (or points) contained in the open (or closed, or semi-closed) interval, are equivalent to each other and also to the set of *all* real numbers (all points of a line). The property of being non-denumerable is not changed by the transition to an equivalent set.

Calling, as usual, each of the sets just mentioned a *continuum* (of numbers or points) — and even *the* continuum as far as the properties common to these sets are concerned — we may formulate

THEOREM 2. *The continuum is an (infinite) non-denumerable set.*

To be sure, we have not affirmed the *existence* of the continuum, which cannot be proved by means of the five axioms (including the axiom of infinity) introduced so far. The existence of the continuum will result by means of an additional axiom (VI) to be introduced in § 5, 3 for a more general purpose.

We shall now give an important, and at its time most surprising, application of our result to a problem outside set theory.

The concept of real transcendental number, as a real number which is not algebraic, was introduced in § 1. Up to the first quarter of the present century, before the discoveries of Gelfond, Siegel, and others [1]), little was known about transcendental numbers, and the proofs that numbers such as e and π are transcendental (1873/1883) are difficult. Though the original method (Liouville, 1851) of proving the existence of transcendental numbers yields a whole class of such numbers, a more far-reaching and most surprising result is obtained by our relatively simple methods.

The set C of all real numbers is the union of the disjoint sets of all real algebraic numbers (A) and all real transcendental numbers (T); $C = A \cup T$. Applying Theorem 5 of § 3 [2]) we have $T \sim C$, for A is denumerable. Hence

THEOREM 3. *The set of the real transcendental numbers, or of the transcendental numbers of an arbitrary interval, is equivalent to the set of a l l real numbers.*

One might say, a real number is "normally" transcendental and "in exceptional cases only" algebraic.

The restriction to real numbers is insignificant as previously. The result is surprising, for the numbers mathematicians have been studying and using are "almost all" algebraic [3]).

To prevent the impression as if Theorem 3 were a merely existential statement we refer to what was said in 3. Let in the proof of the lemma C_0 be an enumeration of the set of all algebraic numbers as constructed in § 3, 4. Then *the uniquely defined decimal d is a transcendental number,* obtained in a constructive way. True, we do not know, in their entirety and simultaneously, the decimal expansions of all algebraic numbers in a

---

[1]) Cf., for instance, Schneider 59.

[2]) The profound theorems 4 and 5 of § 3 are not required for proving that T is an *infinite non-denumerable* set, for from the elementary Theorem 2 of § 3 it follows that T cannot be finite or denumerable.

[3]) It is noteworthy that in his paper of 1874 Cantor mainly stresses the first of the two results contained, namely the denumerability of the set of the real algebraic numbers — a result which seems to us almost trivial. The second, incomparably profounder result, viz. the non-denumerability of the set of all real numbers, appears there rather as an application of the first to the problem of transcendental numbers.

way comparable to our knowledge of, say, the periodic decimals. But we have at our disposal laws for constructing the nth digit of the nth algebraic number in our enumeration for every positive integer n and can accordingly compute the nth digit of the transcendental number d. To make this obvious we constructed d as done above, by taking just the digits 1 and 2.

To be sure, after having advanced to any n we are not in the possession of a transcendental number, for we may then continue, for instance, in a periodic way and hereby obtain a rational number. Yet objections of this kind have no weight; the situation is similar, e.g., for the number π of whose decimal expansion we know finitely many digits only (in contradistinction, for example, to the expansion of rational numbers). It is the *law* underlying the construction of d (or of π) which defines the expansion uniquely. On the other hand, the construction naturally has only a theoretical character and does not yield a transcendental d in an intuitive way.

5. The Concept of Cardinal Number. The Cardinals $\aleph_0$ and $\aleph$. From Theorem 1 we have drawn an important conclusion and other applications will be given later. Now, however, we shall concentrate upon its consequence within set theory proper and point out in what sense the theorem should be considered *the very basis of set theory*. This is done first in an informal way; in subsection 6 a more elaborate analysis of the subject will be given.

In § 2, 4 a procedure was outlined which leads from equivalent *finite* sets to the concept of their common cardinal number, as was done in the seventeenth century by Descartes and later in a more satisfactory way by Hume. Conversely, if two finite sets have the same number of members they are equivalent.

Since that procedure does not utilize the finiteness of the sets it is natural to attribute the same cardinal to *any* equivalent sets, no matter whether they are finite or infinite. While the existence of non-equivalent finite sets is well known, in the case of infinite sets it is Theorem 1 which renders the procedure non-trivial by ensuring that there exist infinite sets which are not equivalent, hence infinite cardinals which are different. (Nobody before Cantor has even ventured to prove this although mathematicians had dealt with infinite sets and one-to-one correspondences between their members long before.) The existence of different (as we shall see in § 5, infinitely many different) infinite cardinals imposes upon us the task of comparing the cardinals and calculating with them.

But first of all we have to *define* infinite cardinals. The situation in the realm of finite quantities (sets and numbers) suggests to distribute the sets, whether finite or infinite, into classes (sets) of sets [1]) such that sets of the same class are equivalent and sets of different classes are not. Now, says Cantor in his final exposition of the theory [2]), the cardinal of a set S should be understood to be the general concept (universal) which by means of our "active mental power" arises from the set S *by abstracting* from both the special nature of the members of S and the order in which they may occur in S. This would reflect just what is common to all sets equivalent to S, i.e. to all sets of the class to which S belongs.

To be sure, Cantor's formulation will hardly be acknowledged as a *definition* of cardinals. Yet one might proceed to a definition by conceiving the very classes defined above as the cardinals, i.e. by defining:

(A) The cardinal of a set S is the class (set) of all sets that are equivalent to S.

This definition seems somewhat paradoxical. However, such definitions are nowadays a matter of course in mathematics; for instance, a real number is defined as a set of sequences of rationals with certain properties, and a rational number as a set of pairs of integers with certain properties. Hence objections to (A) maintaining that "integers are far simpler objects than sets of sets" need not be taken seriously. On the other hand, the "set of all sets equivalent to S" is apt to involve antinomies unless certain precautions are taken; for these see *Foundations*, chapters II and III.

The logician certainly prefers an explicit definition of cardinal such as (A). For the mathematician, however, the explicitness of the definition is not a foremost requirement, for he is rather concerned with handling the mathematical objects than with exploring their nature — somewhat similar to the chessplayer who does not care what the bishop or the pawn "mean" but how one operates with them. Many divergent philosophical theories have, for instance, been proposed to clarify the nature of integers, but the rules of arithmetic are independent of which theory one adheres to. Also with regard to cardinals it is sufficient to give a *working definition* [3]) such as the following, mentioned for finite cardinals above:

---

[1]) The term "class" means here nothing different from "set" and is adopted for the sake of simpler expression only.

[2]) Cantor 1895, p. 481.

[3]) For this concept and its significance in mathematics cf. Carnap 27, Weyl 26/49.

(B) The sets S_1 and S_2 are said to have *equal cardinals* if they are equivalent, i.e. if $S_1 \sim S_2$. Otherwise their cardinals are called *different*.

As may be expected in view of ordinary arithmetic and will be confirmed in the following sections, all relations between cardinals can be reduced, in addition to the membership relation for sets, to the equality and inequality of cardinals, hence in view of (B) to the equivalence and non-equivalence of sets as defined in § 2. Accordingly we need not fix what a cardinal *is* and may translate statements on cardinals into the language of sets.

One may take an additional step by altogether avoiding the use of cardinals, restricting oneself to corresponding *sets* and their equivalence. For ordinary purposes of set theory and most of its applications this would cause considerable inconvenience, though no difficulty of principle, but in axiomatic set theory (see *Foundations*, chapter II, §§ 1–5 and 8) this way proves to be practicable.

By developing the general concept of cardinal and ensuring the existence of different infinite cardinals we are enabled to answer the question "how many members are contained in the set?" for infinite sets in an equally definite sense as for finite sets and not just with the vague expression "infinitely many". To be sure, there is between finite and infinite sets the specific difference that the answer to the above question is not necessarily changed when additional members are inserted into an infinite set, as is the case for finite sets; this is due to the fact that an infinite, but not a finite, set is equivalent to a proper subset.

The cardinals of infinite sets are called *transfinite cardinals*. For their notation *in general* we shall use *bold letters*, as far as possible corresponding to the notation of sets whose cardinals they are; thus the cardinal of S or s will be written **s**, etc. Frequently the general notation also includes *finite cardinals*, i.e. cardinals of finite sets; yet when we confine ourselves to finite cardinals we use italics, e.g. k, n. It is often convenient to follow Cantor's custom who from 1887 on denoted the cardinal of the set S by $\overline{\overline{S}}$ ($=$ **s**); the double bar hints at disregarding both the special nature of the members and their succession.

To denote *particular* transfinite cardinals, corresponding to the notation of the finite cardinals 0, 1, 2, ..., one has universally adopted Cantor's mode of writing $\aleph$ (Alef), the first letter of the Hebrew alphabet, with a suitable index, e.g. $\aleph_0$, $\aleph_1$, $\aleph_n$. This will prove impracticable in the case of the cardinal of the continuum (also called the *power of the continuum*, see § 5 and § 11, 7) for which we therefore write $\aleph$ without index, following Hausdorff (and not Cantor). The cardinal of denumerable sets will prove to be the least transfinite cardinal (§ 5) and is denoted by $\aleph_0$.

6. Further Analysis of the Concept of Cardinal. Cantor's (latest) quasi-definition of the concept was quoted above [1]. The essence of his definition by abstraction as expressed by the symbol $\overline{\overline{S}}$ is not peculiar to set theory. Wherever in mathematics or elsewhere a relation **R** occurs which is reflexive, symmetrical, and transitive (see § 2, 4),[2] a new concept may be formed "by abstraction", as shown by the following examples. Through the relation of (directed) parallelism, the set of all rays yields the concept of *direction;* through the relation of (geometrical) similarity, the set of all plane polygons yields the concept of *shape;* through the relation of congruence *modulo m*, the set of all integers yields the *congruence classes;* etc. In our case, the (finite and infinite) sets yield, through the relation of equivalence in the sense of § 2, 4, the concept of *cardinal*. If we express the validity of $x\mathbf{R}y$ by saying, x and y are of the same **R**-type, we may call the new concept "the **R**-type" of the objects concerned; that is to say, the **R**-types of x and y are equal if and only if $x\mathbf{R}y$ holds true. Or, closer to Cantor's formulation, the **R**-type is formed by disregarding the properties of the objects concerned save those based on the relation **R**; accordingly the cardinal of S would mean the totality of just those properties of S which are shared by all sets equivalent to S.

This definition by abstraction is a particular (most important) case of the definitorial procedure which sometimes is called the *creative mathematical definition* [3]. Still, from the logical point of view the foundation of defining by abstraction as given in the preceding paragraph can hardly be regarded as satisfactory [4]; it has been redeemed by Frege and Russell independently.

---

[1] Essentially the same explanation is found in Cantor 1887, p. 82, where he refers to similar formulations in a lecture in Freiburg (1883) and in a letter to Kurd Lasswitz of 1884. Yet in his earlier papers 1878 and 1879–84 Cantor avoids an explicit definition and contents himself with the working definition (B). Moreover, in his review (1885) of the fundamental book Frege 1884 (reprinted in Cantor 32, pp. 440–441) he uses a definition similar to Frege's.

The difference of opinion between Cantor and Frege on this point is trifling and can hardly substantiate the tension prevailing between these great scientists. In particular, the review mentioned does neither justice to Frege's intentions nor to the importance of his ideas. The mathematical fashion of that period deprecated Frege's attitude and endeavored to conceive numbers as mere signs on paper, thus confusing concepts and their notations.

[2] Ore 42 shows what extensive theory can be developed on the basis of this concept. Cf. also Dubreil–Dubreil 39.

[3] So in Weyl 26/49, No. 2; cf. already Pasch 1882, p. 40; the pith of the procedure can be traced back to Leibniz. Since the turn of the century, also in general philosophical literature the classical (Aristotelian) conception of definition by *genus proximum* and *differentia specifica* has been shifting to a functional conception, based on the *relations* between the *definiendum* and other concepts; cf. Cassirer 10, Schlick 25, Nagel 39. In a more general context, the importance of the process of abstraction (and even of the identification of distinct concepts) inside and outside mathematics has been stressed by Meyerson 31 (cf. Lichtenstein 32).

[4] It is significant that a scholar as strict and careful as Dedekind, to justify the definition by abstraction, appeals to the creative power of man ("we are of divine origin") and opposes a conception in the sense of (A); see Dedekind 30–32 III, p. 489.

Russell's procedure [1]) is quite general. He uses the term *principle of abstraction* rather in the sense of replacing Cantor's conception by an exact logical argument, the essence of which is as follows. Given a symmetrical and transitive relation R, there exists a one-to-many relation [2]) R^* such that xRy implies zR^*x and zR^*y where z is uniquely determined by x (or y) but not conversely. z is called the R-type of x, hence of any u for which uRx. If R is equivalence between sets then z is the cardinal of x. With the methods of modern logic, e.g. those of *Principia Mathematica*, the existence of R^* can be proven; thus the cardinals are vindicated.

Frege's vindication [2]), which preceded Russell's but is restricted to finite cardinals, is still closer to (A) than Russell's. However, like Frege's logical system in general also his definition of cardinals was ignored until Russell pointed out its importance [4]).

As to (B) of 5, it has already been stressed that this is a "working definition". One must not discredit the use of "incomplete symbols" introduced through such definitions by the claim that in principle it should be possible to *eliminate* any symbol introduced through a definition — which is just another expression for asking what the new concept *is* and not what task it performs. At any rate for mathematics this claim goes too far, as shown by the inductive definitions, based on mathematical or transfinite induction (see § 10, 2); here the elimination is in general impossible.

Finally one might propose to define cardinals by means of *effective examples*, namely as particular objects (sets) among those mentioned in definition (A) — in some analogy with the definition of the unit of length through the normal metre kept in Paris. The particular object would, then, represent the cardinal of every set equivalent to it. At first sight this method (representing the cardinal 3, say, as the set {sun, earth, moon}) seems arbitrary and impracticable. In § 11, 2, however, we shall see that along the lines of von Neumann this method can be carried out generally, though it is not practical for all purposes. Its gist may be grasped from the particular case of a *finite* cardinal, which can be defined as the set of all smaller cardinals including 0, i.e.

$$n = \{0, 1, 2, \ldots, n - 1\}.$$

While the preceding explanations make it obvious that the attacks of various philosophers upon the concept of (transfinite) cardinal are unsubstantiated, the attitude of (neo-)intuitionists that there do not exist altogether non-equivalent infinite sets is consistent, though almost suicidal for mathematics; see *Foundations*, chapter IV, where the peculiar status of the continuum is pointed out.

There still remains the question whether our axioms enable us to construct cardinals. The answer is in the negative. Hence, if a strictly axiomatic foundation of set theory (and not a semi-axiomatic one as in the present book) is intended [5]) one of two ways has to be taken. Either one renounces the explicit use of cardinals and contents oneself with contemplating the equivalence and non-equivalence of sets; this is the way of

---

[1]) Russell 03, pp. 166 and 120; Whitehead–Russell 10–13 I, 72.66. Cf. Russell 19, Nicod 22.

[2]) Cf. § 2, 4. "z is the father of x" is such a relation.

[3]) Frege 1884, especially §§ 63–68. The criticism of Frege's logic in Smart 45 is unjustified.

[4]) The monograph Scholz–Schweitzer 35 (cf. F. Bachmann 34) gives a comprehensive account of Russell's and Frege's vindications of the definition by abstraction, together with a criticism of Cantor's and other older procedures. An extension to relations with $2n$ arguments is also included.

[5]) An axiomatization of cardinals independently of axiomatic set theory is given in Baer 29.

Zermelo [1]) and his followers. Or else one introduces cardinals as particular sets in the sense of von Neumann and his followers; these sets can be secured by admission of an additional axiom, the axiom of substitution or replacement (see § 11, 2). However, even in this case it is preferable for many purposes to operate with sets rather than with cardinals. The reader interested in these questions of principle is referred to *Foundations*, chapter II.

7. The Set of all Functions and its Cardinal.

So far we have dealt with two transfinite cardinals $\aleph_0$ and $\aleph$. We shall now construct a third one.

We consider the closed interval I defined by $0 \leqslant x \leqslant 1$. A single-valued real function $f(x)$ is defined in I when by a suitable rule to every x of I a uniquely determined real number $f(x) = y$ is attached. One-to-one correspondence between x- and y-values is not required.

Let F be the set of all such functions $f(x)$. (Here F is taken just as an example; the proof that F exists on account of our axioms including the axiom formulated in § 5, 3 is based on concepts introduced in § 7.) Two members of F, $f_1(x)$ and $f_2(x)$, are considered different if and only if there is at least one $x = x_0$ in I for which $f_1(x_0) \neq f_2(x_0)$.

There are proper subsets of F which are equivalent to the continuum, for instance the set of those functions that are *constant* in I. To show this we may relate the constant function $f(x) = c$ to the real number c. Hence, at any rate F is not denumerable.

To prove that F is not even equivalent to the continuum we use the diagonal method. Let C be the set (continuum) of all numbers of the interval I and F_0 *any subset of F that is equivalent to C*; it will be sufficient to prove that F_0 is, by this assumption, a *proper* subset of F, i.e. that there are functions in F which do not belong to F_0. (Cf. subsections 2 and 3 above.) Using an arbitrary mapping Φ between F_0 and C, we shall name such a function.

The function (member of F_0) which by Φ corresponds to the real number $c \epsilon C$ shall be denoted by $f_c(x)$; $f_{\frac{3}{4}}(x)$, for instance, is the function related by Φ to $\frac{3}{4} \epsilon C$. $\varphi(x)$ shall be the "diagonal" function which, for each $x_0 \epsilon C$, equals the function $f_{x_0}(x)$; in short, $\varphi(x) = f_x(x)$. In other words, to determine the value $\varphi(c)$ of $\varphi(x)$ for $x = c$ we have to take the function $f_c(x)$; its value for $x = c$, i.e. $f_c(c)$, is $\varphi(c)$ [2]). Hereby the function $\varphi(x)$ is uniquely determined.

---

[1])   Zermelo 08a.
[2])   For instance, if $f_{\frac{3}{4}}(x) = x^2 + 2$ we have $\varphi\left(\frac{3}{4}\right) = f_{\frac{3}{4}}\left(\frac{3}{4}\right) = \left(\frac{3}{4}\right)^2 + 2$.

Finally, $\psi(x)$ shall be a function of F which *everywhere* differs from $\varphi(x)$; e.g., $\psi(x) = \varphi(x) + 1$. $\psi(x)$ *does not belong to* F_0. For let $f_c(x)$ be *any* member of F_0; then $\psi(x) \neq f_c(x)$ because, for $x = c$, $f_c(x)$ has the value $f_c(c)$ and $\psi(x)$ the value $\varphi(c) + 1 = f_c(c) + 1 \neq f_c(c)$. Hence F_0 is a proper subset of F, which means

THEOREM 4. *The set F of all single-valued real functions $f(x)$ defined for* $0 \leqslant x \leqslant 1$ *has a cardinal* $\mathfrak{f}$ [1]) *which is different from both* $\aleph_0$ *and* $\aleph$ *(while F has a subset of the cardinal* $\aleph$*).*

The reader will observe the far-reaching analogy between the proofs of Theorem 4 and of the lemma in subsection **2**. While the diagonal method of that proof used digits, i.e. positive integers, here the integers are replaced by real numbers; instead of a_{tt} we here have $f_c(c)$.

One may even consider the very proof of Theorem 4 to be a proof of the lemma, i.e. of the non-denumerability of the continuum, by interpreting the present proof in a new light without formally changing it. For this purpose we regard the functions $f(x)$ as *arithmetical functions* whose argument x ranges over the positive integers and which assume positive integral values only. If

$$D = \{f_1(x), f_2(x), \ldots, f_n(x), \ldots\}$$

is *any denumerable* set of arithmetical functions then the proof of Theorem 4 shows that the arithmetical function $\chi(x) = f_x(x) + 1$, where x ranges over the positive integers, is not contained in D. Hence the set of all arithmetical functions is not denumerable. On the other hand, one easily realizes that the concepts of arithmetical function and of real number essentially coincide; cf. § 7, **5**.

In § 7 we shall see that the proof of Theorem 4 rests upon the enormous generality and arbitrariness of our functions, which permits the construction of the rather "pathological" function $\varphi(x)$. In ordinary analysis one hardly uses such functions and for the cardinal of, for instance, the set of all *continuous* functions we shall obtain a different result.

Exercises

1) Give, by means of rational functions, mappings between the following continua (cf. **1**)

---

[1])   We shall see later why $\mathfrak{f}$ has not been denoted by means of an aleph.

a) the set of real numbers between *a* and *b* and the set of real numbers between *c* and *d* (*a*, *b*, *c*, *d* denoting different real numbers);

b) the set of real numbers between 0 and the positive number *a* and the set of real numbers which are greater than the positive number *b*.

2) Prove the non-denumerability of the set of real numbers when expanded into *dual fractions*

a) directly by a modification of the diagonal method as used in **2**;

b) by using Theorem 5 of § 3.

(Hint regarding a): insert digits 1 into the diagonal fraction *d* so as to exclude a *finite* dual fraction.)

3) Prove that the set of all irrational real numbers and the set of all sequences of natural numbers have the cardinal $\aleph$.

4) Show that the set of all points of the circumference (or an arc) of a circle (ellipse, hyperbola) has the cardinal $\aleph$. (By means of a suitable concept of curve this statement may be generalized.)

5) What modification has the proof of Theorem 4 to undergo if the functions $f(x)$ are defined for *all* real x instead of for $0 \leqslant x \leqslant 1$?

6) How may the proof of Theorem 4 be changed in order to show that F is not equivalent to *any* subset of the continuum C? (Cf. footnote [2]) on p. 68.)

7) On p. 63 the notion of a single-valued real function $f(x)$ was presumed to be known. (We shall introduce it on pp. 111 ff. in a generalized, set-theoretical sense.) To define this notion here, consider $y = f(x)$ to be a set of *ordered pairs* (y, x) of real numbers and indicate suitable conditions which shall be satisfied by the set of all arguments x on the one hand and by the values y on the other. — An *ordered* pair (a, b), with a preceding b, may be conceived as a *plain* set of the form $\{\{a\}, \{a, b\}\}$; see p. 130.

CHAPTER II

EQUIVALENCE AND CARDINALS

§ 5. Arrangement of Cardinals by Magnitude

1. Definition of Order. Among finite cardinals there is a simple definition stating which of two different cardinals is less than the other, namely: if S and T are finite sets and if S is equivalent to a proper subset of T then the cardinal of S is less than the cardinal of T. In particular, the cardinal of a proper subset of T is less than the cardinal of T. For example, $3 < 5$ because $\{s_1, s_2, s_3\}$ is equivalent to a proper subset of $\{t_1, t_2, t_3, t_4, t_5\}$. (Cf. also the end of subsection **4**.)

Our task is to arrange the finite and transfinite cardinals in a corresponding way, i.e. to order them "according to magnitude". Clearly the above way of defining will not do because a set may be equivalent to a proper subset; then it has a cardinal equal to the latter's.

To define a suitable order relation in our case we shall add a new condition which incidentally will relieve us of the restriction to *proper* subsets. The additional condition might be non-equivalence between the two sets, but it proves more convenient [1]) to take the following way introduced by Cantor:

DEFINITION I. If the set S is equivalent to a subset of the set T while T is not equivalent to any subset of S then the cardinal **s** of S is called *less* (smaller) than the cardinal **t** of T. In symbols,

$$\mathbf{s} < \mathbf{t}, \text{ or } \overline{S} < \overline{T}.$$

Evidently this is in accordance with the usual arrangement of finite cardinals with respect to magnitude. We shall now examine how far this

---

[1]) In view of the equivalence theorem (subsection **4**, see particularly Theorem 4) both ways of defining are equipollent. For the present definition includes the non-equivalence between S and T while the equivalence theorem asserts that, if S is equivalent to a subset of T but not to T then T is not equivalent to any subset of S. Yet pending the proof of the equivalence theorem the present definition is preferable.

order relation shares the properties of order relations in mathematics in general (cf. § 8, 2).

a) The relation is *irreflexive*, i.e. s < t implies s ≠ t. For s = t means $S \sim T$, contrary to the second condition of the definition.

It follows that the subset of T mentioned in the first condition is in any event a proper subset (as in the definition of order for finite cardinals mentioned before).

b) The relation is *transitive* (§ 2, 4), i.e. (with a slight extension) $\overline{\overline{S}} \leqslant \overline{\overline{T}}$ [1]) and $\overline{\overline{T}} < \overline{\overline{W}}$ together imply $\overline{\overline{S}} < \overline{\overline{W}}$. To prove this we start, in accordance with the assumption, from mappings of S onto a subset (proper or not) of T and of T onto a subset of W, or — as we henceforth shall say for short — from a mapping of S *into* T and a mapping of T *into* W; together they produce a mapping of S into W. On the other hand, W is not equivalent to any subset of S; for otherwise, by combining a mapping of W into S with a mapping of S into T, we would obtain a mapping of W into T, contrary to the assumption $\overline{\overline{T}} < \overline{\overline{W}}$.

c) The relation is *asymmetrical*, i.e. s < t and t < s are incompatible. For by b) their conjunction would imply s < s, contrary to a).

d) From s < t, s = s′, t = t′ follows s′ < t′ (substitutivity). This is not a special property of the order relation defined above but required of any relation in mathematics, namely that a true statement containing the relation remains true when an argument is replaced by an equal one. In the present case the condition is clearly fulfilled, for s = s′ means $S \sim S'$ etc., and our definition of order depends on equivalence properties only.

For finite sets, the properties a) — d) also apply to the relation "is equivalent to a proper subset of", hence to the order of finite cardinals. The advantage of our definition of order is its appropriateness for both finite and transfinite cardinals.

While the symmetry of the equivalence relation permits to write also $T \sim S$ instead of $S \sim T$, the property c) prevents such interchange for <. To express the statement s < t by starting with t we have, then, to introduce a new symbol. As usual in arithmetic we write t > s (t *is greater than* s), which is not a new relation but merely another expression for s < t; s < t and t > s are just different ways of formulating the same "inequality" statement. Hence the properties a) — d) hold for > also.

---

[1]) As usual, this means "$\overline{\overline{S}} < \overline{\overline{T}}$ or $\overline{\overline{S}} = \overline{\overline{T}}$".

However, by no means have we by a) — d) accomplished our purpose of proving that the order relation defined here has the usual properties of order relations. In fact, given the cardinals **s** and **t**, from a) and c) it follows that *at most one* of the statements

$$\mathbf{s} < \mathbf{t}, \; \mathbf{s} = \mathbf{t}, \; \mathbf{s} > \mathbf{t}$$

holds true. What we wish to prove is that *just one* of them holds; hence we have still to show that *at least one* of them holds, in other words, that for two different cardinals **s**, **t** either $\mathbf{s} < \mathbf{t}$ or $\mathbf{t} < \mathbf{s}$ is true (*connexity* of the relation or *comparability of cardinals*).

We are unable to prove connexity at this juncture. While in the present section (see **4**) some progress will be made, only at the end of the book, and with a considerable detour, shall we accomplish the aim. Cantor ever attempted to accomplish it and never succeeded; this is why he used the more neutral term "*Mächtigkeit*" (power, *puissance*) rather than the term "cardinal" which should entail comparability.

2. Immediate Consequences. Regarding the transfinite cardinals introduced so far, we first prove $\aleph_0 < \aleph$. Conceiving $\aleph_0$ and $\aleph$ as the cardinals of the sets N of all positive integers and of the set C of all real numbers respectively, we have $N \subset C$. Yet by Theorem 1 of § 3 any subset of N is either finite or denumerable, hence not equivalent to C, which shows $\overline{\overline{N}} < \overline{\overline{C}}$.

Secondly, we prove $\aleph < \mathbf{f}$ where $\mathbf{f}$ is the cardinal of the set F of functions introduced in § 4, 7. The above set C with the cardinal $\aleph$ is equivalent to a subset of F, namely to the set of all constant functions. On the other hand, as shown there, F is not equivalent to C [1]) and one easily extends this so as to show that F is, *a fortiori*, not equivalent to any *subset* of C [2]). Hence $\aleph < \mathbf{f}$ holds true.

Of more general results we start with

THEOREM 1. *There exists a l e a s t transfinite cardinal, namely $\aleph_0$. Every finite cardinal is less than every transfinite cardinal.*

Proof. By Theorem 4 of § 3 every infinite set has a subset of the cardinal

---

[1]) Strictly speaking, the proof of § 4 referred to a set (continuum) equivalent to C, which amounts to the same thing.

[2]) With respect to a subset $C_0 \subset C$ one may, for instance, define $\psi(x)$ for the members x of C_0 as done in § 4, 7, and for other x in an arbitrary way, e.g. $\psi(x) = 1$.

$\aleph_0$. On the other hand, a non-denumerable (infinite) set is certainly not equivalent to a subset of a denumerable set, which, by Theorem 1 of § 3, has only finite and denumerable subsets. Hence for a transfinite $s \neq \aleph_0$ we have $\aleph_0 < s$.

If n is a finite cardinal, by the definition of order we have $n < \aleph_0$. The transitivity of $<$, then, yields $n < s$ for every transfinite s, which completes the proof.

Since the proof A of Theorem 4 of § 3 depends on the axiom of choice (cf. § 6, 5) we show how far one can prove Theorem 1 without using this axiom. In fact, for non-inductive cardinals, i.e. cardinals of non-inductive sets (§ 2, 5), the second statement of Theorem 1 can be seen to be true as follows.[1]) If A is a non-inductive set and $a_0 \in A$, the set $A - \{a_0\}$ is not empty. If a_1 is a member of the latter set, $A - \{a_0, a_1\}$ is not empty. This procedure can be continued any *finite* number of times; hence by means of a finite number of choices only we obtain, for every finite k, an inductive subset of A which contains just k members. On the other hand, A is not equivalent to a subset of an inductive set; hence $k < \overline{\overline{A}}$, i.e. every finite (inductive) cardinal is less than every non-inductive cardinal.

For the cardinals of reflexive sets the proof B of Theorem 4 of § 3 is sufficient to yield our theorem, and this proof uses a single choice only.

The inequality $\aleph_0 < \aleph$ raises the question whether a cardinal s exists *between* $\aleph_0$ and $\aleph$ such that $\aleph_0 < s < \aleph$, or whether $\aleph$ is the cardinal *next* to $\aleph_0$. For eighty years, until 1963, mathematicians have been trying to answer this question; see pp. 113 and 229. The question may also be given the form whether every non-denumerable infinite subset of the continuum is equivalent to the continuum or not. (An analogous question arises with respect to cardinals between $\aleph$ and f.) Cantor was from the beginning [2]) convinced that $\aleph$ was next to $\aleph_0$; in 1884 his desperate efforts to enforce a proof of this conviction were partly responsible for a dangerous break-down of his health. Further information with respect to this "continuum hypothesis of Cantor" is given in (§ 7, 3 and) § 11, 7; for a profounder treatment see *Foundations*, 2nd ed., chapter II.

3. Cantor's Theorem. The Power-Set.
A question which is closely connected with the one just raised and which may seem still more important was solved by Cantor in one of his last papers [3]); namely the

---

[1])   As to the first statement, cf. § 10, 6 and *Foundations*, pp. 62 ff. (mediate cardinals).

[2])   Cf. Cantor 1878 and many of his subsequent papers.

[3])   By a different method, which is much more complicated and uses resources not at our disposal by now, Cantor had even earlier (1883) arrived at the main result. See § 11, 5.

question whether to every transfinite cardinal there exist still greater cardinals. The comprehensive and elegant answer is given by

THEOREM 2 (CANTOR'S THEOREM). *To every set S there exist sets of cardinals greater than $\overline{\overline{S}}$; in particular, the set whose members are all subsets of S is of this kind.[1])*

This set shall be denoted by **CS** [2]) and called the *power-set* of S (for a reason which becomes obvious partly below and more generally in § 7, 3).

According to Theorem 2 there exists no greatest cardinal. Just as the series of finite cardinals, beginning with 0, 1, ..., continues without limit so does the (or, a) series of transfinite cardinals beginning with $\aleph_0$. Yet it will turn out (cf. Theorem 7 of § 6) that in the domain of transfinite cardinals the multiplicity is by far greater than in the finite domain.

Proof[3]) of Theorem 2. First, a subset of **CS** equivalent to S may be defined as the set of all unit-sets $\{s\}$ where s ranges over the members of S; relating $\{s\} \in CS$ to $s \in S$ one obtains a mapping as required.

The second part of the proof of $\overline{\overline{S}} < \overline{\overline{CS}}$ consists, according to the definition of order, in showing that **CS** is not equivalent to any subset of S. To render the argument conspicuous we shall prove that **CS** is not equivalent to S itself and as an afterthought add the slight modification required for the (simpler) case of a proper *subset* of S. We shall again use the diagonal method (cf. § 4, 3).

Let φ denote any fixed mapping of S onto a *subset* C_0 of **CS**; we have to prove that, by the assumption $S \sim C_0$, C_0 is a *proper* subset. φ relates to every *member* of S a certain *subset* of S; hence it will be sufficient to produce a subset c^* of S which is not related by φ to any $s \in S$, for then $c^* \notin C_0$.

In view of φ we distribute the members of S to two categories: of those s which are a member of the subset related to s by φ (members of the *first kind*) and of those s which are not a member of that subset (members of the *second kind*). The *set c^* of all members of the second kind* is certainly a

---

[1]) Accordingly, the theorem seems to have a constructive character. However, the general concept of *subset* is not constructive; cf. *Foundations*, chapter II. For the difficulty of reconciling the theorem with a theory of types see, for instance, Quine 37 and in general *Foundations*, chapter III.

[2]) We have adopted C alluding to Cantor's name. Zermelo, Kleene, and others use 𝔘 with reference to the German *Untermenge* (subset).

[3]) Cf. Hessenberg 06, pp. 41–42 and Zermelo 08a, p. 276; the basic idea is found in Cantor 1892 (cf. his letter to Dedekind of 1899, published in Cantor 32, p. 448).

subset of S (the null-set, if all $s \in S$ are of the first kind); we shall now show that c^* *does not belong to* C_0.

If c^* belonged to C_0 there would be an $s^* \in S$ related to c^* by φ; this s^* must be either of the first or of the second kind. The former case expresses that $s^* \in c^*$, contrary to the definition of c^* by which c^* contains members of the second kind only. But if s^* is of the second kind this means that s^* does *not* belong to c^*, which again contradicts the definition by which c^* contains *all* members of the second kind. Hence the assumption $c^* \in C_0$ yields a contradiction, which completes the proof that CS is not equivalent to S.

The argument used here may appear paradoxical to the reader and will do still more if we use a similar argument to produce the *antinomy of Russell* (1902; see *Foundations*, p. 6). We start with the alternative, seemingly sound for any set s, that s is one of its own members (first kind of sets) or is not (second kind), i.e. $s \in s$ or $s \notin s$. The set of all letters printed in this book is certainly of the second kind since it is not a letter. As a set of the first kind one may regard the set of all sets or the set of all abstracts; yet for our argument it does not matter whether sets of both kinds exist.

Now let R be *the set of all sets of the second kind*. R is either of the first or of the second kind. In the former case we have $R \in R$, contrary to the definition of R; in the latter case we have $R \notin R$ which, by the definition of R, just implies that $R \in R$. Our result is that R is a member of R if and only if R is not a member of R — a glaring contradiction derived from plausible assumptions by a sound argumentation.

Similar as the proof of $c^* \notin C_0$ and the derivation of Russell's antinomy may seem, the difference between them is fundamental. In the former case we have by indirect proof, i.e. by arriving at a contradiction, refuted a certain arbitrary assumption, viz. $S \sim CS$. In the latter case, however, we started with a rather vague set R; if we do not venture to refute the principle of the excluded middle, asserting that $R \in R$ or $R \notin R$, or other logical arguments used (for instance, attributing sense to $R \in R$ for each or for some R) then the antinomy proves that the very definition of R is inadmissible. This only shows that Cantor's definition of set (§ 1) has to be abandoned; as a matter of fact, this was an important result of Russell's discovery. Our axioms obviously do not enable us to construct R or a set of similar structure.

To complete the proof of Theorem 2 we have to show that CS is not equivalent to any *subset* of S either. For this purpose, the distinction between members of the first and the second kind should be restricted to the members of the subset. Yet in view of Theorem 3 or 4 below, this supplement becomes unnecessary altogether.

Theorem 2 is naturally valid also for finite sets. The power-set of the null-set O (which has the cardinal 0) is $\{O\}$ since the null-set has no subset save itself; as $\{O\}$ has the cardinal 1 our theorem expresses $0 < 1$. For a unit-set $\{a\}$ (with the cardinal 1), for instance $\{O\}$, we have $C\{a\} = \{O, \{a\}\}$; thus the theorem means $1 < 2$. For a pair such as $\{a, b\}$ or $\{O, \{O\}\}$, the power-set, i.e. $\{O, \{a\}, \{b\}, \{a, b\}\}$ or $\{O, \{O\}, \{\{O\}\}, \{O, \{O\}\}\}$, contains four members; in general, the power-set of a set of n members contains 2^n members, which is a well-known theorem of arithmetic (proven by mathematical induction); this gives a provisional explanation of the name "power-set". Hence for finite sets of a cardinal > 1 the power-set has *not* the next-greater cardinal, in contrast with Cantor's hypothesis for denumerable sets (end of **2**).

The inequalities $\aleph_0 < \aleph < \mathfrak{f}$ (see above) are particular cases of Theorem 2. For, as shown in § 7, **5/6**, the continuum may be conceived as the power-set of a denumerable set, e.g. of the set of all integers, and the set of all functions as the power-set of a continuum.

Theorem 2 refers to a procedure of set formation which is not justified by the axioms introduced so far. True, individual subsets of a given set are warranted, at least to a great extent, by the axiom of subsets (§ 2, **2**); yet this does not entitle us to unite the subsets to a new set whose members they are. The principle required for this purpose is

Axiom (Principle) of Power-Set (VI). Given a set S, there exists its power-set, i.e. the set whose members are all subsets of S.

In particular, this axiom guarantees the existence of the *continuum*, namely of the power-set of a denumerable set, which is ensured by the axiom of infinity (§ 2, **5**).

Certain logical difficulties involved by the interdependence between the axioms of subsets and of power-set are discussed in *Foundations*, chapters II and III.

4. The Equivalence Theorem. At the end of subsection **1** the connexity of the order relation between cardinals was left open. We now resume this question by specifying all possible cases with respect to two given sets S and T in view of the definition or order [1]), as illustrated by the following scheme.

	T is equivalent to a subset of S	T is not equivalent to any subset of S
S is equivalent to a subset of T	first case	third case: $\overline{\overline{S}} < \overline{\overline{T}}$
S is not equivalent to any subset of T	second case: $\overline{\overline{T}} < \overline{\overline{S}}$	fourth case

---

[1]) This logical procedure, sometimes called *complete disjunction*, was first used in set theory for the present purpose: Cantor 32, p. 450 (letter to Dedekind of 1899, cf. Schoenflies 22, pp. 101f.) and Borel 1898, pp. 102f.

While this scheme exhausts all possible cases according to the principle of the excluded middle it does not affirm that each case is realizable.

The definition of order expresses that in the second case the cardinal of T is less than that of S and in the third case the cardinal of S less than that of T. To examine the comparability of sets with respect to their cardinals we then have to consider the first and the fourth case. The answer regarding the first is given by

THEOREM 3 (EQUIVALENCE THEOREM). *If each of two sets is equivalent to a subset of the other, then the sets themselves are equivalent, i.e. their cardinals equal.*

In addition to its fundamental significance, the equivalence theorem has also practical value inasmuch as it ensures the equivalence of sets between which it is difficult to establish a mapping directly while it proves easy to map each onto a subset of the other. A characteristic example will be given in § 7, **6**.

We present two fundamentally different proofs of the equivalence theorem. Afterwards we shall compare their methods and survey the history of the theorem.

First proof. Assuming $S \sim T_1 \subset T$ and $T \sim S_1 \subset S$ [1]) we have to prove $S \sim T$.

Any mapping of T onto S_1 maps the proper subset T_1 onto a proper subset $S_2 \subset S_1 \subset S$ (p. 27), hence $S_2 \subset S$. From $S \sim T_1$ and $T_1 \sim S_2$ we infer $S \sim S_2$. Taking this relation as the assumption of the theorem we may express its statement as $S \sim S_1$, because of $S_1 \sim T$. The equivalence theorem thus assumes the seemingly simpler form: *if S is equivalent to its proper subset S_2 then S is also equivalent to every set S_1 „between"* S_2 *and* S (i.e. which satisfies $S_2 \subset S_1 \subset S$).

The understanding of the proof will be simplified by writing A for S_2, B for $S_1 - S_2$, and C for $S - S_1$. Hence we have

$$S_1 = A \cup B, \quad S = A \cup B \cup C$$

where A, B, C are pairwise disjoint sets. The equivalence theorem, then, asserts that from $A \cup B \cup C \sim A$ follows $A \cup B \cup C \sim A \cup B$.

Let ψ be an arbitrary mapping of $A \cup B \cup C$ onto A. By applying ψ

---

[1]) Obviously the assumptions of the theorem refer to *proper* subsets because otherwise nothing is left to prove. Hence the theorem is void for finite sets which cannot be equivalent to proper subsets.

separately to the complementary subsets A, B, C of the former set we obtain pairwise disjoint subsets A_1, B_1, C_1 of A such that

$$A \sim A_1, B \sim B_1, C \sim C_1, A_1 \cup B_1 \cup C_1 = A.$$

The second step consists in analogically using a mapping ψ_1 of A onto A_1. ψ_1 may be chosen as a part of ψ and a corresponding remark holds for the further mappings ψ_k. By applying ψ_1 separately to the subsets A_1, B_1, C_1 of A we obtain pairwise disjoint subsets A_2, B_2, C_2 of A_1 such that

$$A_1 \sim A_2, B_1 \sim B_2, C_1 \sim C_2, A_2 \cup B_2 \cup C_2 = A_1.$$

Continuing this procedure, we use for the kth step ($k = 3, 4, 5, \ldots$) a mapping ψ_{k-1} (part of ψ) of A_{k-2} onto A_{k-1} which, separately applied to the subsets A_{k-1}, B_{k-1}, C_{k-1} of A_{k-2}, yields pairwise disjoint subsets A_k, B_k, C_k such that

$$A_{k-1} \sim A_k, B_{k-1} \sim B_k, C_{k-1} \sim C_k, A_k \cup B_k \cup C_k = A_{k-1}.$$

This procedure can be continued indefinitely, i.e. for all positive integers k. For though A_k is a proper subset of A_{k-1}, the successive steps, far from exhausting the sets A_k, do not even diminish their cardinals, as shown by the relations

$$A \sim A_1 \sim A_2 \sim \ldots \sim A_{k-1} \sim A_k \sim \ldots,$$

to which we add, for later use, the relations

(1) $$C \sim C_1 \sim C_2 \sim \ldots \sim C_{k-1} \sim C_k \sim \ldots.$$

Our procedure may be illustrated by fig. 8.

Now two cases are possible. Either there exist members common to

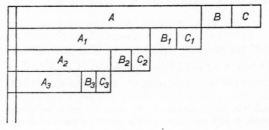

Fig. 8

all sets A_k, i.e. the intersection of all these sets is not empty; the small rectangles on the left hand of fig. 8 hint at this common part of all A_k. Or else there are no common members, then the intersection is the null-set and the rectangles are reduced to strokes. That either case may occur is shown by the examples of pp. 19/20. In both cases the intersection shall be denoted by M.

Whichever case holds, the original set S or $A \cup B \cup C$ is the union of the denumerably many (pairwise disjoint) sets

$$M, C, B, C_1, B_1, \ldots, C_k, B_k, \ldots.$$

For an $x \in A_{k-1}$ which belongs neither to B_k nor to C_k belongs to A_k; hence an $x \in A$ which belongs to *no* B_k or C_k belongs to *each* A_k, therefore to the intersection M. On the other hand, $A \cup B$ arises from $A \cup B \cup C$ by dropping C, i.e. $A \cup B$ is the union of

$$M, C_1, B, C_2, B_1, \ldots, C_{k+1}, B_k, \ldots.$$

(The permutation of every two contiguous terms has been made for practical reasons and is insignificant in view of the commutativity of the union operation; see § 2, **3**.)

After these preparations the proof of the equivalence theorem is easy. To form a mapping of $A \cup B \cup C$ onto $A \cup B$, as required, we first relate M and each B_k (including B) to itself, while C shall be related to C_1 and each C_k to C_{k+1}. Then the union $A \cup B \cup C$ can be mapped onto the union $A \cup B$ by using the identical mapping, which relates every member to itself, with respect to M and the sets B, B_k; as to C and C_k, we rely on the equivalence relations (1) above which are ensured by suitable parts of the mapping ψ that was the starting-point of our proof. Since each member of $A \cup B \cup C$ belongs to one and only one of the sets M, C, B, C_k, B_k, and the analogue holds true for $A \cup B$, a one-to-one correspondence between the members of both sets has been established, which completes the proof of $A \cup B \cup C \sim A \cup B$.

Two sets are called *effectively equivalent* if a mapping between them can not only be shown to *exist* but can be *constructed*. Accordingly a set is called *effectively denumerable* (or "enumerable") if a mapping onto the set of positive integers can be constructed. These concepts are frequently used when the mere existence is not considered sufficient, particularly by mathematicians who identify mathematical existence with construction [1]).

The proof just completed shows that, if ψ is given, a mapping between $A \cup B \cup C$

---

[1]) Cf. Borel 19, Sierpiński 21 and 32, and the exposition in *Foundations*, pp. 56–59 and 299ff.

and $A \cup B$ can be constructed. Hence the equivalence theorem states that, if each of the sets S and T is effectively equivalent to a subset of the other, also S and T are effectively equivalent.

Second proof.[1]) From the assumptions of our theorem, by which there is a mapping φ of the set S onto $T_1 \subset T$ and a mapping χ of the set T onto $S_1 \subset S$, we shall infer that there are subsets $S_0 \subset S$ and $T_0 \subset T$ such that φ maps S_0 onto T_0 and χ maps $T - T_0$ onto $S - S_0$ [2]). Since any member of S belongs either to S_0 or to $S - S_0$ and the situation regarding T and T_0 is analogous, Banach's theorem yields a mapping between S and T as stated by Theorem 3.

To obtain the sets S_0 and T_0 we first relate to every subset $X \subset S$ a subset $X^* \subset S$ in the following way: by φ, to $X \subset S$ corresponds a set $Y \subset T_1 \subset T$, and by χ, to $T - Y$ corresponds a set [3]) $S - X^* \subset S_1 \subset S$. Thus $X^* \subset S$ is uniquely determined by $X \subset S$.

Our aim is to obtain an X for which $X^* = X$. For this purpose we prove:

(a) If X_1 and X_2 are subsets of S and if $X_1 \subseteq X_2$, then $X_1^* \subseteq X_2^*$

For by the nature of φ, $X_1 \subset X_2$ implies $Y_1 \subset Y_2$, hence $T - Y_2 \subset T - Y_1$. From this, by the nature of χ we conclude $S - X_2^* \subset S - X_1^*$, hence $X_1^* \subset X_2^*$. Naturally from $X_1 = X_2$ follows $X_1^* = X_2^*$ since X^* is uniquely determined by X. This completes the proof of (a).

An $X \subset S$ shall be called *distinguished* if $X \subseteq X^*$. There exist distinguished subsets of S, for instance the non-empty set $S - S_1 = D_1$. In fact, by mapping T onto S_1 through χ we obtain members of S_1 and not of D_1; therefore, if φ relates $D_1 \subset S$ to $Y_1 \subset T_1$ and χ relates $T - Y_1$ to $S - D_1^*$, then $S - D_1^*$ contains no member of D_1. Hence, in view of $D_1 \subset S$, we have $D_1 \subseteq D_1^*$, i.e. D_1 is distinguished.

Let S_0 be the *union of all distinguished subsets* of S. For every distinguished subset D we then have $D \subseteq S_0$, hence by (a): $D^* \subseteq S_0^*$. In other words, for every distinguished $D \subset S$ we have

$$D \subseteq D^* \subseteq S_0^*.$$

The relation $D \subseteq S_0^*$, holding true for every distinguished D, holds as well for the union S_0 of all D's, i.e.

(b) $$S_0 \subseteq S_0^*,$$

---

[1]) Beginners may skip this proof at the first reading.

[2]) This theorem which has many applications is due to Banach; see Banach 24, cf. Sikorski 48 and Bruns-Schmidt 58.

[3]) Since $T - Y \subseteq T$, χ maps $T - Y$ onto an $S' \subseteq S_1 \subset S$. Hence we have $X^* = S - S'$.

hence by (a) : $S_0^* \subseteq (S_0^*)^*$. This means that S_0^* is also distinguished; hence by the definition of S_0 : $S_0^* \subseteq S_0$. Together with (b) this shows that $S_0^* = S_0$.

Thus we have reached our aim. According to the definition of X^* by means of X, φ maps $S_0 \subset S$ onto $T_0 \subset T$, and χ maps $T - T_0$ onto $S - S_0$, which completes the proof.

The proof may be summarized as follows. We call "distinguished" those subsets $X \subset S$ for which, if φ maps X onto $Y \subset T$ and χ maps $T - Y$ onto $S - Z$, $X \subseteq Z$ holds true; then the union X of all distinguished sets is again distinguished and for this X we have $Z = X$.

The fundamental difference between our two proofs of the equivalence theorem lies in that the first proof essentially rests upon properties of the sequence (or set) of positive integers while this sequence does not enter the second proof. In fact, the mapping established by the first proof uses Theorem 2 of § 3 (or the relation $\aleph_0 + 1 = \aleph_0$, see § 6, 4). The second proof, on the other hand, has a more abstract character and utilizes a procedure which will appear in § 11, 7 in wider generality; in the present case the chief point is forming the union of a set of sets.[1]

It will prove useful to express the equivalence theorem in another form. If the set S is equivalent to a subset of T there remain (cf. the scheme of p. 72) two exclusive possibilities: that T is also equivalent to a subset of S, or that T is not equivalent to any subset of S. In the first case, according to the equivalence theorem we have $S \sim T$, i.e. $\overline{\overline{S}} = \overline{\overline{T}}$; in the second, by the definition of order $\overline{\overline{S}} < \overline{\overline{T}}$. Hence:

---

[1]   Most proofs of the equivalence theorem belong to one of these two types. The first complete proof published was given by F. Bernstein in 1897 (cf. Cantor 32, p. 450) and appeared in Borel 1898, pp. 103 ff.; it essentially coincides with the first proof given above. A similar proof proposed at the same time by E. Schröder turned out to be defective; see Korselt 11.

The first proof of the second type was given by Dedekind in 1887 and 1899 but not published until 1932; see Dedekind 30–32III, pp. 447–449 and Cantor 32, p. 449. Essentially the same proof was independently rediscovered by Peano (06) and Zermelo (08a, pp. 271f.). To the second proof given above cf., for instance, Banach 24, J. M. Whittaker 27, Reichbach 55.

The proof of J. König 06, belonging to the first type, is distinguished by its lucidity, see below exercise 4); it has yielded remarkable generalizations, in particular the theory of *equivalence with respect to classes of mappings* (cf. § 8, 3) — an important field that contains all results of equivalence theory which are independent of the axiom of choice (§ 6, 5). Cf. Sierpiński 22 and 46/47, Banach 24, Kuratowski 25, Rosenfeld 25, D. König 26, Lindenbaum–Tarski 26, Ulam 29, Otchan 42, Kurepa 53a, and in particular Tarski 28, 29, 30, 48 (pp. 94–98).

THEOREM 4. *Let* s *and* t *be respectively the cardinals of the sets S and T. If S is equivalent to a subset of T, either* s $=$ t *or* s $<$ t, *and vice versa.*

The last statement is evident in view of the definitions of the equality and the order of cardinals.

While we inferred Theorem 4 from Theorem 3, the converse is done as easily. Both theorems, then, are equipollent.

According to Theorem 3 or 4, the definition of order can now be expressed as follows: if S is equivalent to a subset of T but not to T itself, the cardinal of S is less than the cardinal of T. This is also a possible definition of order for finite cardinals in arithmetic.

5. The Problem of Comparability.

Among the cases contained in the scheme of p. 72, the fourth case alone remains unsettled. The reader reflecting upon it will deem it rather paradoxical. If this case occurred it would mean that the sets were *incomparable*; ensuring that any two sets can be compared with respect to their cardinals means excluding the fourth case.

The resources at our disposal by now are not sufficient to prove comparability. Only by the end of this book (§ 11, **6** and **7**) shall we be able to reach this aim and to state:

Of any two sets, one at least is equivalent to a subset of the other. Hence of two different cardinals one is less than the other.

Exercises

1) Prove that the validity of the inequalities between cardinals s $<$ t and t $\leqslant$ w implies the validity of s $<$ w (cf. b) on p. 67).

2) Regarding the classification of the members of S utilized in the proof of Theorem 2, specify members of the first kind and of the second kind under various assumptions about the subset C_0; in particular under the assumption $C_0 =$ CS (which means an *indirect* proof, by *reductio ad absurdum*, of the theorem).

3) How far can the proof of Theorem 2 (and of its special cases mentioned on p. 72) be simplified by using Theorem 4?

4) (For advanced readers) Let be given a mapping of S onto $T_1 \subset T$ and a mapping of T onto $S_1 \subset S$ as assumed in the equivalence theorem, and let correspond by them $t_1 \in T_1$ to $s \in S$, $s_2 \in S_1$ to $t_1 \in T$, $t_3 \in T_1$ to $s_2 \in S$, $s_4 \in S_1$ to $t_3 \in T$, etc. We thus obtain, starting with an arbitrary $s \in S$, a uniquely determined sequence $(s, t_1, s_2, t_3, s_4, \ldots)$. If,

in particular, s belongs to S_1 as well, then we may also continue the sequence leftwards by putting the image of s (in T) before s; if this image belongs also to T_1 we may take an additional step leftwards, etc.

Construct a one-to-one correspondence between the members of S and those of T by distinguishing, for any $s \in S$, between the following three cases:

a) the sequence can be continued leftwards indefinitely;

b) the sequence, after having been continued leftwards as far as possible, starts with a member of S;

c) in the same sense, the sequence starts with a member of T.

(Hint: relate to s either its right-hand or its left-hand neighbor.)

Compare this proof, which essentially is that of J. König 06, with the first proof in **4**.

5) Let us suppose that the cardinal of the union of any two sets one of which at least is infinite, is not greater than the cardinal of either term. Show that this supposition guarantees the comparability of cardinals. (To the supposition itself cf. § 11, **5**.)

§ 6. ADDITION AND MULTIPLICATION OF CARDINALS [1])

1. Introduction. After having studied the comparison of cardinals we now consider operations with them, extending the operations with positive integers. We shall succeed not only in defining such operations but even in proving for them the natural extensions of most *formal laws* of arithmetic, notably [2]) of

$$a + (b + c) = (a + b) + c, \quad a(bc) = (ab)c \quad \text{(associative laws)}$$
$$a + b = b + a \qquad\qquad ab = ba \quad \text{(commutative laws)}$$
$$a(b + c) = ab + ac \qquad\qquad \text{(distributive law) [3]).}$$

On the other hand, we shall see that the *inverse* operations, e.g. subtraction, cannot be defined generally for transfinite cardinals. Also in

---

[1]) Most of the contents of §§ 6 and 7 are due to Cantor; see in particular Cantor 1895.

[2]) For the formal laws of exponentiation see § 7.

[3]) The other distributive law, viz. $(a + b)c = ac + bc$, which has significance in systems with non-commutative multiplication, follows from the above law by the commutative law of multiplication. For a weaker form of the distributive law cf. A. Robinson 41. — Below in subsection **9** a different kind of distributivity (for sets) is considered.

ordinary arithmetic they can be carried out only after suitable extensions of the domain of positive integers which are not practicable in the present case.

It is not surprising that part of ordinary arithmetic — and a far greater part when operations with transfinite order-types are concerned, see § 8 — cannot be preserved in the arithmetic of transfinite cardinals. When the domain of numbers and of the operations with them is expanded so fundamentally as to admit transfinite numbers and infinite sums and products of them one should not expect the new operations to submit to the old laws in their entirety. In mathematics just as in any theory the generalization (extension) of a concept involves abandoning part of the properties of the original concept.[1])

According to H. Hankel's once-famous *principle of the permanence of formal laws* which implicitly or explicitly ought to guide the extension of concepts and relations (operations) in mathematics, the operations for transfinite numbers should be defined, *as far as possible*, in a way preserving the laws of ordinary arithmetic. But after having defined the operations the mathematician cannot go on prescribing (postulating) the formal laws of these operations; on the contrary, he has to examine how far the laws of arithmetic continue being valid and to what extent they are modified.[2]) Hence it is rather a pleasant surprise that the laws of finite arithmetic prove valid to a great extent in the domain of transfinite cardinals.

The failure to perceive this situation has from the beginning handicapped the acceptance of Cantor's ideas. The following sentences from a letter of Cantor's [3]) are characteristic both of his own and of his opponents' attitudes: All pretended proofs against the possibility of actually transfinite number are ... faulty in this respect — and here lies their πρῶτον

---

[1])   For a stricter formulation of this (sometimes misinterpreted) rule see, for instance, Bolzano 1837 (§ 20), Dubislav 31 (§ 63).

[2])   Cantor had this in mind when he prefaced the final exposition of his theory with the motto: *Neque enim leges intellectui aut rebus damus ad arbitrium nostrum, sed tanquam scribae fideles ab ipsius naturae voce latas et prolatas excipimus et prescribimus* (1895, p. 481). Cf. *Thesis III* affixed to his *Habilitationsschrift* (cf. p. 1): *Numeros integros simili modo atque corpora coelestia totum quoddam legibus et relationibus compositum efficere* (Cantor 32, p. 62), and a passage from a letter written by Cantor in 1884: As to everything else [except the art of style and the economy of exposition] this is not my merit; with respect to the *contents* of my research work I am only a kind of reporter and secretary. (Cf. Schoenflies 28, pp. 15ff.)

[3])   Of 1885, addressed to G. Eneström (translated from the German original). See Cantor 1886, p. 226.

$\psi\varepsilon\tilde{v}\delta o\varsigma$ — that from the first they impute to, or rather enforce upon, the numbers in question all properties of finite numbers, whereas the actually transfinite numbers — if they shall be conceivable at all — must, by their contrast to finite number, constitute an entirely new kind of number whose nature completely depends on the situation and should be the object of our investigations but not of our discretion or prejudice.[1])

2. Union of Sets. While in this and the following section emphasis is laid upon operations with *cardinals*, these operations are defined by means of operations with *sets*. First we shall generalize the concept of union of sets introduced in § 2, **3**.

> DEFINITION I. If A is an arbitrary set, the set that contains all members which belong to at least one member of A [2]) is called the *sum-set* $\bigcup A$ or the *union of the members* of A. If a, a', a'', ... are members of A one also writes
>
> $$\bigcup A = a \cup a' \cup a'' \cup \ldots.$$

Accordingly $\bigcup A$ is independent of whether some of its members belong to one or to more of the members of A.

The existence of $\bigcup A$ to any given A is expressed by the axiom of sum-set (§ 2, **3**).

Example. Relate to each point of a straight line a segment of the length 1, extending from the point rightwards. The union of these segments, each conceived as the set of its points (including or excluding the ends), is the set of all points of the line. — This example extends beyond the bounds of Definition III of § 2.

The key for the transition from the sum-set to the sum of cardinals lies in the following remark. If A and B are *equivalent* sets of sets and if, in view of a definite mapping, the image in B of $a \in A$ is denoted by $\varphi(a)$, let us assume $a \sim \varphi(a)$ for each $a \in A$. This clearly does not ensure that

---

[1]) The controversy as to whether the conceptions of mathematics are our creations or (as Cantor presumes) have an existence independent of the human mind, somehow like Platonic ideas, is no less topical in present mathematics than it was in the days of Cantor and Kronecker. The question may be formulated as follows: do we *invent* or *discover* mathematical objects? Cf. Hessenberg 08, Bays 46, Hermes 56, and the discussion in several passages of *Foundations*, in particular p. 333.

[2]) Hence members of A which are not sets, as well as the null-set if it belongs to A, contribute nothing to $\bigcup A$.

the sum-sets $\cup A$ and $\cup B$ are equivalent, as shown by trivial instances such as

$$A = \{a_1, a_2\}, \qquad B = \{b_1, b_2\},$$
$$a_1 = \{1, 2, 3\}, a_2 = \{4, 5\}, \quad b_1 = \{6, 7, 8\}, b_2 = \{8, 9\}$$

in which case $\cup A$ contains five members and $\cup B$ four.

Yet if we moreover assume A and B to be *disjointed* sets then $\cup A \sim \cup B$ can be proven as follows. Let $\psi^{(a)}$ be a mapping between the equivalent sets $a \epsilon A$ and $\varphi(a) \epsilon B$ [1]) and let x be any member of $\cup A$. Since A is disjointed, x belongs to a definite $a \epsilon A$, and by $\psi^{(a)}$ x is related to a uniquely determined $y \epsilon \varphi(a) \epsilon B$; moreover, the correspondence between $x \epsilon \cup A$ and $y \epsilon \cup B$ is biunique since B, too, is disjointed. By mapping $\cup A$ onto $\cup B$ through these correspondences for every $x \epsilon \cup A$ we have proven $\cup A \sim \cup B$, i.e.

THEOREM 1. *If A and B are equivalent disjointed sets such that a certain mapping relates each $a \epsilon A$ to an equivalent $b \epsilon B$ (i.e. $a \sim b$) then we have* $\cup A \sim \cup B$.

3. Addition of Cardinals. To illustrate the problems arising presently in the light of a simple instance we start with the addition of two cardinals only.

DEFINITION II. Given two (finite or transfinite) cardinals a_1 and a_2, let A_1 and A_2 be *disjoint* sets such that $\overline{\overline{A}}_k = a_k$ ($k = 1, 2$; A_k is called a *representative* of a_k). Then the cardinal $s = \overline{\overline{A_1 \cup A_2}}$ of the union is called the *sum* of the cardinals a_1 and a_2; we write

$$s = a_1 + a_2.$$

The following remarks to this definition will prove useful.

1) The definition clearly conforms to the addition of non-negative integers (finite cardinals) as defined in arithmetic. Hence it is a generalization of that addition.

2) The definition seems ambiguous because of the relative arbitrariness of the representatives, hence of their union. Yet in view of Theorem 1

---

[1]) There arises the question of obtaining definite mappings $\psi^{(a)}$ for all $a \epsilon A$ simultaneously. In fact, if A is infinite the axiom of choice is required for this purpose; cf. the remark on p. 91 and the exposition in *Foundations*, pp. 60–62.

this arbitrariness does not affect the sum. For if A_1' and A_2' are other disjoint representatives, hence $A_1 \sim A_1'$ and $A_2 \sim A_2'$, then we have $A_1 \cup A_2 \sim A_1' \cup A_2'$ and obtain the same sum s.

3) Apparently it would be preferable to begin the definition with "given a pair $\{a_1, a_2\}$ of cardinals", which would enable us to begin Definition III with "given a set of cardinals". Yet even for Definition II this would not do because for $a_1 = a_2$ we have not a pair, while certainly sums such as $3 + 3$ or $\aleph_0 + \aleph_0$ have to be considered.

The above formulation virtually means "given the pair $\{1, 2\}$ to each of whose members a cardinal is assigned"; it is this conception which will be generalized in Definition III.

4) In the sum $a_1 + a_2$, a_1 occurs first and a_2 second. Yet this is not an intentional succession; it is due to the deficiency of man who, orally or in writing, cannot express words simultaneously but only successively. Instead of $a_1 + a_2$ we may, according to the definition of union, as well write $a_2 + a_1$. (The situation is different in arithmetic where the sum $n_1 + n_2$ of positive integers is defined inductively, starting with $n_1 + 1$; here from the first the succession is essential and only subsequently is $n_1 + n_2 = n_2 + n_1$ proven.)

Addition of cardinals in general is introduced by

DEFINITION III. Let be given a system of (not necessarily different) cardinals c_t by means of a single-valued function f which assigns to each member t of a non-empty "auxiliary set" T a cardinal $f(t) = c_t$. To form the sum of the given cardinals replace each c_t by a set C_t (*representative* of c_t) of the cardinal c_t such that, for $t_1 \neq t_2$, C_{t_1} and C_{t_2} are disjoint sets. The cardinal s of the union of all representatives C_t for $t \in T$ is called the *sum* of the given cardinals (terms); one writes

$$s = \sum_{t \in T} c_t = c' + c'' + \ldots$$

where c', c'', ... are some of the given cardinals.

In short, the sum of *cardinals* is the cardinal of the union of disjoint *sets* with the respective cardinals:

$$\sum_{t \in T} c_t = \overline{\overline{\bigcup_{t \in T} \{\ldots C_t \ldots\}}}.$$

The remarks 2) and 4) annexed to Definition II remain valid here. In fact, in view of Theorem 1 the sum is independent of the particular choice of the representatives C_t, and the symbol $\sum$ (in contradistinction to the same symbol as used in arithmetic and analysis) does not refer to a definite succession of the terms $\mathbf{c}_t$ [1]).

The remark 3) has been utilized in the formulation of Definition III as far as the function f is concerned. Equal cardinals $\mathbf{c}_t$ occur in a multiplicity corresponding to a subset of T, namely to the multiplicity of equal *functions-values* $f(t)$; if, for instance, T is the set of the real numbers of the interval $0 \leqslant t \leqslant 3$ and if f is defined by $f(t) = 1$ for integral t, $f(t) = 2$ for non-integral rational t, $f(t) = \aleph_0$ for irrational t, then the term 1 appears four times, the term 2, $\aleph_0$ times, the term $\aleph_0$, $\aleph$ times. If a *sequence* of cardinals is given one may take for T the set of all positive integers. — As to the concept of single-valued function used in Definition III, its reduction to the concept of set is sketched on p. 65, and more generally on pp. 89 and 110 ff.; cf. *Foundations*, chapter II.

Definition III, and analogically Definition VI below, are apt to arouse the question of whether representatives C_t in a sufficient quantity are available. This question has two different aspects. First it may mean asking whether, $\mathbf{c}_t$ being given, a set of this cardinal can be produced—which is mistaking the logical relation between set and cardinal; a cardinal is given as *the cardinal of a set* and in this logical order cardinals were introduced in § 4. On the other hand, the question is justified if meaning how *sufficiently many* representatives of $\mathbf{c}_t$ can be produced; in the above example we need a set of the cardinal $\aleph$ of representatives having the cardinal $\aleph_0$, i.e. $\aleph$ different and pairwise disjoint denumerable sets. This can be achieved in the following way. If C_t is a definite set with the cardinal $\mathbf{c}_t$ and the members of C_t are denoted by c_t then the sets of all *ordered pairs* (c_t, t) for each $t \in T$, with c_t ranging over C_t, are pairwise disjoint representatives of $\mathbf{c}_t$ in a quantity corresponding to the cardinal of T. In fact, for $t_1 \neq t_2$ any two ordered pairs (c'_{t_1}, t_1) and (c''_{t_2}, t_2) are different, even in the case $c'_{t_1} = c''_{t_2}$. — As to ordered pairs, they are easily reduced to pairs, i.e. to sets; see § 8, 2.

4. Formal Laws. Examples.

The *commutative law* of addition requires no proof since no order of the terms enters the definition; cf. § 2, 3 and remark 4) in 3.

As to the *associative law* of the addition of cardinals, there is a difference of principle between our case and that of arithmetic. In arithmetic, primarily the addition of two terms only is defined; after proving the associative law $(a + b) + c = a + (b + c)$ and its generalization, the

---

[1]) This "commutativity" may more elaborately be expressed as the possibility of mapping the argument-set T onto itself or an equivalent set; cf. Hausdorff 14, pp. 37f., or exercise 7) at the end of this section. The same applies to the commutativity of the multiplication of cardinals as introduced in Definition VI.

definition can be extended to any finite number of terms. This method does not suffice for the addition defined here, first because there may be infinitely many (even more-than-denumerably many) terms and secondly because, for instance, the equality $a + b + c = (a + b) + c$ which in arithmetic is a definition must here be proven as a theorem.

In the present case the problem is rather that of formulating the associative law than of proving it. We go back to Definition I upon which the addition of cardinals is based and decompose the set A, whose sum-set $\bigcup A$ we consider, arbitrarily into complementary and pairwise disjoint subsets

(1) $A = K \cup L \cup M \cup \ldots.$

Hence every $a \in A$ is either a $k \in K$ or an $l \in L$ or an $m \in M$ etc. The general associative law for unions of sets, then, runs

(2) $\bigcup A = \bigcup K \cup \bigcup L \cup \bigcup M \cup \ldots.$

Contrary to arithmetic, we need not consider other decompositions than the arbitrary one on the right-hand side of (2), for the proof of (2) shows that every other decomposition also yields $\bigcup A$. (The analogue of $\bigcup A$ for a finite number of terms is initially not available in arithmetic.)

To prove (2), i.e. to show that every member of the left-hand union is a member of the right-hand union and conversely, we take into account that every $x \in \bigcup A$ belongs, according to (1), either to a $k \in K$ or to an $l \in L$ or to an $m \in M$ etc., hence either to $\bigcup K$ or to $\bigcup L$ or to $\bigcup M$ etc. Conversely, every $x \in \bigcup K$ belongs to $\bigcup A$, etc.

For (2) we have no need to assume A to be disjointed (nor even the subsets K, L, M, $\ldots$ to be pairwise disjoint). Now we make these assumptions for the purpose of applying (2) to Definition III, conceiving A as the set of all representatives C_t; then the transition from (2) to the cardinals of $\bigcup A$, $\bigcup K$, $\bigcup L$, $\bigcup M$, $\ldots$ yields general associativity for the addition of cardinals, say in the form

$$\sum_{t \in T} c_t = \sum_{t \in P} c_t + \sum_{t \in Q} c_t + \sum_{t \in R} c_t + \ldots$$

where T is the union of the paarwise disjoint sets P, Q; R, etc.

Examples for the addition of cardinals. In a slight generalization of the remark 1) on p. 82, the addition of finitely many positive integers (i.e. of finite cardinals different from 0) as defined in arithmetic is in accordance with Definition III. However, now we can also form the sum of infinitely many such numbers, which has nothing to do with the infinite sums or series of analysis, hence involves no question of convergence; for instance, we obtain

$$1 + 2 + 3 + \ldots + k + \ldots = \aleph_0$$

by taking, in accordance with Definition III, $\{a_0\}$, $\{a_1, a_2\}$, $\{a_3, a_4, a_5\}$, $\ldots$ as the representatives of 1, 2, 3, $\ldots$ respectively; the members a_k are here arbitrary save for the condition $a_k \neq a_m$ for $k \neq m$. In the same way we obtain for a sequence of terms

$$n + n + n + \ldots = \aleph_0 \qquad (n \text{ finite}, \neq 0)$$

and in particular

(3)
$$1 + 1 + 1 + \ldots = \aleph_0.$$

Regarding the term 0, we have $s + 0 = s$ for every cardinal s. Conversely one can only state that the validity of $s + x = s$ for *every* cardinal s implies $x = 0$.

Passing over to transfinite terms, we obtain the results (n finite)

(4)　$\aleph_0 + n = \aleph_0 + \aleph_0 = \aleph_0 + \aleph_0 + \ldots + \aleph_0$ (finitely many terms)
　　　　$= \aleph_0 + \aleph_0 + \aleph_0 + \ldots$ (sequence of terms) $= \aleph_0$

in view of Theorems 2 and 3 of § 3.

The far stronger Theorem 6 of § 3 gives for *every* transfinite cardinal c:

(5)
$$c + n = c + \aleph_0 = c;$$

in particular for the cardinal of the continuum

(5′)
$$\aleph + n = \aleph + \aleph_0 = \aleph.$$

The second relation (5′) is in accordance with the fact that the union of the sets of all real transcendental numbers (Theorem 3 of § 4) and of all real algebraic numbers (§ 3, 4) is the set of all real numbers.

No *general* theorem enables us so far to evaluate sums in which the term $\aleph$ occurs several times. Yet for this purpose we may utilize Theorem 2 of § 4; taking as representatives of finitely many terms $\aleph$, or of a sequence of such terms, linear continua of, say, unit-length we obtain

(6)　$\aleph + \aleph + \ldots + \aleph = \aleph + \aleph + \aleph + \ldots$ (sequence) $= \aleph.$

5. Cartesian Product. The Axiom of Choice. To introduce the multiplication of cardinals we need a new operation with sets, whose result is usually called "Cartesian product".

The connection between this concept and a product of cardinals derives from a well-known consideration. Multiplication in arithmetic is defined as repeated addition; e.g., $3 \cdot 4$ as $3 + 3 + 3 + 3$ (or $4 + 4 + 4$). To evaluate $m \cdot n$ according to Definition III would then require representatives which together contain $m \cdot n$ different members. Yet we may reduce this to $m + n$ members only by starting with the disjoint sets $\{a_1, a_2, \ldots, a_m\}$, $\{b_1, b_2, \ldots, b_n\}$ and by considering the set of all combinations $\{a_k, b_l\}$, i.e. pairs of one member out of each set. Dropping the restriction to finite sets we arrive at

> DEFINITION IV. Given the disjoint sets R and S, the set P of all pairs $\{r, s\}$ with $r \in R$ and $s \in S$ is called the *Cartesian product of R and S* and denoted by $P = R \times S$. R and S are called *factors* of the product.

Other expressions for "Cartesian product" are "combination set" or "outer product" (as distinguished from the intersection as "inner product"). Cantor, who introduced the concept for the present purpose, called it *Verbindungsmenge*, while calling the union *Vereinigungsmenge*.

Example: $R =$ set of all positive integers, $S = \{s_1, s_2\}$. We have $R \times S = \{\{1, s_1\}, \{1, s_2\}, \{2, s_1\}, \{2, s_2\}, \{3, s_1\}, \ldots\}$ which is also a denumerable set.

For the purpose of multiplication of cardinals we generalize Definition IV in two different directions. The one is nothing new: we introduce any multitude of factors in the same way as done in the beginning of Definition III, namely by means of an auxiliary set T; it will turn out that in the case of multiplication this method is desirable not only for cardinals but even for sets, in contrast with the operation of union where (Definition I) it is sufficient to consider a *set* of sets.

The second generalization involves a more delicate problem. For certain applications it is advantageous to get rid of the condition that R and S be disjoint, and in the general case, that any two factors be disjoint sets. This present a difficulty, for if r_1 and r_2 are members of both R and S we should distinguish between the pair $\{r_1, r_2\}$ with $r_1 \in R$ and $r_2 \in S$, and the pair $\{r_2, r_1\}$ with $r_2 \in R$ and $r_1 \in S$ — though according to extensionality $\{r_1, r_2\} = \{r_2, r_1\}$. Moreover, taking r_1 from both R and S

we do not get a pair at all. For instance, if $R = \{1, 2\}$ and $S = \{1, 2, 3\}$ then $R \times S$ would contain only the three pairs $\{1, 2\}$, $\{1, 3\}$, $\{2, 3\}$ and in addition the unit-sets $\{1\}$ and $\{2\}$, instead of six pairs as intended.

This difficulty may be solved in two ways. First, one might consider *ordered pairs* (r, s), stipulating that r be a member of R and s a member of S and making an extra provision that includes pairs of the form (r, r). While in the case of Definition IV this appears feasible (cf. the end of subsection **3**) it would not be sufficient for the general case of Definition V where, instead of ordered pairs, *ordered sets in general* are needed. The reduction of the concept of ordered set to the set concept is an intricate matter (§ 8) and, which is more important, the introduction of order at this juncture is not pertinent to our subject since order does not enter the concept of Cartesian product.

A more relevant method is marking the members of the pairs occurring in Definition IV explicitly *as members of the respective set* (R or S). This may be done through replacing the members by pairs consisting of the member and the respective set, i.e. by writing $\{\{r, R\}, \{s, S\}\}$ instead of $\{r, s\}$ in Definition IV.[1]) Then the "loss" of pairs (members of the Cartesian product) as cited above cannot occur; if, as assumed above, r_1 and r_2 are members of both R and S then the four pairs in question will now be written as

$$\{\{r_1, R\}, \{r_1, S\}\}, \{\{r_1, R\}, \{r_2, S\}\}, \{\{r_2, R\}, \{r_1, S\}\}, \{\{r_2, R\}, \{r_2, S\}\}.$$

Though this method is unobjectionable it is far simpler, and sufficient in principle, to consider *disjoint* factors only. Yet for certain applications, especially to the concept of power (§ 7), this restriction proves inconvenient; even *equal* factors are then used.

From the case of two factors we thus proceed to

DEFINITION V. Let S be a non-empty set of sets s; more generally, consider a system of (not necessarily different) sets s_t given by means of a single-valued function f which assigns to each member t of a non-empty set T a set $f(t) = s_t$. The set whose members are all

---

[1]) In certain "pathological" cases where not only $r \in R$ but at the same time $R \in r$, one ought to take ordered pairs instead of plain pairs. Even this does not mean the method which was rejected in the preceding paragraph because it does not involve ordered sets *in general*; an ordered *pair* is a quite simple concept not requiring order (see § 8, **2**).

different sets (*complexes*) that contain a single member out of each
s or s_t, is called the *Cartesian product* of S or of all sets (*factors*) s
or s_t and is denoted by

$$\mathbf{P}S, \text{ or } \prod_{t \varepsilon T} s_t. \, {}^1)$$

If $s_{t_1}, s_{t_2}, \ldots$ are some of the factors we also write

$$\prod_{t \varepsilon T} s_t = s_{t_1} \times s_{t_2} \times \ldots.$$

The term "complex" is adopted *ad hoc* as an abbreviation for a set that
contains one member out of each factor. In effect, then, a complex is a
single-valued function which assigns to each t (or s_t) a member of s_t, and
the Cartesian product is the set of all such functions. (A function is a set of
ordered pairs, see pp. 65 and 110 ff.) Hence the factors of the product
need not be disjoint or even different.

For the *existence* of the Cartesian product see footnote ^{3}) on p. 90.

Examples.

a) $S = \{\{1, 2\}, \{3, 4\}, \{5, 6\}, \ldots\}$,

i.e. a denumerable disjointed set of pairs. Then

$$\mathbf{P}S = \{1, 2\} \times \{3, 4\} \times \{5, 6\} \times \ldots =$$
$$= \{\{1, 3, 5, \ldots\}, \{2, 3, 5, \ldots\}, \{1, 4, 5, \ldots\}, \{2, 4, 5, \ldots\}, \{1, 3, 6, \ldots\}, \ldots\}$$

which set will prove to have the cardinal of the continuum (§ 7).

b) $S = \{\{1, 2\}, \{3, 4\}, \{5\}, \{6\}, \{7\}, \ldots\}$. Then
$\mathbf{P}S = \{\{1, 3, 5, 6, \ldots\}, \{2, 3, 5, 6, \ldots\}, \{1, 4, 5, 6, \ldots\}, \{2, 4, 5, 6, \ldots\}\}$,

i.e. a set of the cardinal 4.

If the null-set O occurs among the members of S or among the factors
s_t then *the Cartesian product is clearly the null-set* because no complex
exists, for no member can be chosen from O. One will ask whether this
statement can be inverted, i.e. if the Cartesian product is non-empty
provided each factor is non-empty. This question, apparently quite
simple, is one of the most discussed problems in modern mathematics.

---

^{1})   The symbol Π is usually applied to products of numbers (cardinals) and not to
Cartesian products of sets. But in view of the close relation between these (see Definition
VI) and since no confusion will arise we shall not introduce a new symbol for the
present purpose.

The answer seems to lie in choosing a single member in each factor and uniting the chosen members to a set; this set, then, is a complex, i.e. a member of the Cartesian product, which shows that this product is not empty.

However [1]), on account of the axioms introduced so far we seem to be unable to choose members as described, except when the members of S are unit-sets or when S is a finite set [2]). To render the situation more perspicuous let us assume S to be a *disjointed* infinite set of non-empty sets; then every complex, if any, is a subset of the union $\cup S$, namely a subset with the property π that its intersection with each member of S is a unit-set. Yet the axiom of subsets (§ 2, 2) does not yield the construction of such a subset; in fact, save for trivial cases there is not a single subset with the property π but infinitely many. (True, by means of the axioms of subsets and of power-set one can form the Cartesian product, that is to say the set that contains *all* subsets of $\cup S$ with the property π, but this does not involve that the product is different from O, i.e. that there *exists* a subset of $\cup S$ as desired.[3]))

We therefore introduce a new axiom, the last one used in this book.

Axiom (VII) of Choice, or Multiplicative Principle. The Cartesian product PS of a disjointed set S which does not contain the null-set is different from the null-set. In other words, the union $\cup S$ contains at least one subset which has a single member common with each member of S, these members assumed to be non-empty sets.

If S is not disjointed then the corresponding statement must be expressed in a different way; for instance, as affirming the existence of a single-valued function which assigns to each member x of S a member of x. This generalized form can be derived from the above axiom by means of our other axioms, as Zermelo has shown.

The multiplicative principle for disjointed sets S was formulated by Bertrand Russell in 1906. Previously, in 1904, the axiom had been formulated and utilized by Zermelo without assuming S to be disjointed; in 1908, it was given the general ("functional") form by Zermelo, from

---

[1]) The following arguments up to Theorem 2 are somewhat difficult and may be skipped by beginners at the first reading.

[2]) Regarding the latter eventuality, we may start with the case that S contains a single member and proceed to any finite set by mathematical induction.

[3]) For explaining this in detail and pointing out the problems connected with the axiom of choice in general, see *Foundations*, pp. 45 ff. (Add Fraïssé 58 to the literature there given.) The Cartesian product is just the subset of those members of the power-set of $\cup S$ (i.e., of those subsets of $\cup S$) which have the property π.

whom originates the name "choice" in the sense of choosing a single member out of each member of S.[1])

Implicitly we have used the axiom of choice previously, notably in the first proof of Theorem 4 of § 3 and in the proof of Theorem 1 on p. 82 upon which the addition of cardinals is based. As to the latter proof, cf. the footnote on p. 82. (While the set of *all* mappings $\psi^{(a)}$ between a and $\varphi(a)$, and even the set which contains all these sets for each $a \in A$, can be shown to exist on account of the preceding axioms, the axiom of choice is required to simultaneously choose a single such mapping for each a.)

By joining the multiplicative principle (hence its name) to the remark on the bottom of p. 89, we obtain

THEOREM 2. *The Cartesian product of a disjointed set S is the null-set if and only if the null-set is a member of S.*

To pass over from Cartesian products to the multiplication of cardinals we need the analogue of Theorem 1. If A and B are equivalent sets of sets [2]) and if, in view of a definite mapping, the image in B of $a \in A$ is denoted by $\varphi(a)$, let us assume $a \sim \varphi(a)$ for each $a \in A$. We prove $PA \sim PB$ as follows. Let $\psi^{(a)}$ be a mapping [3]) between the equivalent sets $a \in A$ and $\varphi(a) \in B$ and let x be a member of PA, i.e. a complex; then x biuniquely determines, by simultaneous mappings $\psi^{(a)}$ of the members of A onto the corresponding members of B, an image which is a complex of PB. Hence

THEOREM 3. *If A and B are equivalent sets of sets such that a certain mapping relates each $a \in A$ to an e q u i v a l e n t $b \in B$ (i.e. $a \sim b$) then we have $PA \sim PB$.*

6. Multiplication of Cardinals and its Formal Laws. Theorem 3 enables us

---

[1])   Zermelo 04, 08, 08a; Russell 06.

[2])   In contrast with Theorem 1, disjointedness is not required since every member of a complex is conceived as a member of the respective set (i.e. of a member of A or B).

By speaking of "sets of sets" we refer to the first formulation in the opening of Definition V; if the use of functions f (with the same auxiliary set T) is necessary the argumentation is not changed.

[3])   Here again the axiom of choice is used. Without it we can form the set whose members are the sets of all mappings $\psi^{(a)}$ while a ranges over A; yet we need the axiom to choose a *single* mapping for each a. By uniting the chosen mappings we obtain the correspondences desired between the complexes of PA and PB.

to define the multiplication of cardinals in a way largely analogous to
their addition (Definition III).

DEFINITION VI. Let be given a system of (not necessarily different) cardinals c_t by means of a single-valued function f which
assigns to each member t of a non-empty set T a cardinal $f(t) = c_t$.
To form the product of the given cardinals replace each c_t by a set
C_t (*representative* of c_t) of the cardinal c_t. The cardinal **p** of the
Cartesian product of all representatives C_t for $t \in T$ is called the
product of the given cardinals (*factors*); one writes

$$\mathbf{p} = \prod_{t \in T} c_t = \mathbf{c}' \, \mathbf{c}'' \ldots$$

where $\mathbf{c}'$, $\mathbf{c}''$, ... are some of the given cardinals.

In short, the product of *cardinals* is the cardinal of the Cartesian
product of *sets* with the respective cardinals:

$$\prod_{t \in T} c_t = \overline{\overline{\prod_{t \in T} C_t}}.$$

In contrast with Definition III, there is no need to take for the representatives disjoint nor even different sets, for the reason given on
p. 91. Analogically to Definition III, the product is independent of the
particular choice of the representatives in view of Theorem 3, and also
independent of a possible succession of the factors (see p. 84). In the
case of finitely many finite factors, the definition clearly conforms to the
multiplication of non-negative integers as defined in arithmetic.

As to the *associative law* of the multiplication of cardinals, the situation
is similar to that described in the beginning of **4**. To formulate the law
let S, as in Definition V, denote the set whose Cartesian product $\mathbf{P}S$ shall
be formed, and let

(1) $S = K \cup L \cup M \cup \ldots$

be any decomposition of S into complementary and pairwise disjoint
subsets [1]). Hence, every $s \in S$ is either a $k \in K$ or an $l \in L$ or an $m \in M$ etc.
The general associative law for Cartesian products of sets, then, runs
(cf. subsection **4**)

(2) $\mathbf{P}S \sim \mathbf{P}K \times \mathbf{P}L \times \mathbf{P}M \times \ldots.$

---

[1]) Starting from the more general (second) formulation of Definition V, one has to
decompose the auxiliary set T; for the rest the argumentation remains unchanged.

Clearly this equivalence cannot be transformed into an equality, for the members of $\mathbf{P}S$ are complexes each of which has the cardinality of S while the members of the right-hand set have only the cardinality of the set that contains the subsets $K, L, M, \ldots$ which appear in (1).

To prove (2) we relate to each member (complex) x of $\mathbf{P}S$, which according to Definition V contains a single member out of each member of S, the complex belonging to the Cartesian product on the right-hand side of (2) whose *members* contain the same members as x [1]). We thus obtain a one-to-one correspondence between the Cartesian products on both sides of (2), which expresses their equivalence.

To illustrate this proof let S be disjointed and $= \{s_1, s_2, s_3, s_4, s_5\}$ $(s_k \neq O)$, $K = \{s_1, s_2, s_3\}$, $L = \{s_4, s_5\}$, hence $S = K \cup L$. If $\sigma_k \epsilon s_k$, the above-defined correspondence relates

$$\{\sigma_1, \sigma_2, \sigma_3, \sigma_4, \sigma_5\} \epsilon \mathbf{P}S \text{ to } \{\{\sigma_1, \sigma_2, \sigma_3\}, \{\sigma_4, \sigma_5\}\} \epsilon (\mathbf{P}K \times \mathbf{P}L).$$

In this case we may express the associative law (2) by

$$s_1 \times s_2 \times s_3 \times s_4 \times s_5 \sim (s_1 \times s_2 \times s_3) \times (s_4 \times s_5).$$

With a view to applications in § 7 we shall write the associative law (2) in another form, using the symbol $\prod$ for the Cartesian product of *sets* as done in Definition V. First, expressing (2) through the factors rather than through the sets of factors, we replace (2) by

$$(3) \qquad \prod_{y \epsilon S} y \sim \prod_{y \epsilon K} y \times \prod_{y \epsilon L} y \times \prod_{y \epsilon M} y \times \ldots.$$

Still the formulations (1), (2), (3) suffer from the use of dots, owing to the expression of the decomposition (1) (as also of (1) on p. 85) by the casual letters K, L, etc. This shortcoming is easily redressed by writing (1) in the form $S = \bigcup_{t \epsilon T} \{..K_t..\}$, where T is a suitable auxiliary set to whose members t the complementary and pairwise disjoint subsets K_t are assigned; $\{..K_t..\}$ means the set of all K_t for $t \epsilon T$. Then (3) can be written as

$$(4) \qquad \prod_{y \epsilon S} y \sim \prod_{t \epsilon T} \left(\prod_{y \epsilon K_t} y\right),$$

where S is the union of the pairwise disjoint sets K_t.

---

[1]) As pointed out on p. 88, if S is not disjointed then each member of the members $y \epsilon S$ has to be taken with regard to its belonging to y, say as a pair one of whose components is y.

Finally, since the cardinals of equivalent sets are equal, the transition from any of the equivalence statements (2), (3), (4) between *sets* to the respective *cardinals* yields the full associative law for the multiplication of cardinals c_t, say in the form

$$\prod_{t \varepsilon T} c_t = \prod_{t \varepsilon P} c_t \prod_{t \varepsilon Q} c_t \prod_{t \varepsilon R} c_t \ldots$$

where T is the union of the pairwise disjoint sets P, Q, R, $\ldots$.

The *distributive law* connecting addition and multiplication of cardinals may be expressed in the following form which is sufficient for the needs of the arithmetic of cardinals:

$$(5) \qquad c \sum_{t \varepsilon T} c_t = \sum_{t \varepsilon T} (c \cdot c_t).$$

In view of the commutativity of the multiplication we may also let the sum precede c ("second" distributive law).

To prove (5) we replace the cardinals c and c_t by pairwise disjoint set-representatives, the sums by unions, the products by Cartesian products; then obviously the originating left-hand and right-hand sides are even equal (not only equivalent) sets.

Joining these results to those of **4**, we have

THEOREM 4. *Addition and multiplication of cardinals are commutative and associative operations connected by the distributive law of arithmetic.*

The insertion "of arithmetic" excludes the second distributive law of Boolean algebra (below, subsection **9**).

Obviously the multiplication with 1, even any number of times, does not change the result; cf. the second example on p. 89. Conversely one can only state that the validity of $c \cdot x = c$ for *every* cardinal c implies $x = 1$.

In arithmetic, multiplication is usually defined not according to Definitions IV and VI but as repeated addition. This procedure can be generalized from two to any finite number of factors by mathematical induction but is not convenient for the general case of Definition VI; instead it shall now be introduced as a provable *theorem*.

Let us first stipulate that in the product ab the first factor a be regarded as multiplicand and the second b as multiplier. This (arbitrary) stipulation, though insignificant in the present case because of the commutativity of multiplication, will prove essential in § 8.

We prepare the general case by taking one of the two factors as a finite cardinal $n \neq 0$. Then the equality, valid for any cardinal c,

(6)
$$\underbrace{c + c + \ldots + c}_{n \text{ terms}} = c \cdot n$$

expresses that a set representing the left-hand sum is equivalent to the Cartesian product of sets of the cardinals c and n. To show this let C_k ($k = 1, 2, \ldots, n$) be pairwise disjoint sets with the cardinal c, whose union has the cardinal $c + c + \ldots + c$. Taking fixed mappings of C_1 onto each other C_k, we denote an arbitrary member of C_1 with c_1 and its image in C_k by those mappings with c_k. If $F = \{f_1, f_2, \ldots, f_n\}$ is a set of n members which do not belong to a C_k then the Cartesian product $C_1 \times F$ is equivalent to the union of the C_k, as shown by relating $c_k \in C_k$ to $\{c_1, f_k\} \in (C_1 \times F)$; this equivalence is another expression for the equality (6).

In the general case, i.e. for any multiplier d, the proof is quite similar. For let c and d be represented by the disjoint sets C and D; $\{c, d\}$ may denote the members of the Cartesian product $C \times D$. If d^* is a fixed member of D, the pairs $\{c, d\}$ with $c \in C$ for which $d = d^*$, form a subset of $C \times D$ which is equivalent to C; hence, if d^* ranges over all members of D, we obtain a set equivalent to D of pairwise disjoint subsets of $C \times D$ each of which is equivalent to C; $C \times D$ is the union of these subsets. According to Definition III the cardinal cd of $C \times D$ is, then, represented as a sum each of whose terms equals c and such that the terms occur in the multiplicity (cardinal) d. In particular, if C is a unit-set (hence $C \times D \sim D$), we obtain the cardinal of D in the form of a sum each term of which is 1. Hence

THEOREM 5. *The product* cd *of two cardinals* [1]) *can be obtained by reiterated addition of the term* c *"d-times", i.e. according to an auxiliary set of the cardinal* d *in the sense of Definition III. In particular, any cardinal* $d \neq 0$ *can be obtained by repeated addition (according to* d) *of the unity* 1.

Of course, we may derive the latter statement also directly from Definition III by taking $c_t = 1$ for each $t \in T$, and $C_t = \{t\}$. On the other hand, one obtains the first statement from the second by multiplying by c and using the distributive law.

---

[1]) Properly we should condition $d \neq 0$. Yet by the commutativity of multiplication we may include $d = 0$, stipulating that "adding 0-times" means obtaining the sum 0.

Theorem 2 (p. 91) runs in terms of cardinals:

THEOREM 6. *A product of cardinals equals 0 if and only if at least one of the factors equals 0.*

This theorem is well known from arithmetic where (besides its being restricted to finitely many finite factors) it is based on the distributive law (for "if") and the possibility of division (for "only if").[1]) In the present case, however, "if" derives straight from Definition V (see p. 89) and "only if" from the axiom of choice.

Theorems 4, 5, 6, the analogues of which hold in arithmetic, show that the definitions of addition and multiplication (III, V, VI) are natural and appropriate.

7. Inverse Operations. Inequalities. In contrast with the success reached for the "direct" operations of addition and multiplication, their inversions can generally not be carried out for cardinals.

That one cannot subtract **b** from **a** or divide **a** by **b** if **b** > **a** is trivial, since no "negative cardinals" or "fractions" [2]) exist according to the introduction of cardinals as *cardinals of sets*. (For the case **a** > **b** see Theorem 5 of § 3 and, more generally, § 11, **5** and **7**.) But also in the case **a** = **b** subtraction and division yield no definite results, as shown by the equalities (where n is any finite cardinal $\neq 0$, **c** any transfinite cardinal)

$$\aleph_0 + 0 = \aleph_0 + n = \aleph_0 + \aleph_0 = \aleph_0 \qquad \text{(p. 86)}$$
$$\aleph + 0 = \aleph + n = \aleph + \aleph_0 = \aleph + \aleph = \aleph \qquad \text{(p. 86)}$$
$$\mathbf{c} + 0 = \mathbf{c} + n = \mathbf{c} + \aleph_0 = \mathbf{c} \qquad \text{(p. 86)}$$
$$\aleph_0 \cdot n = \aleph_0 \cdot \aleph_0 = \aleph_0 \qquad \text{(p. 95)}$$
$$\aleph \cdot n = \aleph \cdot \aleph_0 = \aleph \cdot \aleph. \qquad \text{(pp. 95 and 103)}$$

For more far-reaching equalities of the same kind cf. § 11, **5**.

At the bottom of the impossibility of inverse operations lies the equivalence of infinite sets to proper subsets, which is also responsible

---

[1]) The arguments in arithmetic are in short as follows:

a) $a \cdot 0 = a (0 + 0) = a \cdot 0 + a \cdot 0$, hence $a \cdot 0 = 0$. Analogically one proves $0 \cdot a = 0$.

b) $ab = 0$ with $b \neq 0$ implies, in view of a):

$$0 = (ab)\frac{1}{b} = a\left(b \cdot \frac{1}{b}\right) = a \cdot 1 = a.$$

[2]) For special limited purposes "transfinite rationals" have been introduced in Olmsted 45.

for the deviation of *inequalities* between cardinals from the simple situation in arithmetic.

From the inequalities

(1) $$\mathbf{a}_1 \leqslant \mathbf{b}_1, \quad \mathbf{a}_2 \leqslant \mathbf{b}_2$$

it still follows that

(2) $$\mathbf{a}_1 + \mathbf{a}_2 \leqslant \mathbf{b}_1 + \mathbf{b}_2, \quad \mathbf{a}_1 \mathbf{a}_2 \leqslant \mathbf{b}_1 \mathbf{b}_2,$$

as in arithmetic for non-negative a_k, b_k. To prove this we take as representatives disjoint sets A_1, A_2 and disjoint sets B_1, B_2; by (1) there exist subsets $B_1' \subseteq B_1$ and $B_2' \subseteq B_2$ such that $A_1 \sim B_1'$, $A_2 \sim B_2'$. Hence by Theorems 1 and 3

$$A_1 \cup A_2 \sim B_1' \cup B_2', \quad A_1 \times A_2 \sim B_1' \times B_2'.$$

Since $B_1' \cup B_2' \subseteq B_1 \cup B_2$ and $B_1' \times B_2' \subseteq B_1 \times B_2$, the last equivalences mean $\mathbf{a}_1 + \mathbf{a}_2 \leqslant \mathbf{b}_1 + \mathbf{b}_2$, $\mathbf{a}_1 \mathbf{a}_2 \leqslant \mathbf{b}_1 \mathbf{b}_2$ by Theorem 4 of § 5.

It is easy to extend the inequalities (2), as consequences of (1), to any (finite or infinite) number of terms and factors; see exercise 3) at the end of this section.

Yet in arithmetic stricter inequalities hold, namely (for positive a_k)

(3) $a_1 \leqslant b_1$ and $a_2 < b_2$ imply $a_1 + a_2 < b_1 + b_2$, $a_1 a_2 < b_1 b_2$,

and in particular (for non-negative a_k)

(4) $a_1 < b_1$ and $a_2 < b_2$ imply $a_1 + a_2 < b_1 + b_2$, $a_1 a_2 < b_1 b_2$.

Clearly the inequalities (3) do not hold for transfinite cardinals, as shown by instances such as $\aleph + n = \aleph + \aleph_0$, $\aleph \cdot n = \aleph \cdot \aleph_0$ (for $n \neq 0$) in spite of $\aleph \leqslant \aleph$, $n < \aleph_0$. The inequalities (4) do hold for transfinite cardinals but can be proved only by means of essentially different and more profound resources as developed in § 11, 5 and 7 [1]).

An almost evident statement which, however, has far-reaching consequences is expressed by

THEOREM 7. *If C is a set of cardinals among which there is no greatest one then the sum* $\mathbf{s}$ *of the cardinals of C is greater than any member of C.*

---

[1]) Not only does the proof of (4) for transfinite cardinals require the axiom of choice but, as shown in Tarski 24, this axiom can also be derived from either inequality (4).

Proof. We have $c \leqslant s$ for every $c \, \epsilon \, C$, by Definition III (and Theorem 4 of § 5). If there existed a $c^* \, \epsilon \, C$ such that $c^* = s$ then every other $c \, \epsilon \, C$ were less than c^*, i.e. c^* were the greatest cardinal of C.

Remark. One may also prove our theorem by assuming that for every $c \, \epsilon \, C$ there is a *greater* cardinal in C. Yet this assumption is slightly stronger, pending a proof of the comparability of cardinals.

Theorem 7 expands the domain of cardinals in the following sense. Cantor's Theorem (2 of § 5) yields, *for any given cardinal,* a greater one; by the axiom of infinity, then, there exist infinitely many transfinite cardinals. Beyond this, Theorem 7 secures, *for any given set of cardinals,* a greater one: if there is a maximum in the set then the cardinal yielded by Cantor's theorem, and otherwise the sum of the cardinals contained in the set. Hence the variety of transfinite cardinals incomparably surpasses that of finite cardinals.

In connection herewith arises the *antinomy of the set of all cardinals;* this "set" satisfies the condition of Theorem 7, hence it should yield a cardinal "greater than any cardinal". Cf. *Foundations,* chapter 1, § 2.

Skipping various more special inequalities [1]) we conclude with a most general one, which is remarkable both for its strange structure and for its (somewhat difficult) proof based on the diagonal method.

Let us first remark that if two sequences of cardinals (a_k) and (b_k) with $a_k < b_k$ for each $k = 1, 2, 3, \ldots$ are given then one cannot conclude $\sum_k a_k < \sum_k b_k$ or $\prod_k a_k < \prod_k b_k$ but only $\sum_k a_k \leqslant \sum_k b_k$ and $\prod_k a_k \leqslant \prod_k b_k$ [2]). We have, for instance, *equality* between the sums and between the products if $a_k = k$, $b_k = k + 1$. The following theorem, however, states *inequality* if, in addition to $a_k < b_k$, we compare the *sum* of the a_k with the *product* of the b_k — even in more general cases than sequences.

THEOREM 8.   (*Inequality of König–Jourdain–Zermelo* [3]).) *If the single-valued functions f and g assign to each member t of a non-empty set T cardinals $f(t) = a_t$ and $g(t) = b_t$ such that $a_t < b_t$ for each $t \, \epsilon \, T$, then*

$$\sum_t a_t < \prod_t b_t.$$

[1])   Cf., for instance, Bernstein 05, § 3; Lindenbaum-Tarski 26, § 1. Cf. also below § 11.

[2])   The products may even be equal if a further assumption regarding the quantity of the b_k is added; see Tarski's result mentioned in § 7, 4.

[3])   J. König 05; Jourdain 08; Zermelo 08a, p. 277. The theorem was proven by König for sequences only, with a view to an application to the continuum problem.

Proof.[1]) As representatives of the cardinals $\mathbf{a}_t$, $\mathbf{b}_t$ we take sets A_t, B_t of these cardinals respectively such that the sets B_t are pairwise disjoint and that

$$A_t \subset B_t, \text{ hence } C_t = B_t - A_t \neq O.$$

Accordingly, the sets A_t are also pairwise disjoint. The union S of all A_t has the cardinal $\sum_t \mathbf{a}_t$, the Cartesian product P of all B_t has the cardinal $\prod_t \mathbf{b}_t$. According to Theorem 4 of § 5 it is sufficient to prove that

a) S is equivalent to a subset of P,

b) S is not equivalent to P itself.

Ad a). Using the axiom of choice, we choose in every $C_t = B_t - A_t$ an arbitrary member c_t which shall henceforth remain fixed; for $t_1 \neq t_2$ we have $c_{t_1} \neq c_{t_2}$. Particular members of P, i.e. complexes that contain one member out of each $B_t = A_t \cup C_t$, shall be formed as follows: for *a single* $t = \tau$ the member shall be *any* $a_\tau \in A_\tau$, while for every $t \neq \tau$ we take the *fixed* $c_t \in C_t$. To make this rule perspicuous we write some t's as $1, 2, \ldots, k, \ldots$; then corresponding particular complexes of P have the form

$$\{a_1, c_2, \ldots, c_k, \ldots\} \qquad (a_1 \in A_1)$$
$$\{c_1, a_2, \ldots, c_k, \ldots\} \qquad (a_2 \in A_2)$$
$$\cdot$$
$$\cdot$$
$$\{c_1, c_2, \ldots, a_k, \ldots\}. \qquad (a_k \in A_k)$$

The set of those complexes in which, for a certain t, a_t ranges over the set A_t is obviously a subset of P equivalent to A_t. These subsets are pairwise disjoint; for if $t' \neq t''$ then the set of the complexes with $a_{t'} \in A_{t'}$ and the set of the complexes with $a_{t''} \in A_{t''}$ have no common member since $A_{t'}$ and $A_{t''}$ are disjoint. Hence the union of all those subsets of P is equivalent to the union S of all sets A_t, i.e. S is equivalent to a subset of P.

Ad b). Assume $P_0 \subseteq P$ to be *equivalent to S*. We shall prove that this implies $P_0 \neq P$.

Let φ be a fixed mapping of S onto P_0; we split P_0 into its complementary, pairwise disjoint subsets which, in view of φ, correspond to the

---

[1]) Beginners may skip this proof at the first reading.

subsets $A_t \subset S$, and we denote the subset of P_0 corresponding to a certain A_t by $P_0^{(t)}$; then $P_0^{(t)} \sim A_t$. The members of P_0, hence of each $P_0^{(t)}$, are complexes which contain a single member out of each B_t; yet by means of the diagonal method we shall show that *not all* such complexes belong to P_0.

Let $t = \tau$ be a fixed member of T. The special member belonging to B_τ of a member (complex) h of $P_0^{(\tau)}$ shall for short be called a *diagonal member*: the diagonal member $b_{\tau,\tau}$ of h. (The first index τ refers to the subset $P_0^{(\tau)} \subset P$ to which h belongs, the second to the factor B_τ of P to which $b_{\tau,\tau}$ belongs.) The set D_τ of all diagonal members $b_{\tau,\tau}$ occurring in the complexes h of $P_0^{(\tau)}$ is a subset of B_τ and has, in contrast with the cardinal $\mathfrak{b}_\tau$ of B_τ, a cardinal $\leqslant \mathbf{a}_\tau$ only; for $P_0^{(\tau)} \sim A_\tau$, and the diagonal members belonging to different complexes h are not necessarily different. Hence for each τ the difference

$$E_\tau = B_\tau - D_\tau \neq O$$

since even the cardinal of D_τ is less than that of B_τ by our initial assumption $\mathbf{a}_t < \mathbf{b}_t$.

Finally, using the axiom of choice, we choose a single member e_t in each E_t; these members are different because the sets B_t, hence also E_t, are pairwise disjoint. The set e^* of all chosen e_t is a member (complex) of P, for e^* contains a single member out of each factor $B_t = D_t \cup E_t$. We maintain that e^* *is not contained in the subset P_0 of P*. In fact, every member (complex) h of P_0 belongs to a certain $P_0^{(t)} \subset P_0$ as defined above, and the member of h belonging to the particular factor B_t — namely the diagonal member $b_{t,t}$ — is contained in $D_t \subset B_t$, contrary to the member of e^* belonging to B_t, which has been chosen from the complement $E_t \subset B_t$. Hence $h \neq e^*$ for every $h \in P_0$; in other words, P_0 is a *proper subset* of P, which completes the proof.

As an example for Theorem 8 we take the sequence of inequalities $0 < 1, 1 < 2, \ldots, k < k + 1, \ldots$; we obtain

$$0 + 1 + 2 + \ldots + k + \ldots (= \aleph_0) < 1 \cdot 2 \cdot 3 \cdot \ldots \cdot k \cdot \ldots.$$

The analogue applies to any sequence of increasing (finite or transfinite) cardinals. For further examples see § 7, **5** and **6**.

8. Examples of the Multiplication of Cardinals. The Cardinal of a Two-Dimensional Continuum. In analogy to the multiplication table of

arithmetic we calculate the products of the transfinite cardinals $\aleph_0$ and $\aleph$ by themselves and by finite cardinals $\neq 0$. (For the factor 0 see Theorem 6.) Most results are easily obtained by means of Theorem 5.

In accordance with (4) and (6) of subsection **4** we have for finite $n \neq 0$

$$\aleph_0 \cdot n = \aleph_0 + \aleph_0 + \ldots + \aleph_0 = \aleph_0, \quad \aleph_0 \cdot \aleph_0 = \aleph_0 + \aleph_0 + \ldots = \aleph_0,$$
$$\aleph \cdot n = \aleph + \aleph + \ldots + \aleph = \aleph, \quad \aleph \cdot \aleph_0 = \aleph + \aleph + \ldots = \aleph.$$

As an example for obtaining these results directly from Definitions IV — VI we illustrate the equality $\aleph_0 \cdot \aleph_0 = \aleph_0$ by the "diagonal method of Cauchy", i.e. the re-arrangement of a double sequence to a simple one, according to the following array (cf. § 3, **3**):

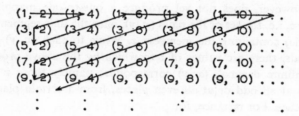

The sets of all odd and of all even positive integers are here used as representatives of the two equal factors $\aleph_0$, $\aleph_0$. — Of course, the result is also contained in Theorem 3 of § 3.

The product $\aleph \cdot \aleph$ cannot be evaluated in the same way. Its geometrical meaning is the cardinal of the set of all points of a square or of a plane (cf. Theorem 2 of § 4). If, for instance, we consider (see fig. 9) the unit-square (whose side is 1) and regard each interior point, including the points of two adjacent sides (say the upper and the right-hand sides with their intersection), as the ordered pair [1]) of its coordinates (x, y) then the Cartesian product S required contains all pairs of real numbers x and y from the intervals $0 < x \leqslant 1$, $0 < y \leqslant 1$. (As the axes we have chosen the lower and the left-hand

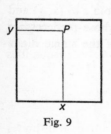

Fig. 9

---

[1]) For the transition from ordered pairs to plain pairs cf. § 8, **2**. In the present case we may also contemplate the unit-square defined by $0 < x \leqslant |$ and $2 < y \leqslant 3$, whereby the factors of the Cartesian product with the cardinal $\aleph \cdot \aleph$ become *disjoint* sets; then plain pairs $\{x, y\}$ are sufficient. Hence we shall simply speak of "pairs".

sides of the square.) Thus we arrive (cf. §4, **2**) at a one-to-one correspond-ence between all members (points) of S and all pairs of *infinite decimals* beginning with 0. ..., viz.

$$x = 0.x_1x_2 \ldots x_k \ldots, \quad y = 0.y_1y_2 \ldots y_k \ldots.$$

By interlacing these decimals we obtain the following decimal of the corresponding interval $0 < z \leqslant 1$

$$z = 0.x_1y_1x_2y_2 \ldots x_ky_k \ldots,$$

a result which obviously is based upon the equality $\aleph_0 + \aleph_0 = \aleph_0$ (cf. § 7, **6**). Thus we have related to every pair (x, y) a uniquely determined z; different pairs yield different values of z.

This, however, does not yet produce a one-to-one mapping of the unit-square, i.e. the set of the pairs (x, y), onto the unit-segment (say, the square side) containing the members z. While to each (x, y) a single z corresponds, there are values of z to which by the above procedure no pair of infinite decimals (x, y) corresponds; namely those z in whose expansion at all odd or at all even places, from a certain place on, the digit 0 occurs. For instance, for

$$z = 0.123405060506 \ldots \text{ our procedure yields } x = 0.13, y = 0.245656\ldots.$$

Yet pairs of an infinite and a terminating decimal are not members of S. Our rule, then, defines a mapping of the square *into* (not onto) the square side.

There are various methods of redressing this shortcoming. Presumably the simplest one consists in using, for the transition from z to (x, y) and vice versa, *groups of digits* ending with a digit $\neq 0$ whose predecessors equal 0 (which includes single digits $\neq 0$) instead of the single digits used above. Accordingly, for instance,

$$z = 0.3 \mid 5 \mid 07 \mid 9 \mid 001 \mid 2 \mid 6 \mid 0004 \mid \ldots$$

yields the pair of

$$x = 0.3070016\ldots, \quad y = 0.5920004\ldots;$$

thus terminating decimals x, y are excluded and a one-to-one mapping is established. Hence we have

THEOREM 9. $\aleph \cdot \aleph = \aleph$. *In other words, the set of all points of a square, or of all points of a plane — in short, a two-dimensional continuum — is equivalent to a one-dimensional continuum, for instance to the set of all points of a segment.*

Naturally, one may express our equivalence relation in various other ways; for instance, by taking a rectangle etc. instead of a square, or by taking the set of the complex numbers $x + iy$ instead of the set of the pairs (x, y).

The history of Theorem 9 is remarkable [1]). Cantor, after having proved in 1874 that there exist infinite sets which are not equivalent, by showing that the one-dimensional continuum is not denumerable (see § 4), looked for transfinite cardinals different from $\aleph_0$ and $\aleph$. His first guess was progressing from the one-dimensional continuum to multi-dimensional continua. When his attempt to prove $\aleph \cdot \aleph \neq \aleph$ remained unsuccessful he conferred with some leading mathematicians who advised him that this inequality was self-evident and required no proof; otherwise there would be no distinction between functions of one and of more variables or between different dimensions. Only after three years of fruitless efforts did he become convinced that his guess was false. A first proof of $\aleph \cdot \aleph = \aleph$ by means of decimal expansions (1877) suffered from the shortcoming mentioned above; then the publication of a correct proof (Cantor 1878) met with a delay caused by Kronecker and was finally made possible only with the help of Weierstrass. The result was a surprise for Cantor himself who wrote to Dedekind: *je le vois, mais je ne le crois pas.*

As a matter of fact, Cantor's result and its easy generalization to any finite number of dimensions and even to $\aleph_0$ dimensions (see § 7, 6), far from destroying the concept of dimension as Cantor had supposed, paved the way for clarifying this concept in a logico-mathematical and not merely intuitive way. Dedekind at once stressed the importance of *continuous* mappings in this context, confirming Leibniz' assertion that space constitutes an order and not just an aggregate (set). In the years following Cantor's publication it was proven, notably by Lüroth [2]), that continua of one, two, and three dimensions cannot be related by

---

[1]) The original proof (by means of expansions into continued fractions) is found in Cantor 1878. For the following cf. Cantor–Stäckel 1897 and Cantor–Dedekind 37, pp. 20–41.

[2]) See the comprehensive exposition Lüroth 07. An attempt made by Cantor in 1879 proved a failure.

one-to-one and continuous (for short, homeomorphic) mappings [1]). The general case, meaning the proof for any m- and n-dimensional continua, is a profound problem of topology and was only solved in 1911 [2]); but even for $m = 2$, $n = 3$ the proof is not too simple.

The problem does not belong to our subject-matter since the notion of continuity is outside *abstract* set theory. Yet the reader may grasp the gist of the problem even in the quite simple case $m = 1$, $n = 2$, for which we prove

THEOREM 10. *There is no single-valued continuous real function $z = f(x, y)$ of two real arguments x, y which yields a one-to-one correspondence between the ordered pairs (x, y) and the values z (i.e. which assumes different values for different argument-pairs). In short, a one-dimensional continuum (say, a line) cannot be mapped continuously onto a two-dimensional continuum (a plane).*

Remark. As the following proof shows, we need not assume f to be continuous in both arguments; it is sufficient that f is a continuous function of either argument when the other remains constant. As to the domain, instead of infinite lines and planes we may consider bounded closed continua; for instance, the square $-1 \leqslant x \leqslant 1$, $-1 \leqslant y \leqslant 1$ in the plane and a segment which contains the points $f(-1, 0)$ and $f(1, 0)$ on the line (cf. the proof).

We *prove* the theorem indirectly, assuming that $f(x, y)$ were a function with the properties mentioned and deriving a contradiction from this assumption. By taking y constant, $= 0$, we obtain the continuous function of a single argument $f(x, 0) = \varphi(x)$; let $\varphi(-1) = a$, $\varphi(1) = b$. By hypothesis $a \neq b$. According to a well-known theorem on continuous functions, $\varphi(x)$ assumes each real value between a and b as x increases from -1 to 1. Hence, by hypothesis, $z = f(x, y)$ *does not assume any value of the interval* $\langle a, b \rangle$ (i.e., $a \leqslant z \leqslant b$) when $y \neq 0$.

The remaining task is to make use of a value $x = c$ for which $f(x, 0)$ assumes an *interior* value of the interval $\langle a, b \rangle$; then, by its continuity, $f(c, y)$ will assume a

---

[1]) For bounded closed sets, the biuniqueness and continuity (in one direction) of the mapping implies that it is also continuous in the other direction. That this is not the case for more general sets was shown by Kuratowski 21.

Yet if the mapping is only unique (defined by a single-valued function) then the additional property of continuity is not sufficient. In fact, the surprise caused by Cantor's proof was increased when Peano defined a plane *curve* — in other words, a couple of single-valued continuous functions $f(t)$, $g(t)$, or a continuous motion of a point — which passes through every point of a square (Peano 1890); this means that the points of a square can be related to the points of a segment in such a way that different segment-points correspond to different square-points and neighboring square-points to neighboring segment-points while to neighboring square-points do not always correspond neighboring segment-points, and sometimes the same square-point corresponds to different (incidentally, to not more than four) segment-points.

Hilbert 1891 gives a geometrical form to Peano's analytical proof; cf. Hahn 13, Kamiya 27. For a generalization to n dimensions, which means a movable point passing through every point of an n-dimensional space, see Sierpiński 36.

[2]) Brouwer 11, cf. 13. For the history of the problem and its general background cf., for instance, Menger 28, Alexandroff 32, Hurewicz–Wallman 41. The first serious attempt to define dimension had already been made in Bolzano 1851 (see p. 80 of the 1920 edition).

value still belonging to $\langle a, b \rangle$ when y is slightly shifted from 0. Let, therefore, $x = c$ be the value in $\langle -1, 1 \rangle$ for which $\varphi(c) = f(c, 0) = \dfrac{a+b}{2}$. By hypothesis, $f(c, y) = \psi(y)$ is a continuous function of y for which $\psi(0) = \dfrac{a+b}{2}$; hence a y which is $\neq 0$ but sufficiently close to 0 will yield a value $\psi(y) = f(c, y)$ which still belongs to $\langle a, b \rangle$. Since this contradicts the end of the preceding paragraph, Theorem 10 has been proved.

It would even suffice to assume that f is continuous in one argument only.

In contrast with the homeomorphic mappings used to show the invariance of dimensionality, the mapping used to prove Theorem 9 is just biunique and not continuous; the points of the segment corresponding to neighboring points of the square are, in general, not neighboring points, and conversely. Yet the mapping used in proving Theorem 9, in spite of its arbitrariness, still defines a function of the segment-points which is continuous at every irrational point.[1])

9. Intersection of Sets. Boolean Algebra.[2]) Of the operations with sets defined in § 2, 3 we used in this section *union* only and added to it the Cartesian product, but the operation of *intersection* was disregarded; for while intersection (in concurrence with union) is important in many fields of mathematics it has no significance for the arithmetic of transfinite numbers. Still we shall here generalize and extend what was said about intersection and its connection with union in § 2, thus enabling the reader to comprehend the problems in question.

The definition of intersection can be generalized to *any set A of sets* just as the definition of union is generalized by Definition I on p. 81. The existence of the intersection $\bigcap A = a \cap a' \cap \ldots$ in this general case is proven by means of our axioms, in particular the axioms of sumset and of subsets, verbatim as on p. 20. While commutativity is contained in the very definition, the associativity of the operation can be formulated in full analogy to (1) and (2) on p. 85 and proven just as there. Both distributive laws of p. 22 may be generalized and proven in the same way; cf. example 1) below. The examples given in exercise 1) of § 2 (cf. exercise 4) of § 7) for the connection between inclusion, union, and intersection are also generalized easily.

We call a sequence (S_n) of sets *ascending* if, for every n, $S_n \subseteq S_{n+1}$ and *descending* if always $S_{n+1} \subseteq S_n$. As is easily seen, the union of the

---

[1])   This rather surprising result is due to Sierpiński 27.
[2])   This subsection is not used in the following sections.

sets of any sequence (T_n) can be represented as a union of ascending sets, the intersection as an intersection of descending sets, as follows:

$$T_1 \cup T_2 \cup T_3 \cup \ldots = T_1 \cup (T_1 \cup T_2) \cup (T_1 \cup T_2 \cup T_3) \cup \ldots$$
$$T_1 \cap T_2 \cap T_3 \cap \ldots = T_1 \cap (T_1 \cap T_2) \cap (T_1 \cap T_2 \cap T_3) \cap \ldots.$$

Starting with an arbitrary *"universal"* set V we consider its subsets S and their *complements* $S' = V - S$. Clearly we have $V' = O$ and $(S')' = S$. If S_k $(k = 1, 2, \ldots, n)$ are finitely many subsets of V we obtain

$$V = (S_1 \cup S_2 \cup \ldots \cup S_n) \cup (S_1' \cap S_2' \cap \ldots \cap S_n') =$$
$$= (S_1 \cap S_2 \cap \ldots \cap S_n) \cup (S_1' \cup S_2' \cup \ldots \cup S_n').$$

For each member of V belongs either to *at least one* S_k, hence to their union, or else to *no* S_k, hence to the intersection of their complements S_k'. This proves the first equality; the second follows from it if the S_k, which are arbitrary subsets of V, are replaced by their complements S_k'. These equalities, called *de Morgan's laws* (but known already to Occam), state: the complement of a union of sets is the intersection of their complements; the complement of an intersection, the union of the complements. Obviously these laws remain valid for infinitely many sets. (The restriction to subsets of V is irrelevant since this universal set can be chosen as comprehensive as desired.)

Hence we obtain the following *law of duality*. Let C be a set secured from sets S_k by repeated operations of union and intersection. Then the complement C' is obtained by replacing the sets S_k with their complements S_k', union with intersection, and intersection with union. Since $S = T$ implies $S' = T'$, any *equality* resulting from these operations remains true if those replacements are carried out on both sides. The result can be extended to inequalities (relations of inclusion) expressed by $\subset$; for $S \subset T$ implies $S' \supset T'$ (which is another expression for $T' \subset S'$), hence we have yet to replace $\subset$ with $\supset$ and vice versa.

For instance, $S \cup S' = V$ yields $S' \cap S = O$.

If we start from an *identity* between the subsets S_k of V, i.e. from an equality which is true for any choice of these sets, we need not replace the sets by the complements; the dual identity is obtained by a mere exchange of union and intersection. Moreover, if we have an inequality using $\subset$ then in addition $\subset$ and $\supset$ must be exchanged. To be sure, if constant sets occur in the identity, they must be replaced by their complements; for instance, from $S \cup O = S$ we conclude $S \cap V = S$; from $S \cap O = O$, $S \cup V = V$; from $S \subseteq V$, $S \supseteq O$.

Examples. 1) From the distributive law [1]

$$S \cap (T_1 \cup T_2 \cup \ldots \cup T_n) = S \cap T_1 \cup S \cap T_2 \cup \ldots \cup S \cap T_n,$$

which is proven (even for infinitely many sets T_n) just as in § 2, **3**, we obtain the dual distributive law

$$S \cup T_1 \cap T_2 \cap \ldots \cap T_n = (S \cup T_1) \cap (S \cup T_2) \cap \ldots \cap (S \cup T_n).$$

2) The associative law of union yields, as its dual, the associative law of intersection, and vice versa.

3) From $S \subseteq S \cup T$ we obtain $S \supseteq S \cap T$.

4) The *characteristic functions* introduced in § 7, **3** and exercise 4) of § 7.

It is noteworthy that all statements based on inclusion, union, intersection, and complementation can be formally derived from a few of them, without reference to the *meaning* of these relations and operations; for instance, taking union and complement as primary, from the commutative and associative laws of union and the law

$$(S' \cup T')' \cup (S' \cup T)' = S.$$

Then we may *define* the intersection $S \cap T$ by $(S' \cup T')'$ and the inclusion $S \subseteq T$ by $S \cup T = T$. Abstract systems whose members satisfy the three laws mentioned, or else laws equipollent to them, are called *Boolean algebras* [2] after G. Boole who, together with A. de Morgan, created the logical calculus to be described presently. These algebras play an important part in mathematics [3] and logic; during the last decades they have yielded new branches such as the theory of *lattices* (cf. § 8, **2**).

---

[1] For certain independence questions regarding distributivity see Wernick 30, Tarski 35.

[2] For the introduction and axiomatic foundation of Boolean algebra it may suffice to refer to Stone 35, Tarski 35 and 38, Birkhoff-MacLane 53. For an important extension (Boolean rings) see, for instance, Mostowski-Tarski 39; for connections with topology and abstract algebra, Stone 34 and 37, von Neumann-Stone 35, Tarski 38b. Cf. Whitesitt 61, Sikorski 64, and some references in § 8, **2**.

[3] Including applied mathematics, e.g. probability, insurance, switching circuits; see, for instance, Broderick-Schrödinger 40, Koopman 40, Berkeley 37, Shannon 38. The latter paper has started a series of important researches in this and other fields of electronics.

Disjunction and conjunction are the logical equivalents of union and intersection [1]) (cf. § 2, 3), which explains the significance of Boolean algebra in *logic*. To obtain equivalents of other notions used above let us remember the axiom of subsets (§ 2, **2**), which by definite properties determines subsets of a given set. If for the latter we take the universal set V then V corresponds to properties fulfilled by *each* member of V. If $S \subseteq V$ is determined by a given property then the contrary [2]) property determines the complement S', which accordingly corresponds to logical negation. Similarly inclusion corresponds to implication, in other words to "all s are t"; for if $S \subseteq T$ then the members s of S, i.e. the objects with a property characteristic of S, have also properties characteristic of T, which is logically expressed by "S implies T" or "if S then T".

By the operations of disjunction, conjunction, negation, and implication (with their derivations) a broad field of logic is covered, which frequently is called *algebra of logic* and can be formalized by our symbols. The following instances will be sufficient to show this.

Logical statement	A corresponding set-theoretical statement
There is no s	$S = O$
Every object is an s	$S = V$
Some s are t	$S \cap T \neq O$
Some s are not t	$S \cap T' \neq O$
There is neither an s nor a t	$S \cup T = O$ (or $S' \cap T' = V$)
Law of contradiction	$S \cap S' = O$
Law of excluded middle	$S \cup S' = V.$[3])

Exercises

1) Show that the sum of denumerably many finite cardinals $\neq 0$ equals $\aleph_0$.

2) Evaluate the sums $\mathbf{f} + \aleph$ and $\mathbf{f} + \mathbf{f}$ where $\mathbf{f}$ is the cardinal defined in § 4, **7**.

---

[1])   Set operations can also be related to the transfinite extensions of logical disjunction and conjunction, viz. to existential and universal quantification ("some" and "all"); see Kuratowski-Tarski 31.

[2])   "Contrary" is taken in the sense of mere negation; the contrary of 'black' is not 'white' but 'not-black'.

[3])   For a more detailed and profound elaboration of this and related points see Sierpiński 51, in particular § 19.

3) Let to each member t of a non-empty set T be assigned cardinals a_t and b_t such that $a_t \leqslant b_t$; prove that $\sum_{t\varepsilon T} a_t \leqslant \sum_{t\varepsilon T} b_t$ and $\prod_{t\varepsilon T} a_t \leqslant \prod_{t\varepsilon T} b_t$.

4) Prove $\aleph_0 \cdot \aleph_0 = \aleph_0$ by decomposing the set of positive integers into denumerably many pairwise disjoint denumerable subsets and show that there are infinitely many such decompositions.

5) Prove that the set of all *finite* sets of positive integers is denumerable (in contradistinction to the set of *all* such sets).

6) Show that the universal library described on p. 6 is a denumerable set of books if the restriction imposed on the size of a (finite) book is dropped, or if $\aleph_0$ different types are admitted.

7) Let the set T, occurring in Definitions III and VI, be replaced by a set $U \sim T$, and let ψ be an arbitrary mapping of T onto U. Denoting by $\psi(t)$ the $u \in U$ that corresponds by ψ to $t \in T$, assign to $\psi(t) \in U$ the cardinal $f(t)$ assigned in Definitions III and VI to $t \in T$. (Hence every term or factor occurs in the new sum or product in the same quantity as in the old one.) Prove that this transition from T to U leaves the sum and the product unchanged, and reflect in what sense this statement may be considered to express the commutative laws of the addition and multiplication of cardinals.

8) Prove $\aleph \cdot \aleph = \aleph$ by expanding real numbers into continued (instead of decimal) fractions. What is the advantage of this procedure?

9) Generalize the method of proving Theorem 9 so as to map the set of all points of a cube or of the three-dimensional space onto a segment.

§ 7. Exponentiation of Cardinals. Transfinite Numbers and Infinitesimals

1. Exponentiation as Repeated Multiplication. Exponentiation shall first be introduced in the same way as in the arithmetic of positive integers, namely by repeating the operation of multiplication.

To form $c^2 = c \cdot c$ for cardinals c, according to Definition VI of § 6, we have to take sets S_1 and S_2 with $\overline{\overline{S}}_1 = \overline{\overline{S}}_2 = c$; c^2 is then the cardinal of the Cartesian product $S_1 \times S_2$. Restricting ourselves at present to the case that the factors of the Cartesian product are different (for equal factors, see **2**), we generalize the case of a pair $\{S_1, S_2\}$ of factors by the following

DEFINITION I. To form the power c^d, where c and d are any cardinals ($d \neq 0$) [1]), let D be a set of the cardinal d each member of which is a set with the cardinal c. The cardinal of the Cartesian product PD is called the dth *power of* c and denoted by c^d; c is called the *base* and d the *exponent* of the power.

According to Definition VI, c^d is a product in which each factor equals c and the multitude of the factors is d. We need not prove that the power is independent of the choice of D, for this follows from Theorem 3 of § 6.

2. The Insertion-Set.

We now turn to the method by which Cantor originally introduced the power c^d, a method which is more convenient for applications than Definition I and also reveals the close connection with the concept of *function*.

Given the non-empty sets S and T, consider the single-valued functions $s = f(t)$ whose argument t ranges over T while the values s belong to S. (We shall chiefly be interested in the *cardinality of the set* of all functions $f(t)$.) The nature of such functions shall be illustrated by three examples; the first two are rather trivial.

i) Four dice shall be marked respectively by 1, 2, 3, 4. An individual throw of the set of dice may be regarded as a function $s = f(t)$ where $t \, (= 1, 2, 3, 4)$ denotes the numeral of the respective die and s the number of spots shown by the die t; accordingly s is one of the values 1, 2, 3, 4, 5, 6, and different dice t may assume the same value s. Two functions are considered equal only if the same $s = f(t)$ is assumed for each t. According to the preceding paragraph we have $S = \{1, 2, 3, 4, 5, 6\}$, $T = \{1, 2, 3, 4\}$. As the result related to each die is independent of the others, there are 6^4 different functions $s = f(t)$ each of which biuniquely corresponds to a certain throw; for short, these functions may be denoted by the *ordered* set (s_1, s_2, s_3, s_4) where s_t is the result regarding the die t. (To be sure, our definition of equality differs from the usual practice of the game according to which, for instance, the throws (1, 2, 3, 6) and (6, 3, 2, 1) are considered equal.)

2) An example the terminology of which is more similar to the mathematical applications is a musical "program", i.e. a set T of pieces of music such that each member s of a certain set S of musicians can perform

---

[1]) The case $d = 0$ has here, in contrast with arithmetic, but little importance. We define $c^0 = 1$ for $c \neq 0$, though the reasons for this definition in arithmetic (division, continuity of the function c^x) are absent; cf., however, Theorem 2 below. $c = d = 0$ remains excluded altogether.

any piece of T. A definite cast for the program is formed by assigning a single musician to each piece of the program (possibly the same artist to several pieces), i.e. by relating one $s \epsilon S$ to each $t \epsilon T$. We may call this, *inserting* the set S of musicians into the program by means of a single-valued function $s = f(t)$ where t ranges over T and the values s are taken from S. The set of all possible casts with respect to given sets T and S has the cardinal s^t where $s = \overline{\overline{S}}$ and $t = \overline{\overline{T}}$, because each piece of T can be performed by any musician of S independently of the performances of the other pieces.

In the examples 1) and 2), where the sets S and T are finite, the set of all functions (insertions) coincides with a well-known notion of combinatorial analysis, namely the set of all ways of placing **s** objects into **t** holes with repetitions (the set of **t** th-class variations of **s** objects).

3) A mathematically significant example is presented by *decimal fractions* (or similar expansions). A given decimal $D = s_0. s_1 s_2 \ldots s_k \ldots$ with $s_k = 0, 1, 2, \ldots, 9$ (which is an infinite or terminating expansion of a real number x of the interval $0 \leqslant x \leqslant 10$) may be conceived as a certain insertion of the set of digits $S = \{0, 1, 2, \ldots, 9\}$ into the denumerable set (sequence) of places $T = \{0, 1, 2, \ldots, k, \ldots\}$; in other words, as a certain function $s = f(t)$ with t ranging over T, which assumes values out of S. The totality of all such functions, also named the insertion-set of S into T, contains all decimals D as defined above. Accordingly two decimals D_1, D_2 are considered equal only if they are identical (and not also if they are expansions of the same real number, as are $D_1 = 0.4999\ldots$ and $D_2 = 0.5$).

Using the notion of complex as introduced in Definition V of § 6, we may conceive the decimals D as complexes which in the present case are infinite *sequences* of digits $(s_0, s_1, s_2, \ldots, s_k, \ldots)$ with $s_k \epsilon S$. In the same sense every throw of the dice (example 1)) and every cast for the program (example 2)) constitutes a complex, which in both cases is a finite sequence. In these cases we have to regard the complexes either as ordered sets or else as plain sets of ordered pairs (s, t), t ranging over T.

In the light of these examples we introduce the general notion of an *insertion-set*; Cantor's term was *Belegungsmenge*. Starting, as in the beginning of this subsection, with non-empty[1]) sets S and T, we denote by $(S \mid T)$ the set of all insertions of S into T, i.e. the set of all functions

---

[1]) Only $T \neq O$ is actually required. If $S = O$ then nothing can be inserted, i.e. no complex exists; hence the insertion-set is the null-set, in accordance with $0^t = 0$ for $t \neq 0$.

$s = f(t)$ with t ranging over T and the s belonging to S. Two insertions are equal if and only if the same s is assigned to each $t \in T$; this is in accordance with equality between functions in analysis. Every member of the insertion-set may be written as a set, equivalent to T, of ordered pairs $\{\ldots (s, t) \ldots\}$, where each $t \in T$ appears as the second component of a single pair while the first components belong to S. According to Definition V of § 6, the set of *all* these sets, i.e. $(S \mid T)$, is the Cartesian product defined by the auxiliary set T if to each $t \in T$ the set S is assigned, i.e. the product $S \times S \times S \times \ldots$ where T defines the multitude of the factors. Comparing this with Definition I of subsection **1**, we have

THEOREM 1, simultaneously DEFINITION II. *The power* s^t *is the cardinal of an insertion-set* $(S \mid T)$ *with* $\overline{\overline{S}} = s$ *and* $\overline{\overline{T}} = t$, *i.e. of the set of all single-valued functions* $s = f(t)$ *where* t *ranges over a set of the cardinal* t, *and the values* s *belong to a set of the cardinal* s.

The paragraph preceding this theorem gives a set-theoretical definition of the notion of a single-valued *function* $s = f(t)$ by means of the set T of the arguments and of the set S of the function-values: a function is conceived as a set, having the cardinal $\overline{\overline{T}}$, of ordered pairs as specified above. (Ordered pairs may also be regarded as plain pairs; see § 8, **2**.)

The advantage of this new definition, in view of its easy applicability, becomes manifest in the following subsections.

3. The Power-Set. Returning to the concept of power-set (§ 5, **3**), we now conceive an arbitrary subset T_0 of T as the insertion into T of a set of two members, say $\{1, 0\}$ or $\{yes, no\}$: 1 (or "yes") shall be assigned to those $t \in T$ that belong to T_0, 0 (or "no") to the other $t \in T$. Conversely, any such insertion defines a certain subset of T. (T or the null-set corresponds respectively to the assignment of 1 or 0 to *each* $t \in T$.) Accordingly the power-set CT, i.e. the set of *all* subsets of T, may be regarded as the insertion-set $(\{1, 0\} \mid T)$ and has the cardinal 2^t. Hence, in view of Cantor's theorem (Theorem 2 of § 5) we have

THEOREM 2. *For any set* T *of the cardinal* t, *the power-set* CT, *i.e. the set of all subsets of* T, *has the cardinal* 2^t. CT *may be conceived as the insertion-set* $(p \mid T)$ *where* p *is a pair.*

Hence we have $2^t > t$ *for every cardinal* t.

While the theorem has been proved for $t \neq 0$ only, it is also true for $t = 0$ because of $CO = \{O\}$, $2^0 = 1$. (Cf. the footnote on p. 110.)

The meaning of the theorem for finite T was touched upon on pp. 71/2.

Theorem 2 may be considered a particular case of the inequality of Zermelo (Theorem 8 of § 6). For if we take the constant functions $f(t) = 1$ and $g(t) = 2$ for $t \epsilon T$ then the inequality states $\sum_{t \epsilon T} 1 < \prod_{t \epsilon T} 2$, hence by Theorem 5 of § 6 and Definition I above, $\mathbf{t} < 2^{\mathbf{t}}$.

If $\mathbf{t}$ is *finite* and > 1, $2^{\mathbf{t}}$ is greater but not next-greater than $\mathbf{t}$. The conjecture that for every *transfinite* $\mathbf{t}$ the power $2^{\mathbf{t}}$ *is next to* $\mathbf{t}$ is called the *generalized continuum hypothesis*; for $\mathbf{t} = \aleph_0$ it signifies (see subsection 5) that $\aleph = 2^{\aleph_0}$ is next to $\aleph_0$. (Cf. § 5, 2; § 11, 7; *Foundations*, pp. 72 and 92–94.)

By means of the new notation for the cardinal of the power-set, the process of attaining ever increasing cardinals (p. 98) can be described more simply. Starting with any finite or transfinite cardinal $\mathbf{c}_0$ and denoting $2^{\mathbf{c}_k}$ by $\mathbf{c}_{k+1}$, we first reach $\mathbf{c}_n$ for every finite n, then $\sum \mathbf{c}_n$ with n ranging over all finite n; this sum is greater than each $\mathbf{c}_n$ and may again be used for a start instead of $\mathbf{c}_0$, etc. Starting with $\mathbf{c}_0 = 0$ we thus reach transfinite cardinals of enormous magnitude.

The functions defined by the insertion of a pair into a set T (Theorem 2) also play an important part in certain applications of set theory. They correspond, as shown above, biuniquely to the subsets of T and are called *characteristic functions* [1]). Cf. exercise 4) at the end of § 7.

4. Formal Laws of Exponentiation.

In arithmetic the following formal laws of exponentiation hold

$$m^n \cdot m^p = m^{n+p}, \; m^n \cdot p^n = (mp)^n, \; (m^n)^p = m^{np}.$$

They are also valid, in a more general form, for (finite and transfinite) cardinals, namely

THEOREM 3. *If* $\mathbf{a}, \mathbf{b}, \mathbf{c}$ *are cardinals and if to every member t of a non-empty set T a cardinal $f(t) = \mathbf{k}_t$ is assigned, the following formal laws hold:*

(1)
$$\prod_{t \epsilon T} \mathbf{a}^{\mathbf{k}_t} = \mathbf{a}^{\sum_{t \epsilon T} \mathbf{k}_t}$$

(2)
$$\prod_{t \epsilon T} \mathbf{k}_t{}^{\mathbf{b}} = \left(\prod_{t \epsilon T} \mathbf{k}_t \right)^{\mathbf{b}}$$

(3)
$$(\mathbf{a}^{\mathbf{b}})^{\mathbf{c}} = \mathbf{a}^{\mathbf{bc}}.$$

---

[1]) See, in particular, de la Vallée Poussin 16.

Hence in particular

(1') $\qquad a^{k_1} \cdot a^{k_2} = a^{k_1 + k_2}$, $\qquad$ (2') $\quad k_1{}^b \cdot k_2{}^b = (k_1 k_2)^b$.

Proof. The important one among these laws is (1), from which (3) immediately follows. To prove (1) we use the associative law for Cartesian products of sets in the form (4) of p. 93. If each member y of all sets K_t has the same cardinal a and if $\overline{\overline{K}}_t = k_t$ then the Cartesian product $\prod\limits_{y \varepsilon K_t} y$ has the cardinal a^{k_t} by Definition I. On the other hand, the union S has the cardinal $\sum\limits_{t \varepsilon T} k_t$, hence the Cartesian product on the left-hand side of (4), the cardinal $a^{\sum\limits_{t \varepsilon T} k_t}$. Since equivalent sets have the same cardinal, (1) has been proven.

(2) is less important and will be used in the form (2') only. (2') is almost evident in view of the associative and commutative laws of the multiplication of cardinals; roughly speaking, one relates to each factor k_1 a corresponding factor k_2, on account of the equalling exponents, and then unites the factors $k_1 k_2$. For a formal proof cf. exercise 5) at the end of § 7. — The general form (2) can be proven in the same way.

Finally, if in (1) the same cardinal $k_t = b$ is assigned to each $t \varepsilon T$ and if $\overline{\overline{T}} = c$ then the left-hand side of (1) becomes $(a^b)^c$ by Definition I, while the exponent of the right-hand side turns to bc by Theorem 5 of § 6.

Inequalities. We found in § 6 that $a_t \leqslant b_t$ implies $\prod\limits_{t \varepsilon T} a_t \leqslant \prod\limits_{t \varepsilon T} b_t$ (cf. (2) on p. 97). Hence, if $a_t = a$ and $b_t = b$ for each t and if $\overline{\overline{T}} = c$ we have

(4) $\qquad\qquad\qquad a \leqslant b$ implies $a^c \leqslant b^c$.

In view of the footnote on p. 110 this remains true for $c = 0$.

An analogous inequality follows from the corresponding assumption regarding the exponents. Let the set C be equivalent to $D_0 \subseteqq D$, i.e. $c \leqslant d$ where $c = \overline{\overline{C}}$, $d = \overline{\overline{D}}$, and write $D - D_0 = D_1$, $\overline{\overline{D}}_1 = d_1$, hence $c + d_1 = d$. By (4) we have for every cardinal $a \neq 0$

$$1^{d_1} \leqslant a^{d_1},$$

which after multiplication of both sides by a^c, in view of $1^{d_1} = 1$, yields

(5) $\qquad\qquad\qquad c \leqslant d$ implies $a^c \leqslant a^d$.

This also holds for $a = 0$ if $c \neq 0$.

The difficulty with respect to "strict" inequalities is analogous to the situation found in § 6, 7. One still might expect that the assumptions $a < b$, $c < d$ would imply $a^c < b^d$; this, however, is false.[1]

That the latter inequality does not generally hold true if either the bases or the exponents are equal is obvious; for instance, we shall presently prove that

$$\aleph^{\aleph_0} = \aleph \; (= \aleph^1), \qquad \aleph^{\aleph_0} = 2^{\aleph_0}.$$

Regarding the particularly important base 2, one has not yet succeeded in proving that $c < d$ implies $2^c < 2^d$ — not even by using the axiom of choice.[2] The converse, however, easily follows by means of the axiom of choice, namely through the *comparability of cardinals* (see § 11, 7). For assume that $2^c < 2^d$. Then $d \leqslant c$ cannot hold true since by (5) this would imply $2^d \leqslant 2^c$; hence by comparability we obtain $c < d$.

5. The Power-Set of a Denumerable Set.

We start with evaluating the power $10^{\aleph_0}$. Using Definition II, we insert a set containing 10 members, say $M = \{0, 1, 2, \ldots, 9\}$, into the denumerable set $N = \{1, 2, \ldots, k, \ldots\}$. As in example 3) of 2, we conceive an insertion $(a_1, a_2, \ldots, a_k, \ldots)$ with $a_k \in M$ as the decimal fraction $0.\, a_1 a_2 \ldots a_k \ldots$; then the insertion-set $(M \mid N)$, having the cardinal $10^{\aleph_0}$, is the set D of all (infinite and terminating) decimals beginning with 0., provided that decimals differing formally are considered different.

Since the set D_0 of all infinite decimals of D has the cardinal $\aleph$ of the continuum (§ 4, 2 and 5) and the set D_1 of all terminating decimals, as a subset of all rationals, is denumerable, $D = D_0 \cup D_1$ has the cardinal $\aleph + \aleph_0 = \aleph$. Hence

$$(1) \qquad\qquad 10^{\aleph_0} = \aleph.$$

The occurrence of 10 in this formula derives from a biological and not mathematical source, namely from our using the decadic scale of notation, including decimals, in accordance with the number of our fingers. As mentioned in § 4, 3, for the expansion of real numbers we may as well use system fractions with any base $n > 1$, in particular with $n = 2$ (dual fractions), instead of $n = 10$; hence

$$(2) \qquad\qquad 2^{\aleph_0} = \aleph = n^{\aleph_0}. \quad (n > 1)$$

---

[1] Tarski 25a, p. 10 shows that in spite of these assumptions $a^c = b^d$ may hold true.

[2] However, this statement is obtained immediately by using the generalized continuum hypothesis (see above, 3); cf. Sierpiński 34/56, p. 167.

While this is a roundabout way of proving (2) inasmuch as we used, in addition to the expansion of real numbers into decimals, also expansions into other system fractions, we may derive (2) straight from (1). We restrict ourselves to $n = 2$; any n can be treated similarly.

The following proof [1]) establishes a mapping of the set F_2 of all dual fractions into the set F_{10} of all decimals and a mapping of F_{10} into F_2, wherefrom follows $F_2 \sim F_{10}$ by the equivalence theorem; we limit ourselves again to fractions between 0 and 1. F_2 is certainly equivalent to a proper subset of F_{10} since each dual fraction may formally be comprehended as a decimal in which only the digits 0 and 1 occur. On the other hand, we relate to each decimal f_{10} a dual fraction f_2 by the rule that each digit d_k of f_{10} shall be replaced in f_2 by d_k zeros followed by 1 (hence $d_k = 0$ by 1). Thus F_{10} is mapped onto *a proper* subset of F_2, because F_2 also contains dual fractions with more than nine consecutive zeros. In view of Theorem 2 we may formulate (2) as

THEOREM 4. *The power-set of a denumerable set has the cardinal* $2^{\aleph_0} = \aleph$ *of the continuum. More generally,* $n^{\aleph_0} = \aleph$ *for every finite* $n > 1$.

This quantitative conception of the continuum as the power-set of, say, the set of non-negative integers is closely connected with example 3) of **2** on the one hand and several examples in **6** and in exercise 7) on p. 125 on the other.

6. Further Examples of Exponentiation. We begin with powers of $\aleph$. By repeated application of $\aleph \cdot \aleph = \aleph$ (Theorem 9 of § 6) we obtain

(1) $$\aleph^n = \aleph. \quad (n \text{ finite}, \neq 0)$$

(1) follows also from Theorem 4 and (3) of Theorem 3 by

$$\aleph^n = (2^{\aleph_0})^n = 2^{\aleph_0 \cdot n} = 2^{\aleph_0} = \aleph.$$

Using $\aleph_0 \cdot \aleph_0 = \aleph_0$ (§ 6, **8**) we even obtain

(2) $$\aleph^{\aleph_0} = (2^{\aleph_0})^{\aleph_0} = 2^{\aleph_0 \cdot \aleph_0} = 2^{\aleph_0} = \aleph.$$

Obviously these are "logarithmic" calculations with the base 2, reducing multiplication and exponentiation respectively to addition and multiplication (as also done in the proof of $\aleph \cdot \aleph = \aleph$ in § 6). When Cantor,

---

[1]) Due to J. König 14, p. 219.

after twenty years of pioneer work in set theory, presented these short
and rather mechanical calculations [1]) he proudly compared them with the
great effort he had displayed in 1878 to prove (1), then meeting with
incredulity and antagonism in the mathematical world. Such operations
with cardinals, including the use of their formal laws, are — like the
operations with ordinals, see below §§ 8 and 11 — but another pattern of
a development found frequently in mathematics (most conspicuous in
calculus and its applications): the invention of a new mechanism which
rather automatically carries out processes that had previously demanded
creative invention.

In § 6, 8 the relation $\aleph^2 = \aleph$ was interpreted geometrically by using
coordinates. In the same way $\aleph^3$ is the cardinal of a cube or of the
infinite three-dimensional space, both regarded as the sets of their
points, and $\aleph^n$ or $\aleph^{\aleph_0}$ are respectively the cardinals of the set of points
of an n-dimensional space or of a space of denumerably many dimensions.
(In the latter space a point biuniquely corresponds to an infinite sequence
of real coordinates.) Hence

THEOREM 5. *The sets of points contained in three-dimensional space,
n-dimensional space, $\aleph_0$-dimensional space have each the cardinal $\aleph$.
The same applies to continuous parts of these spaces, for instance cubes.*

The surprising aspect of this result may be expressed by saying that all
points of space can be related in a one-to-one correspondence to the
points of an arbitrarily small segment.

Regarding powers of $\aleph_0$, we first generalize $\aleph_0{}^2 = \aleph_0$ to $\aleph_0{}^n = \aleph_0$
for finite $n \neq 0$. To evaluate $\aleph_0{}^{\aleph_0}$ we use $2^{\aleph_0} = \aleph$ and the formal laws
(Theorem 3) by the following specimen of calculating

$$\aleph_0{}^{\aleph_0} = (\aleph_0 \cdot 2)^{\aleph_0} = \aleph_0{}^{\aleph_0} \cdot 2^{\aleph_0} = \aleph_0{}^{\aleph_0} \cdot 2^{\aleph_0 \cdot \aleph_0} = \aleph_0{}^{\aleph_0} \cdot (2^{\aleph_0})^{\aleph_0} =$$
$$= (\aleph_0 \cdot 2^{\aleph_0})^{\aleph_0} = (\aleph_0 \cdot \aleph)^{\aleph_0} = \aleph^{\aleph_0} \text{ (see § 6, 8)} = \aleph, \text{ i.e.}$$

(3) $$\aleph_0{}^{\aleph_0} = \aleph.$$

As shown in § 3, 3, the set of the lattice-points in the plane has the
cardinal $\aleph_0^2 = \aleph_0$, and the same applies to the set of the lattice-points in
the n-dimensional space. On the other hand, (3) and (2) show that the
set of the lattices-points in $\aleph_0$ dimensions has the same cardinal as the

---

[1])   Cantor 1895, p. 488. Cf. some calculations in Hölder 30.

set of *all* points of this space; in $\aleph_0$ dimensions, then, it makes no quantitative difference whether we consider the space in its entirety or its lattice-points only.

As to the exponent $\aleph$, i.e. insertions into the continuum, $\aleph^\aleph$ is the cardinal of all single-valued real functions $f(x)$ whose argument x runs over a continuum; in § 4, **7** this cardinal was called **f**. A logarithmic calculation as above yields

(4) $\aleph^\aleph = (2^{\aleph_0})^\aleph = 2^{\aleph_0 \cdot \aleph} = 2^\aleph.$

$\aleph^\aleph$, then, is the cardinal of the power-set of the continuum, i.e. of the set of all sets of real numbers. Hence Theorem 4 of § 4 is a particular case of Cantor's theorem (2 of § 5).

By considering functions of a complex variable $x + iy$, or of n or denumerably many variables $x_1, x_2, \ldots, x_n(,\ldots)$, we obtain argument sets whose cardinal is $\aleph$, according to (1) and (2). Hence a set containing all such functions has also the cardinal $\mathbf{f} = \aleph^\aleph$.

Further equalities, some of which were proved before in less simple ways, may be inferred by means of the inequality "$\prod_k \mathbf{a}_k \leqslant \prod_k \mathbf{b}_k$ if $\mathbf{a}_k \leqslant \mathbf{b}_k$" (p. 109) or of (4) on p. 114. For instance, $n^{\aleph_0} = \aleph$ follows from $2^{\aleph_0} = \aleph_0{}^{\aleph_0} = \aleph$; in the same way we obtain $1 \cdot 2 \cdot 3 \cdot \ldots k \ldots = \aleph$ (cf. p. 100).[1]) Similarly, $2^\aleph = \aleph^\aleph$ yields $\aleph_0{}^\aleph = \mathbf{f}$. Hence it makes no difference for the cardinal of the set of all functions defined on a continuum whether the functions may assume all real values, or rational (or integral) values only, or even just two values, say 0 and 1.

One might suspect that the reason why $\aleph_0{}^{\aleph_0}$ is greater than the base $\aleph_0$ while $\aleph^{\aleph_0}$ equals the base $\aleph$ (see (2) and (3)) is that $\aleph$ is "too great to further increase through the exponentiation by $\aleph_0$". This is not true; there are two types of cardinals $\mathbf{c}$, those with $\mathbf{c}^{\aleph_0} > \mathbf{c}$ and those with $\mathbf{c}^{\aleph_0} = \mathbf{c}$, and *both types include cardinals as great as desired,*[2]) as we shall now show.

If $(\mathbf{c}_k)$ $(k = 1, 2, \ldots)$ is a sequence of increasing cardinals ($\mathbf{c}_k < < \mathbf{c}_{k+1}; \mathbf{c}_1 \neq 0$) then $\sum_k \mathbf{c}_k = \mathbf{c}$ belongs to the first type (and is of an arbitrarily great magnitude since the choice of $\mathbf{c}_1$ is arbitrary). For by

---

[1]) For other (transfinite) factorials cf. Kurepa 54.

[2]) It is remarkable that the distinction between these two types is important for a problem of field theory which has a solution for the second type only; see F. K. Schmidt 33. (For applications of set theory to abstract algebra in general, cf. § 12.) For another effect of the distinction see Rabin 59.

the inequality of König (Theorem 8 of § 6) we have

$$c = \sum_k c_k < c_2 c_3 c_4 \ldots \leqslant c_1 c_2 c_3 c_4 \ldots.$$

Denoting the latter product by d, we have (cf. exercise 3) on p. 109) in view of $c_k < c$ for every k

$$d \leqslant c^{\aleph_0}.$$

The combination of $c < d$ and $d \leqslant c^{\aleph_0}$ gives $c < c^{\aleph_0}$.

On the other hand, every cardinal of the form $c = b^{\aleph_0}$ with any base b (however great) belongs to the second type since

$$c^{\aleph_0} = (b^{\aleph_0})^{\aleph_0} = b^{\aleph_0 \cdot \aleph_0} = b^{\aleph_0} = c.$$

Finally, we shall use the equivalence theorem to calculate the cardinal of a set of functions not contemplated above, viz. the set C of all *continuous functions*; say, of the continuous real functions $f(x)$ of a real variable. We only need the following property of continuity: if (x_k) is a sequence of real numbers converging towards the limit $\bar{x}$, i.e. $\lim_{k \to \infty} x_k = \bar{x}$, then the value of $f(x)$ for $x = \bar{x}$ is uniquely determined by the totality of values $f(x_k)$. (Actually we have $f(\bar{x}) = \lim_{k \to \infty} f(x_k)$, yet we shall not use this.)

Given a rational or irrational $\bar{x}$, there are sequences (x_k) of *rationals* such that $\lim_{k \to \infty} x_k = \bar{x}$. For instance, we may expand $\bar{x}$ into a decimal fraction and take for x_k the terminating decimal obtained by stopping the expansion at the kth place after the decimal point. (For more general ways cf. § 9, 1 and 2.) Hence a continuous function is certainly determined by its values for all rational arguments; in other words, two such functions are equal if they coincide at every rational place. One cannot, however, invert this in the sense that, given any assignment of values of f for each rational x, there exists a continuous function which there assumes these values; this would contradict the continuity at the rational places, whereby the values at these places, too, are determined by the values at neighboring rational places. For example, there exists no continuous function equalling x^2 for integral x and $x^2 + 1$ for fractional x. Yet owing to our applying the equivalence theorem we need not enter into the intricate problem of the interdependence of the values for rational arguments.

We consider the following three sets: the set K of all *constant* functions, the set C of all continuous functions as introduced above, and the insertion-set $(D \mid R)$ of a continuum D into the set R of all rational numbers. Every constant function is continuous but not conversely, hence $K \subset C$; every continuous function corresponds, as explained above, to a certain insertion of real numbers into R but not to every such insertion does a continuous function correspond, hence $C \sim E \subset (D \mid R)$. K has the cardinal $\aleph$ (cf. § 4, 7) and $(D \mid R)$ has the cardinal $\aleph^{\aleph_0} = \aleph$; according to the equivalence theorem, then, C has also the cardinal $\aleph$ [1]). (It is rather difficult to specify a subset E of $(D \mid R)$ which can effectively be mapped onto C.) Hence

THEOREM 6. *The set of all continuous real functions of a real variable has the cardinal of the continuum. In other words, there is a real function $F(x, y)$ of two real variables x and y such that F is continuous in x for every fixed y and that any given continuous function $f(x)$ equals $F(x, y_0)$ for a single y_0.*

The set of all *continuous* functions, then, has a cardinal less than the cardinal of all functions (§ 4, 7). Hence the set of all differentiable functions has also the cardinal $\aleph$ as every such function is *a fortiori* continuous. The same applies to all monotonic functions [2]). On the other hand, contrary to a guess of Cantor's, the set of all integrable functions (even in Riemann's sense) has the cardinal $\mathfrak{f}$ of all functions [3]); roughly we may then say, it is a "normal" property of a function to be integrable but "abnormal" to be differentiable or even continuous.

For other sets of functions with the cardinal $\aleph$ cf. exercise 7) at the end of this section.

7. The Problem of Infinitesimals.[4]) The present section concludes our treatment of transfinite cardinals, save for the special subjects of § 11, 5 and 7. Hence this seems to be a proper opportunity for dealing with the question raised occasionally in mathematical and philosophical literature: whether, in parallelism to infinitely great magnitudes as represented by

---

[1]) Cantor 1879–84 V, p. 590. Regarding an effective mapping, see Szymański 44.
[2]) Hausdorff 06–07 II, p. 111.
[3]) See Jourdain 05, pp. 178–179; Schoenflies 13, p. 367. (Cantor 1879–84 V, p. 590.) Cf. Obreanu 47.
[4]) Readers not interested in the subjects of 7 and 8 are advised to skip these subsections. Their contents are not used in the later parts of the book.

transfinite cardinals, it is possible and useful to introduce also *infinitely small magnitudes*, and what the possible applications of such magnitudes might be.

While in the present subsection this question is treated from a general, in particular philosophic, viewpoint, in **8** we shall deal with a certain mathematical problem related to this subject.

Cantor, when undertaking a "continuation of the series of real integers beyond the infinite" (see above p. 3) and showing the usefulness of this generalization of the process of counting, refused to consider infinitely small magnitude beyond the "potential infinite" of analysis based on the concept of limit.[1]) The "infinitesimals" of analysis, as is well known, refer to an infinite *process* and not to a constant positive value which, if greater than zero, could not be infinitely small (cf. however **8**).[2]) The process of counting, even if starting with 0, jumps to (or begins with) 1 without an intermediate.[3])

Opposing this attitude, some schools of philosophers (notably the trend of Neo-Kantians headed by Hermann Cohen, in full vigor in the beginning of the present century) and later sporadic mathematicians proposed resuming the vague attempts of most 17th and 18th century mathematicians to base calculus on infinitely small magnitudes, the so-called infinitesimals or differentials. After the introduction of transfinite numbers by Cantor such attitudes pretended to be justified by set theory because there ought to exist reciprocals (inverse ratios) to the transfinite numbers, namely the ostensible infinitesimals of various degrees representing the ratios of finite to transfinite numbers.[4])

These views have been thoroughly rejected by Cantor [5]) and by the mathematical world in general. The reason for this uniformity was not dogmatism, which is a rare feature in mathematics and then almost invariably fought off; nobody has pleaded more ardently than Cantor

---

[1]) For a certain use of the limit concept with regard to transfinite cardinals see Kaluza 17. This method is different from the intuitionistic (or "naturalistic") attitude taken in Lusin 33, p. 125.

[2]) Cf., however, the discussion between Leibniz and John Bernoulli as quoted in Weyl 26/49, No. 7, which appears to us extremely strange, used as we are to the triumph of Leibniz' attitude.

[3]) This also applies to Cantor's earliest introduction of (finite and transfinite) ordinal numbers: not as ordinals of sets but as orders of derivations (see § 9, Definition V).

[4]) For the New-Kantian attitude see Natorp 23 and the literature cited in this book. Cf. Peirce 1892/1923 (especially pp. 208 ff. and 217 ff.), also Baer 32.

[5]) Notably in Cantor 1887–88, 1895a; cf. the footnote at the end of 1879–84 III.

himself that liberty of thought was the essence of mathematics and that prejudices had but a short life. The argument was not even that the admission of infinitesimals was self-contradictory (cf. **8**), but just that it was *sterile and useless* — a fact at which Gauss hinted by the remark quoted on p. 1. A repeated challenge to prove, for instance, the Theorem of Rolle by using infinitesimals instead of the limit method has never been responded to; other attempts, e.g. regarding the definition of the (definite) integral, led to similar failure. This uselessness strikingly contrasts with the success of the transfinite numbers regarding both their applications and their task of generalizing finite counting and ordering.

8. Non-Archimedean Domains. The incongruity between infinitely great and infinitely small magnitudes should not be exaggerated to mean that the latter cannot exist. Certain profound and impressive, though not always consistent foundations of geometry, for instance, were given by means of using infinitesimal segments of various orders, in addition to points and finite segments.[1]) But this does not mean inverting the transfinite magnitudes of set theory which, as shown in § 6, **7**, do not admit of an inversion of the direct operations.

At an early stage of Greek mathematics, in the fourth century B. C., a decisive idea was initiated by Eudoxos — who also, in some connection with this idea, was apparently the first to originate the theory of proportions found in the fifth book of Euclid's *Elements* (cf. § 9, **1**) and the method of exhaustion further developed by Archimedes. The idea is the postulate, later called the *Axiom of Archimedes*, that the difference between any two different magnitudes, when added to itself a sufficient number of times, can be made to exceed any given magnitude; or in modern language: given positive real numbers (or segments) a and b with $a < b$, there is an integer n such that $na > b$ (na meaning $a + a + \ldots + a$ with n terms a). Obviously this means the exclusion of magnitudes which are infinitely small (or infinitely great) in comparison with others.

While this postulate plays an important rôle in the foundations of ordinary geometry and arithmetic [2]), systems of magnitudes which do not satisfy the postulate have also been considered; they are called *non-archimedean domains*. In such domains, then, there exist magnitudes a and b with $a < b$ such that *all* multiples na remain below b, i.e. that a is

---

[1]) Notably in Veronese 1891 and Levi–Civita 1893. Cf. Wiener 20.

[2]) Cf. Hilbert 1899/1930 (particularly from the 2nd ed. on) and its *Anhang VI*.

infinitely small compared with b. An example treated already in Greek antiquity and then discussed from the middle ages over Newton, Voltaire, Cantor to the modern foundational researches [1] is the theory of *horn angles*, i.e. angles between a curve and its tangent, or more generally, between two curves with a common tangent. A more recent and significant example is that of *orders of infinity* regarding the growth of functions [2]; this subject, broached around 1880 by Paul du Bois Reymond, was somewhat connected with the beginnings of set theory. An almost trivial example of a non-archimedean domain is that of polynomials $p(x)$ with, say, integral coefficients, if one defines $nx < 1$ for every n. Especially in modern algebra [3] such domains fulfil an important task.

Of course, the cardinals (and ordinals, see § 11) of set theory also constitute non-archimedean domains since, $f(\neq 0)$ being a finite and t a transfinite cardinal, any finite sum of terms f is less than t. The situation differs from other non-archimedean domains chiefly in two respects; first, the cardinals and ordinals in their entirety are introduced with a view to their counting or ordering quality and thus are "natural" generalizations of the integers; moreover, the non-archimedean character is only due to the restriction to finite sums whereas Theorem 5 of § 6 ensures that every cardinal can be reached by repeated addition of the unity, i.e. of the least cardinal $\neq 0$. This contrast explains in what sense other non-archimedean domains contain "relatively infinite" magnitudes while the transfiniteness of cardinals and ordinals is an "absolute" one.[4]

The difference between the transfinite domains of set theory and non-archimedean domains in general is somewhat related to Cantor's distinction between the *transient* and the only *immanent* reality of concepts.[5] This difference explains why the definitions of order and of operations for cardinals and ordinals are natural and quasi-compulsory, in contradistinction to the more formal and arbitrary definitions in general non-archimedean domains. (Cf. Cantor's words quoted in § 6, 1.) When infinitesimals are correctly introduced they belong to the second category and do not constitute a counterpart to transfinite magnitudes. See, however, the *Remark* on p. 125.

---

[1] Cf. the literature given in Kasner 45.

[2] Cf. Hardy 24.

[3] From among the pioneer work, Hahn 07, Artin–Schreier 27, Baer 27 may be mentioned.

[4] Expert readers will understand that this assertion is not opposed to the so-called relativization of cardinals in the sense of Skolem; see *Foundations*, pp. 105–109.

[5] Cantor 1879–84 V, § 8.

Exercises

1) Show directly, without using Definition I, that if $S \sim S'$ and $T \sim T'$ then also $(S \mid T) \sim (S' \mid T')$.

2) Prove that either definition of exponentiation, I or II, implies $c^1 = c$ and $1^c = 1$ for every cardinal c.

3) Prove the following theorem for the functions (insertions) introduced in **2**. Let M be a finite set and F the set of those functions $f(m)$ defined in M which assume values of M, subject to the condition: $f(m') \neq f(m'')$ if $m' \neq m''$. Then there exist in F two functions $f_1(m)$ and $f_2(m)$ such that each function of F can be obtained by reiterating f_1 and f_2 a finite number of times.

If $M = \{1, 2, \ldots, k\}$, the following functions may be used:

$$f_1(1) = k, f_1(m) = m - 1 \text{ for } m \neq 1,$$
$$f_2(k - 1) = k, f_2(k) = k - 1, \ f_2(m) = m \text{ for } m < k - 1.$$

The proof is not as simple as it may seem at first sight.[1]

4) Prove the following properties of the ch(aracteristic) f(unction)s (see 3) corresponding to the subsets of a given set, properties which show the close connection between ch. fs. and the operations of Boolean algebra (or logic):

a) the ch. f. corresponding to the intersection of two or more subsets is the product of the ch. fs. corresponding to the individual subsets;

b) the ch. f. corresponding to the union of two or more *pairwise disjoint* subsets is the sum of the ch. fs. corresponding to the individual subsets.

By what rule has b) to be replaced if the subsets are not pairwise disjoint (say, in the simple case of two subsets)?[2]

5) Prove the formal law (2′) of subsection **4**

     a) by using Definition II of exponentiation,

     b) by using the associative law (4) of § 6, **6** (which was also used for proving the formal law (1) of **4**).

Hint to b). First, regard the set S occurring on the left-hand side of (4) as the union of two disjoint *equivalent* sets and assign k_1 to each member of the one, k_2 to each of the other. Secondly, after having chosen a certain mapping between these sets, use pairs of *corresponding* members; the union of all pairs then equals S. In view of (4), these two procedures yield sets which prove equivalent.

---

[1] See Piccard 35. It is also proven there that if the condition $f(m') \neq f(m'')$ is dropped then three primitive functions are required instead of two.

[2] For profounder properties of the ch. fs. cf. Whitney 33, Stone 45.

6) Prove $\aleph^{\aleph_0} = \aleph$ without formal calculation, analogically to the proof of $\aleph \cdot \aleph = \aleph$ in § 6, 8.

7) Prove that each of the following sets has the cardinal $\aleph$:

a) the set of all *sequences* of positive integers, and even the set of the sequences which emerge from the single sequence $(1, 2, 3, \ldots)$ by merely changing the succession of the members;

b) the set of all denumerable subsets of the continuum;

c) the set of all analytical functions of a complex variable;

d) the set of all formal (convergent or not) power series with real coefficients;

e) the set of all functions that can be represented as series of continuous functions.

Considering that the set of all integrable functions has the cardinal $2^\aleph$, we may conclude *by set-theoretical arguments* that "in general" an integrable function cannot be represented as a series (uniformly convergent or not) of continuous functions.

8) Two subsets of a denumerable set shall be called *almost disjoint* if their intersection is finite. Prove the following theorem by expanding the real numbers into dual fractions: The set of the positive integers, as well as any denumerable set, can be written as a sum-set $\bigcup T$ with $\overline{T} = \aleph$, the members of T being pairwise almost disjoint denumerable sets. (Cf. the footnote [3]) on p. 14; the literature cited there [especially Tarski] contains generalizations of the above theorem.)

Remark to pp. 121–123. Recently an unexpected use of infinitely small magnitudes, in particular a method of basing analysis (calculus) on infinitesimals, has become possible and important by means of a non-archimedean, non-standard, proper extension of the field of the real numbers. For this surprising development the reader is referred to the literature.[1])

---

[1]) A. Robinson 61 and 63 (ch. IX), Laugwitz 61, Luxemburg 62, and further literature cited there.

CHAPTER III

ORDER AND SIMILARITY. ORDER-TYPES AND ORDINALS

§ 8. Ordered Sets. Similarity and Order-Types

1. Introduction. So far infinite sets were investigated only with regard to properties common to *equivalent* sets: cardinal numbers, their comparison, operations with them. This restriction is justified by the simplicity of transfinite cardinals which shows in the analogy to finite integers, and also by the importance of their applications.

Yet equivalent sets still display much diversity, apart from the particular nature of the members which shall be disregarded as hitherto. The trait of diversity with which the remainder of this book deals (except for § 9, 5 and 6) is the succession or *order* in which the members occur in the set, a trait which was neglected purposely up to now. If, for instance, N is the set of all positive integers and R the set of all positive rationals, each ordered by the succession from smaller to greater numbers, then the sets are fundamentally different in spite of $N \sim R$; N has a first (least) member (1) and R not, each member of N but none of R has an immediate successor, etc. Incidentally, this diversity does not derive from the diversity of the members (integers versus rationals), as shown by the possibility of arranging R in form of a sequence, i.e. of an enumerated set, just as N (§ 3, 3). A few essentially different arrangements of the set of all integers are [1])

a) $(\ldots, -3, -2, -1, 0, 1, 2, 3, \ldots)$

b) $(0, 1, -1, 2, -2, 3, -3, \ldots)$

c) $(0, 2, -2, 4, -4, \ldots 1, -1, 3, -3, \ldots)$

d) $(\ldots, -8, -4, 0, 4, 8, \ldots \ldots -7, -3, 1, 5, \ldots \ldots -6, -2, 2, 6, \ldots \ldots -5, -1, 3, 5, \ldots)$.

The systematic treatment of ordered sets beginning with subsection 2

---

[1]) To point out that the succession of the members is not disregarded any more, in contrast with the axiom of extensionality (cf. § 2, **2** and § 4, **5**), we shall use parentheses ( ) to denote ordered sets, instead of the brackets { } introduced in § 2 for plain sets. The succession between the parentheses marks, or hints at, the succession in the ordered set.

shall be preceded here by some informal preliminary remarks. Many discussions have been devoted to the question whether ordinal or cardinal number is the primary concept, hence whether ordered sets should precede plain sets [1]) or the other way round. We shall not deal here with the psychological and historical aspects of this question; there is hardly a doubt that psychologically the ordered set is primary, owing to our experience with spatial order and temporal succession, and that the plain set is derived by an abstraction. From the logico-mathematical point of view the decision is less simple. On the one hand, the plain set is the more general and abstract notion, based on membership alone, and since the systematic exposition in mathematics usually proceeds from the general to the particular it seems natural to begin with plain sets and cardinals and to introduce ordered sets and ordinals by adding the order relation to the membership (and equivalence) relation, as done in the present book and in most expositions of set theory. On the other hand, there are also arguments for the converse direction,[2]) notably the problem of the comparability of cardinals (cf. § 5, 5 and § 11, 7) which cannot be solved without the explicit or implicit use of order; von Neumann [3]) was the first to base the definition of cardinals upon that of ordinals.

The introduction of order and ordinals is motivated by the needs of mathematics. Transfinite cardinals are a unilateral extension of the concept of integer, for integers serve not only the purpose of counting (cardinal, how many?) but also that of enumerating (ordinal, marking succession). In the domain of finite number this distinction is hardly felt owing to an arithmetical theorem [4]), which states that one ordinal only corresponds to each finite cardinal (cf. below p. 135); in other words, that any arrangement of n objects always terminates with the same place (an nth object). This enables language to use the same root for corresponding cardinals and ordinals ("three" and "third", etc.), except for the least or the two least numbers; our being accustomed hereto is

---

[1]) In contrast with ordered sets as considered in this and the following sections, we shall use the name *plain set* when referring to an un-ordered set in the sense of §§ 2–7.

[2]) Cassirer 29 attributes priority to ordinals even from a purely logical viewpoint.

[3]) In particular von Neumann 25. Cf. below, § 11, 2 and 5, and *Foundations*, pp. 101f.

[4]) Schröder seems to have been the first who stressed this fact explicitly, but he erroneously interpreted it as empirical. Proofs of the theorem (by mathematical induction) are given in textbooks of arithmetic; cf. also Russell 19.

responsible for often overlooking the distinction. The introduction of infinite sets and numbers compels us to become aware of it, as shown below.

Cantor, to be sure, introduced transfinite ordinals as derived from ordered sets in his later publications only while originally he had conceived them as a continuation of the finite process of counting with a view to the successive derivations of an un-ordered set of points (see § 9, 5). We here follow his later attitude which is more general and corresponds to the way taken for cardinals.

Besides the intrinsic importance of ordered sets and ordinal numbers, especially of their particular kinds dealt with in §§ 10 and 11, the order concept is also significant for the applications of set theory to analysis and geometry. The notion of order, or else other notions such as neighborhood, dimension etc., are indispensable for such applications because the notion of equivalence of sets alone is too general, eliminating as it does the more delicate differences between equivalent sets; cf. subsection 3.

In §§ 6 and 7 arithmetical operations were defined for sets and cardinals and in the present section certain analogous operations are introduced for ordered sets and their "types". Thus naturally the question arises whether one may cover both these theories within a common comprehensive frame. This problem, though less simple than it may appear, was tackled with some success, and in particular interesting results were obtained regarding exponentiation.[1])

2. Order-Relation and Ordered Sets. We introduce the concept of ordered set, as usual in algebra and geometry, by means of a rule which for any two distinct members of the set states which one precedes the other. Subject to certain formal properties of order in logic and mathematics, the rule is arbitrary and does not just mean order "by magnitude" as in § 5, 1. As a neutral linguistic term we shall use "preceding" (or "succeeding") instead of, for instance, "less" (or "greater"), without implying a spatial or temporal succession; for the same reason we use new symbols $\prec$ and $\succ$ instead of $<$ and $>$ which usually mean a succession according to magnitude. The properties required are contained in

DEFINITION I *(Definition of ordered set)*. Let be given a set S

---

[1]) Birkhoff (37 and) 42; cf. Day 45. These theories use the concept of partly ordered set, see **2**. Some of the ideas were anticipated in *Principia Mathematica* (by means of its theory of relations); cf. Whitehead–Russell 10–13 II, §§ 162 and 172.

and a rule which establishes, for any two members a and b of S, a relation $\prec$ (*relation of order*) such that

a) if $a \neq b$, at least one of the statements $a \prec b$, $b \prec a$ holds true (*connexity*),

b) the validity of $a \prec b$ implies the invalidity of $b \prec a$ (*asymmetry*),

c) for no a does $a \prec a$ hold (*irreflexivity*).

d) $a \prec b$ and $b \prec c$ together imply $a \prec c$ (*transitivity*),

e) $a \prec b$, $a = a'$, $b = b'$ together imply $a' \prec b'$ (*substitutivity*).

The conjunction of S and the rule for $\prec$ is called an *ordered set*, more strictly a "simply and totally ordered" set. (We shall content ourselves with "ordered" since, except for a few remarks in the present subsection, n-tuply ordered sets or partly ordered sets hardly occur in this book.)

We express $a \prec b$ by "*a precedes b*". According to b) we cannot express this statement symbolically by starting with b; therefore we write $b \succ a$ ("*b succeeds a*") synonymously with $a \prec b$.[1])

As to the conditions a) to e), asymmetry is a consequence of transitivity and irreflexivity (see § 5, **1**). Nevertheless, it would not be practical to drop asymmetry, since for certain purposes it is suitable to drop transitivity and then asymmetry becomes indispensable. (Cf. Definition I and exercise 1) of § 10.) Connexity is just the condition which so far we were unable to prove for the arrangement of cardinals according to magnitude; cf. § 5, **1**, where for this arrangement b) to e) were *proven* (while here the above conditions *define* an order relation). Substitutivity is a property of equality rather than of order (and quite insignificant in the present case since a member occurs in a set once only).

The relation which orders a set obviously also orders each subset. Hence we shall always consider *a subset of an ordered set to be ordered*.

From our definition we immediately conclude

THEOREM 1. *If a and b are members of an ordered set then one and only one of the statements*

$$a \prec b, \quad a = b, \quad a \succ b \text{ (i.e. } b \prec a\text{)}$$

holds true.

---

[1]) For a profounder analysis of the properties of the order relation (or serial order) cf. Carnap 34, § 5, and 58, § 31.

We shall denote ordered sets, as plain sets, by a single letter S, s, T etc. without referring to the rule (order relation) separately. For the notation by means of the members see the footnote on p. 126.

> DEFINITION II. The ordered set S is *equal* to the ordered set T if the sets are equal as plain sets (§ 2, 1) and the ordering rule is the same in both sets (i.e. if $a \prec b$ in S implies $a \prec b$ in T).

Clearly this equality is reflexive, symmetrical, and transitive. Henceforth we shall, as a rule, *drop the attribute "ordered"* and simply speak of "sets" whenever no misunderstanding is possible.

If S is a finite set the rule of order can be expressed by specifying, for every two members of S, which one precedes the other. For an infinite set, a law (formula, function) is required, just as for a mapping between infinite sets (§ 2, 4); the law may often, also for a finite set, be hinted at by arranging some of the members and using dots for the rest. For instance, the rules of order defining different ordered sets which contain all integers as given on p. 126 may be formulated as follows:

a) smaller integers precede greater ones;

b) integers with a smaller absolute value precede, and of two integers with equal absolute values the positive integer precedes;

c) even integers precede odd ones, of two even or two odd integers the one with the smaller absolute value precedes, and in the case of equal absolute values the positive integer precedes;

d) integers of the forms $4m + n$ $(0 \leqslant n < 4)$ precede each other according to smaller values for n, and in the case of equal values n the smaller integer precedes.

The set of all different infinite *sequences* of positive integers may, for instance, be ordered *lexicographically* (cf. 7), i.e. just as words are arranged in a dictionary, the succession of letters in the alphabet being replaced by the sequence $(1, 2, 3, \ldots)$.

The notion of order becomes insignificant for the *null-set* and for *unit-sets*. Nevertheless, they shall also be considered to be ordered sets when the context requires it; see, for instance, subsection 5, example 2. The unit-set $\{a\}$, then, is also written as (a) when required by the context. The simplest case in which order is essential is that of an *ordered pair*; from the pair $\{a, b\}$ we obtain the different ordered pairs (a, b) and (b, a). In view of the particular importance of this case *we reduce an ordered pair to a plain set* by identifying (a, b) with the plain set $\{\{a\}, \{a, b\}\}$;

according to this convention, the member of the unit-set has precedence over the other. (The set $\{a, \{a, b\}\}$ would not do because a might be a pair which contains the member $\{a, b\}$.) [1])

Cantor proposed to contemplate, in addition to simply ordered sets, also doubly and n-tuply ordered sets where two or n (positive integer) order relations are defined independently of one another, each being irreflexive and transitive. The set of all complex numbers may serve as an example. If we define

$$a + ib \prec a' + ib' \text{ if } a < a', \text{ or if } a = a' \text{ and } b < b'$$

we have a simply ordered set. Yet if we introduce two order relations $\prec$ and $\{$ by defining

$$a + ib \prec a' + ib' \text{ if } a < a'; a + ib \{ a' + ib' \text{ if } b < b'$$

then two different complex numbers are connected by at least one and in general by both relations, i.e. we have a doubly ordered set.

Cantor had in mind far-reaching applications of n-tuply ordered sets but his expectations have not materialized so far.[2])

Far more important than this direction proves a *weakening*, hence extension of the concept of ordered set by renouncing the condition of connexity. Thus *partly ordered sets* are obtained in which, in addition to the cases $a \prec b$, $a = b$, $b \prec a$, the *incomparability* of a and b is also admitted. Some authors recently say "ordered" for what here is called "partly ordered", and "totally ordered" (or "chain") for "ordered" set.

An obvious example of a partly ordered set is the power-set CS of any finite or infinite set S if the members of CS, i.e. the subsets s of S, are ordered by the rule: $s \prec s'$ if $s \subset s'$. Since, of two given subsets, in general neither is a subset of the other, the relation does not satisfy condition a) of Definition I. *Finite* partly ordered set, e.g. CS for finite S, are conveniently represented by graphs.

During the last decades partly ordered sets have gained an ever increasing importance in many branches of mathematics.[3]) In particular, there is a close connection between partial order and the theory of

---

[1])   For the history of this concept cf. Quine 60, § 53.

[2])   Cantor's and his students' work in this direction is found in Cantor 1887–88 II and H. Schwarz 1888; cf. Riesz 05 and Stöhr 42. Blumberg 36 deals with the principle of induction in such sets. Lindenbaum 34 gives an important extension and in particular considers n-tuply *well-ordered* sets (§ 10). A profounder concept of n-tuply ordered sets, fit for applications in geometry, is introduced in Hudekoff 30; cf. G. Schwarz 54.

[3])   The significance and applicability of partly ordered sets seems to have been recognized at first by Hausdorff (see 14, pp. 139 ff.). It will suffice to mention, in addition to Birkhoff's researches cited at the end of 1 and in the following footnote, Kurepa 35 and 37; MacNeille 37; Kurosh 39 (for partly ordered finite sets); Kurepa 50 (for "partly well-ordered" sets, each ordered subset of which is well-ordered); Altwegg 50 (for an axiomatic treatment).

lattices, which were already studied by Dedekind but did only since the 20's show their significance in algebra, topology, projective geometry, and other branches, including physics [1]); Boolean algebra (§ 6, 9) and the theory of lattices are closely related subjects.

The transition from plain to ordered sets raises two questions of principle.

First, *can every set be ordered?* More exactly, given any plain set S, does there exist a relation which orders S in the sense of Definition I? (The meaning of "existence" in this context is clarified in the following paragraph.) This problem of ordering is discussed in detail in *Foundations*, Chapter II, §§ 4 and 8; in general it cannot be solved in the affirmative without the axiom of choice. For the particular way of *well-ordering* (§ 10) the problem will be solved in full detail in § 11, 6. The question is simple for finite sets S; see § 10, 6.

Secondly, order has above been defined by introducing a separate order relation $\prec$, contrary to our procedure in §§ 2–7 where all required concepts and relations, including equivalence, were based on the single primitive relation of membership. Hence the question arises whether *the order relation can be reduced to the membership relation*. If so, the possibility of *ordering* a given set S means the existence of a set M which, according to that reduction, establishes an order in S; but the existence of *sets* is established by means of the axioms of set theory which use the membership relation only.

In point of fact, a reduction as required is possible, even in different ways. Moreover, one can prove without the axiom of choice that, to a given set S and a certain way of reduction, there *exists the set* M *whose members are all possible orders* M *of* S in the way adopted. Yet this result, far-reaching as it is, does not answer the above question whether every set can be ordered, for without the axiom of choice it cannot be proved that $M \neq O$, i.e. that there *exists* an order M.

The reduction of order to membership is also remarkable beyond the limits of mathematics, for it shows that *the concept of order is independent of temporal or spatial ingredients*, contrary to views sometimes expressed.

An elegant reduction, due to Hessenberg–Kuratowski, is described in

---

[1]) Dedekind 30–32II, pp. 103–147 and 236–271 (originating from 1897/1900); cf. certain early attempts of Peirce reprinted in Peirce 33. Of modern literature, the comprehensive expositions Birkhoff 48, Tarski 49 (§ 15), Hermes 55, and the general analysis in J. Schmidt 57a should be mentioned.

Foundations, pp. 127–131. Another one, more easily handled for practical purposes, is outlined below at the end of **4**.

Finally we introduce a few abbreviating terms in connection with ordered sets S.

a) If $a \prec b \prec c$ (short for: $a \prec b$ and $b \prec c$) one says, b is (lies) *between* a and c (or c and a).

b) If $a \prec b$ and there is no $x \in S$ with $a \prec x \prec b$ then b is called *the sequent of a*, or a and b *consecutive* members of S. In contrast, "*b* is a successor of *a*" and "*a* is a predecessor of *b*" are just other expressions for $a \prec b$; hence a member has at most a single sequent but in general various successors in S.

If b is the sequent of a then a may be called the "immediate predecessor" of b. The term *neighbor* includes both sequent and immediate predecessor.

c) If S contains a member a such that $a \prec s$ for every $s \in S$ which is $\neq a$, then a is called the *first* member of S; clearly a is uniquely determined. Likewise b is called the *last* member of S if $s \prec b$ for every other $s \in S$. If S has both a first and a last member they are called the *ends* of S; if it has neither a first nor a last member, S is called *open*.

d) The term "sequent" can now be generalized as follows. If $S' \subset S$ and the subset of those members of S which succeed every $s' \in S'$ has a first member b, then b is called *the sequent of S'* in S. (Accordingly the first member of S, if any, is the sequent of the null-set.) Hence if S' has a last member a, then the sequent b of S', if any, is also the sequent of a, and vice versa. Clearly there is no member "between S' and b". The sequent of S' is uniquely determined.

If, on the other hand, *no $s \in S$ succeeds every $s' \in S'$* then S' is called *confinal* with S. This does not involve that *all* $s \in S$ which succeed a fixed member or a fixed subset of S must belong to S' (a particular case of which would be that S has a last member also contained in S'); for instance, the subset of all positive *even* numbers is confinal with the set of all positive integers arranged according to magnitude.

e) A subset $S' \subseteq S$ that contains, together with any $s_0 \in S'$, also all predecessors of s_0 in S (i.e. all $s \in S$ for which $s \prec s_0$ in S), is called an *initial of S*. Likewise $S' \subseteq S$ is called a *remainder of S* if, together with any $s_0 \in S'$, all successors of s_0 in S belong to S'. S itself and the null-set are, then, both initials and remainders of S; an initial or remainder different from S is also called a *proper* initial or remainder.

A particular kind of initials of S are those which contain just the members that precede a certain member s of S. Such an initial is called a *section* of S; more precisely, the section of S *determined by s.* (If S has a first member then this determines the null-set as the corresponding section.) Accordingly, S is not a section of itself.

3. Similarity. We proceed from ordered sets to the relation of similarity just as we proceeded from plain sets to equivalence in § 2, **4.**

> DEFINITION III. The ordered set S is called *similar* to the ordered set T, in symbols: $S \simeq T$, if the members of T can be related to those of S by *a one-to-one mapping which preserves the order*; i.e. by a mapping such that, s_1 and s_2 being different members of S, t_1 and t_2 their respective images in T, from $s_1 \prec s_2$ follows $t_1 \prec t_2$ (hence also vice versa). Each such mapping is called a *similar mapping* of T onto S.

As in the case of equivalence, the relation of similarity is reflexive, symmetrical, and transitive. Hence we may speak of similarity, or of a similar mapping, *between S and T,* of two similar sets, and also of a *similar one-to-one correspondence* between the members of S and of T. (Obviously the condition that $s_1 \prec s_2$ implies $t_1 \prec t_2$ would enable us to do with the uniqueness of the mapping only, instead of its biuniqueness; yet it is more convenient to define similarity by *complementing equivalence* with a further condition.)

While by Definition III similar sets are (all the more) equivalent, the converse cannot hold since equivalent sets need not even be ordered. If they are then in general they are not similar. For instance, the sets

$$M = (1, 2, 3, \ldots) \text{ and } N = (\ldots, 3, 2, 1),$$

though containing the same members, are not similar since (for example) M has a first member (1) and N not; hence no mapping between them can be similar because to the true statement "$1 \prec m$ for every $m \in M$, $m \neq 1$" no corresponding statement exists for a possible image in N of $1 \in M$. Generally, a set which is similar to a set with a first (last) member has clearly itself a first (last) member.

A plain set which is equivalent to an ordered set S can always be ordered (cf. p. 140), for instance similar to S; we need only take a certain mapping between the equivalent sets and arrange the images of the members of S according to the order in S.

The definition of an infinite set as a set equivalent to a proper subset (VII of § 2) is apt to raise the question whether every infinite ordered set is similar to a proper subset. The answer is in the negative.[1])

The question raised on p. 27 with respect to equivalence may also be asked here, namely whether the concept of similarity can be reduced to the membership relation; the answer is again in the affirmative. Given two disjoint ordered sets, the set of *all* mappings between them exists as shown on p. 27. A subset of this set, namely the set of all similar mappings, can be defined by using the concept of order as based on membership (p. 132); hence it exists on account of the axiom of subsets. Finally, S and T are similar if and only if the set of all similar mappings between them is not empty.

Subsequently one can get rid of the condition that the sets be disjoint; cf. *Foundations*, chapter II, § 8.

The far-reaching parallelism between the properties of equivalence and similarity and even of analogous relations which satisfy additional conditions, suggests the introduction of a *general concept of relation* comprehending those mentioned as particular cases. (Cf. the question regarding *operations*, raised at the end of 1.) The general relation will then be "equivalence of sets with respect to a class (group) [2]) G of mappings or functions", and we write $S \underset{G}{\sim} T$ if there is a function in G which maps S onto T. Of course, the generality of this concept excludes the development of a theory as elaborate as the theory of similarity; nevertheless a theory far from trivial can be based upon that concept and certain statements regarding ordinary equivalence or similarity appear in this theory as particular cases.[3])

The situation is somewhat analogous to the classification of various geometries according to the groups of transformations characteristic of them *(Erlanger Programm)*. The use of a rather comprehensive group, say of the projective (or even homeomorphic) transformations, eliminates geometrical properties which are still invariant relative to a subgroup, for instance of the affine or the similar transformations. Analogically most properties of similarity between ordered sets are lost by proceeding from the group of similar mappings to the more comprehensive one of plain (equivalence) mappings. Equivalence is an isomorphism with respect to equality only (one-to-one correspondence), similarity an isomorphism with respect to order.

Examples of similarity. 1) Any two equivalent *finite* ordered sets, for instance any two ordered sets with a million members, are similar. Moreover, every finite set can be ordered, by taking first an arbitrary member, then any member of the remainder, etc. Both are theorems of arithmetic to be proven by mathematical induction (starting with defining a finite set as *inductive*; § 2, Definition VI). Cf. § 10, **6**.

2) If N and R denote the sets of all positive integers and of all rationals respectively, both ordered according to *increasing magnitude*, these

---

[1])   See Dushnik–Miller 40 where a counter-instance is formed by means of the axiom of choice. For *denumerable* ordered sets, however, the answer is in the affirmative. Cf. § 10, 5.

[2])   See exercise 10) at the end of § 8.

[3])   Cf. the literature cited in the footnote on p. 77, notably the papers of Tarski.

(denumerable) sets are certainly not similar; cf. p. 126. Yet if the members of R are rearranged so as to form a sequence (§ 3, 3) then we obtain similar sets; in fact, any two *enumerated* sets are similar, which is shown inductively by relating the first members, the second ones, and generally the kth members for every positive integer k to each other. For instance, the subset $(k, k + 1, k + 2, \ldots)$ of N is similar to N.

Moreover, the similar mapping established is *the only similar mapping* between two enumerated sets — in contrast to mappings between equivalent plain sets with more than one member where always various mappings exist, and infinitely many between equivalent infinite sets. We shall see that the uniqueness of the mapping in the present case, as well as in the case of finite ordered sets, is a particular case of a general theorem (13 of § 10). Yet in other cases there are different similar mappings of a set onto itself or a similar set, as shown by various examples in the present and the following section.

3) Let R be again the set of all rationals r, Q the set of all rationals except those of the interval $0 < r \leqslant 1$, both sets ordered according to magnitude. We obtain a similar mapping (one from among infinitely many) of R onto Q by the following rule: each negative r, as well as 0, is related to itself, while a positive $r \in R$ shall be related to $(1 + r) \in Q$ (hence a positive $r \in Q$ to $(r - 1) \in R$).

We shall see (§ 9, 3) that similarity continues to hold between these sets if, for instance, 0 is removed from Q. If, however, 1 is added to the members of Q then the new set, to be written Q', is not similar to R. For then 0 and 1 are consecutive members of Q while R has no pair of consecutive members, because between any two rationals (in the sense of magnitude) there are infinitely many rationals. But the images of consecutive members, in view of a similar mapping, are also consecutive; this follows just as shown on p. 134 for first (or last) members.

The addition of a single member, then, may destroy an infinite ordered set's similarity to another, in striking contrast to plain sets for which

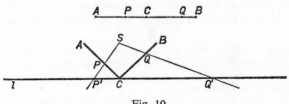

Fig. 10

not even the addition of denumerably many members changes the validity of an equivalence (§ 3, Theorem 6).

4) We resume a procedure used in § 4, **1** to deduce more far-reaching conclusions this time. Drawing a straight line l and a segment $\overline{AB}$ *without* its ends (see figure 10), we conceive the line and the segment as *ordered sets* L and M respectively of their points, say in the order from left to right. To prove that these sets are similar we bend the segment in its center C just as on p. 49 and lay it in C upon the line, the ends diverging symmetrically upwards as done in figure 10; in the new position the segment shall also be considered ordered from left to right. Taking the point S, midway between the new positions of A and B, as center of projection we obtain, precisely as in § 4, a mapping of L onto M by relating to each other the intersections with every (intersecting) ray from S, for instance P and P', Q and Q', and also C and C (related to itself). In view of our present task, we perceive that the mapping is *also similar*, since no two rays from S intersect one another. Hence our sets of points are similar.

Yet the sets cease being similar if to the segment one of its ends is added. For then M has a first or a last member, in contrast with L.

By means of the "line of numbers" (§ 1, fig. 2) our result is transferred to sets of real numbers and then runs as follows: the set of all real numbers is similar to the set of the numbers x of any open interval $a < x < b$, if the numbers are arranged according to magnitude.

5) On account of 4) we may form a similar mapping of a square

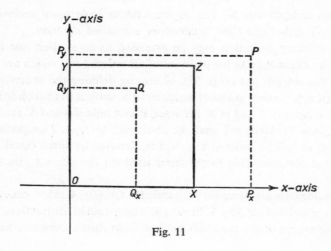

Fig. 11

onto the infinite plane, each regarded as a (simply) ordered set, as follows.

Let $OXZY$ be a square in a plane with a system of Cartesian coordinates (figure 11); O is the origin, and the square sides $\overline{OX}$ and $\overline{OY}$ with their prolongations are the x- and y- axes respectively. The set S of the points of the plane and the set T of the points of the square, excluding the points of the sides, shall be ordered by the following rule: if x_1, x_2 are the abscissae and y_1, y_2 the ordinates of the points P_1 and P_2 respectively, let $P_1 \prec P_2$ if $x_1 < x_2$, or if $x_1 = x_2$ and $y_1 < y_2$. In figure 11, then, we have for instance $O \prec Q \prec Z \prec P$, $X \prec Z$.

To map S similarly onto T we conceive the points of S as the ordered pairs of their coordinates or, which amounts to the same, as the pairs of the respective feet on the axes, i.e. P as (P_x, P_y), Q as (Q_x, Q_y). In example 4) a rule was formed which similarly maps the entire x-axis onto the open square side $\overline{OX}$ and the entire y-axis onto the open square-side $\overline{OY}$; hence to each point (P_x or P_y) of either axis, a point (Q_x or Q_y) of the respective square side corresponds biuniquely. Thus a mapping of S onto T is formed by relating to the point $P = (P_x, P_y)$ of the plane the point $Q = (Q_x, Q_y)$ of the square, and this mapping is clearly similar, for if $P_1 \prec P_2$ then we have for the respectively corresponding square points Q_1, Q_2 also $Q_1 \prec Q_2$.

4. Order-Types. We proceed from the relation of similarity to the concept of order-type just as we did from equivalence to cardinal number (§ 4, **5** and **6**). Without repeating the earlier remarks we define (cf. (B) on p. 60):

The ordered sets S_1 and S_2 are said to have *equal order-types* if $S_1 \simeq S_2$. Otherwise their order-types are called *different*.

This working definition may be extended to an explicit one by conceiving an order-type as the plain set of all ordered sets which are similar to a given set (cf. (A) on p. 59), or else by defining the order-type of a set S as a new symbol uniquely assigned to S, subject to the condition that the order-types of S and of S' are equal if and only if S and S' are similar.

The term "order-type" shall be shortened to *type*. *Transfinite types*, i.e. those of infinite ordered sets, will be denoted by small Greek letters, in general corresponding to the letter used for the set; e.g., the type of S by σ.

In analogy to his notation of cardinals (p. 60), Cantor denoted the type of the ordered set S by $\overline{S}$, hinting at a single act of abstraction, namely from the nature of the members but not from their succession. Since the result of a double act of abstraction is the cardinal $\overline{\overline{S}}$, consistently $\overline{\overline{S}} = \mathbf{s}$ is also written as $\overline{\sigma}$, σ being the type of S, and σ is called *a type of the cardinal* $\mathbf{s}$. If $\overline{\sigma} = \aleph_0$ (or $> \aleph_0$) we speak of a *denumerable* (or *non-denumerable*) *type* σ.

Since any two equivalent *finite* ordered sets are similar (p. 135) there is a one-to-one correspondence between finite cardinals and finite types. This is why both finite cardinals and types may and shall be denoted by the same symbols 0, 1, 2, ..., n, ...; in fact, n is apt to mark the type of *any* ordered set with n members. (Since the null-set and unit-sets are also considered to be ordered sets it is reasonable to admit 0 and 1 as types, too.) Incidentally, there is no danger of confusion between finite cardinals and types; for statements containing finite numbers only are independent of whether we regard them as cardinals or types, and if transfinite numbers (cardinals, types) enter a statement we have to interpret finite numbers in the statement according to the nature of the transfinite ones.

If S is an infinite set of the type σ then the type of the set which originates from S by *inverting its order* (i.e. by replacing each $s_1 \prec s_2$ with $s_1 \succ s_2$) is denoted by $*\sigma$. (Whether $*\sigma \neq \sigma$ or $*\sigma = \sigma$ depends on σ.)

In particular, *the type of an enumerated set*, e.g. of the set $(1, 2, 3, ...)$, *is denoted by* ω. Hence we have $\overline{\omega} = \aleph_0$; $*\omega \neq \omega$ since ω has a first member and $*\omega$ has not (which is an abbreviation, used frequently, for "every set of the type ω has a first member"). $*\omega$, the type of $(..., 3, 2, 1)$, has a last member.

While transfinite order-types, as well as transfinite cardinals, constitute infinite magnitudes they have the drawback of *being incomparable* in general. (For this reason they are not called numbers, whereas the distinctive title of "ordinal numbers" is conferred on the particular types dealt with in §§ 10 and 11.) In fact, the analogy to cardinals would suggest to call σ "less than" τ if σ is similar to a subset of τ but τ not similar to any subset of σ (which again is short for "if a set of the type σ is similar to a subset of a set of the type τ, etc."). An instance as simple as $\sigma = \omega$, $\tau = *\omega$ illuminates the situation: every subset of $*\omega$ has a last member as in contrast to ω, and every subset of ω has a first as in contrast to $*\omega$; accordingly no judicious comparison between ω and $*\omega$ is conceivable. Another instance, also of denumerable types, is $\sigma = 1 + \eta$, $\tau = \eta + 1$ (see § 9, 3). Cf. exercise 5) at the end of § 8.

Nevertheless, one may profitably introduce a *partial order* by magnitude between types (p. 131) by defining just as suggested above; namely, if S and T are sets of the types σ and τ respectively, we call σ *less than* τ ($\sigma < \tau$) if S is similar to a subset of T but T not similar to any subset of S.[1]) Then, in addition to $\sigma = \tau$ and $\sigma < \tau$, the case where *either set is similar to a subset of the other while the sets are not similar* should be distinguished as a third case, and the types σ and τ will be called *incomparable* only if none of these cases applies, as for $\sigma = \omega$ and $\tau = {}^*\omega$.[2])

The following theorem [3]) may serve as an example of applying this partial order of types: there exist linear sets (§ 9) H and K of the cardinal $\aleph$ such that $\overline{H} < \overline{K}$ while no type lies between them, being greater than H and less than K.

Order-types, i.e. the types of simply ordering relations, constitute a particular case of general relation-types.[4])

THEOREM 2. *The set* $T(\mathbf{c})$ *of all different types of a given cardinal* $\mathbf{c}$ *satisfies the inequality*

$$\overline{\overline{T(\mathbf{c})}} \leqslant 2^{\mathbf{c}^2}.$$

As to transforming this inequality to the corresponding equality, it can certainly not be done for *finite* $\mathbf{c} > 0$, for then there exists only a single type of the cardinal $\mathbf{c}$ while the right-hand side is > 1. For $\mathbf{c} = \aleph_0$ we shall succeed in proving the equality by means of the addition of types (6, Theorem 5). That in the general case an equality cannot be attained with "elementary" resources follows from the remark on p. 132 about ordering a given set; if this is not generally possible there remains the risk of $T(\mathbf{c}) = O$, and even when this can be excluded by an effective example, as for $\mathbf{c} = \aleph$ (linear continuum!), still considerable difficulties are left. Only by means of the well-ordering theorem (§ 11, 6) can we prove that $\mathbf{c}^2 = \mathbf{c}$ and that the cardinal of $T(\mathbf{c})$ *equals* $2^{\mathbf{c}}$.

Proof. A) Let $\tau = \overline{T}$ be an arbitrary member of $T(\mathbf{c})$ — which includes the *existence* of an ordered set T of the cardinal $\mathbf{c}$ — and denote by S any (not necessarily ordered) set with the cardinal $\mathbf{c}$. Then S *can be ordered according to the type* τ, namely by establishing in S the order prevailing in T by means of a mapping of S onto T.

B) Hence $T(\mathbf{c})$ *is equivalent to a subset of the set* V *whose members are all ordered sets containing the members of an arbitrary set* S *of the cardinal* $\mathbf{c}$. For, by A), every type of the cardinal $\mathbf{c}$ belongs to some of the sets of V; yet as different sets need not have different types we can only speak of a *subset* of V.

---

[1]) See Fraïssé 48. More simply we may say: there is a similar mapping of S into T but none of T into S.

[2]) Cf. Ginsburg 54. This interesting paper chiefly deals with *fixed points* of ordered sets S, i.e. members of S which, by every similar mapping of S into S, become related to themselves. A main problem is the occurrence of fixed points in ordered sums and products of sets which possess fixed points.

[3]) See Sierpiński 50b, cf. Ginsburg 53.

[4]) These general types and their (relational) addition are comprehensively treated in Tarski 56.

C) Now an ordered set corresponding to S may be considered to be *a certain set of ordered pairs* (s_1, s_2) with $s_1 \in S$, $s_2 \in S$; for instance, of the pairs (s_1, s_2) for which $s_1 \prec s_2$ holds in the ordered set (which implies that the pairs satisfy conditions as formulated in a) — d) of Definition I). Hence the set V defined in B) is equivalent to a *subset* of the set Y whose members are *all* sets of ordered pairs (s_1, s_2) out of S.

D) As shown in § 6, 5, a set of (ordered) pairs out of S is essentially a subset of the Cartesian product $S \times S$. Hence, according to C), V is equivalent to a subset of the power-set $C(S \times S)$ which has the cardinal $2^{c \cdot c}$ (§ 7, 3). Therefore, by B), $T(c)$ has a cardinal $\leqslant 2^{c^2}$, as maintained in our theorem.

By means of C) and D) it can be proven that, given an un-ordered set S. there exists the set whose members are *all ordered sets containing the members of* S. (Cf. above p. 132.) This proof, as well as the proof of Theorem 2, makes no use of the axiom of choice but uses the axiom of subsets in the following way. In C) we formed the set Y whose members are all sets of ordered pairs out of S. Among these sets there are those which correspond to the conditions of order expressed in Definition I. The axiom of subsets, then, yields the subset $Y' \subset Y$ which contains these particular sets of pairs. However, as pointed out above, the axiom of choice is required to prove that Y' is not empty.

5. Addition of Two Order-Types. Operations with types can be defined to a certain extent — addition fully, multiplication partly — in analogy to the operations defined for cardinals in § 6. However, only part of the formal laws there proven are valid in the arithmetic of types.

DEFINITION IV. To add the types σ and τ in this succession, the union $S \cup T$ of disjoint set-representatives with $\overline{S} = \sigma$, $\overline{T} = \tau$ shall be ordered by the following rule:

a) if x_1 and x_2 belong both to S or both to T then $x_1 \prec x_2$ holds in the union if it holds in S or in T;

b) If $x_1 \in S$ and $x_2 \in T$ then $x_1 \prec x_2$ holds in the union.

This rule transforms the union into an ordered set $S + T$ whose type is called the *ordered sum* $\sigma + \tau$ *of the given types*; $S + T$ is called the *ordered sum of S and T*.

In short, the ordered sum of types is the type of the union of corresponding disjoint ordered sets, provided that in the union the order of either set is retained and the members of the first term precede those of the second. In symbols, $\overline{S} + \overline{T} = \overline{S + T}$. (Cf. Definition II of § 6.)

The following remarks will prove useful.

1) While the disjointedness was required in § 6 for the sum of *cardinals* only and not for the union of plain sets, it is here also necessary for the addition of ordered *sets*; otherwise the rule of order would be ambiguous (for instance, if $x_1 \prec x_2$ in S and $x_2 \prec x_1$ in T).

2) Clearly $S + T$ satisfies the conditions of order, including transitivity.

3) In view of the (arbitrary) rule b) the succession of σ and τ must be given from the first; hence we speak of *ordered* sums.

4) The symbol $+$, employed for the addition of cardinals in § 6, is here used for the addition of types; this cannot lead to confusion since the nature of the terms (cardinals or types) clarifies the meaning of $+$ (except for finite σ and τ for which the meaning is indifferent).

5) Similarly as in § 6, $\sigma + \tau$ is uniquely defined by σ and τ, notwithstanding the arbitrariness of their set-representatives. For the following theorem holds: If $S \simeq S'$, $T \simeq T'$, and if S and T, as well as S' and T', are disjoint sets, we have $S + T \simeq S' + T'$. This theorem is proven like Theorem 1 of § 6 (for *pairs A and B*), in view of the rules a) and b) of our definition; hence $\overline{S + T} = \overline{S' + T'}$, i.e. the sum of the types is independent of the choice of the representatives.

6) A comparison between our definition and Definition II of § 6 yields $\overline{\overline{\sigma + \tau}} = \overline{\overline{\sigma}} + \overline{\overline{\tau}}$, i.e. *the cardinal of the sum of two types equals the sum of the cardinals of the types.*

Examples. 1. Between the finite order-types 3, 4, 7 we have the equalities $3 + 4 = 4 + 3 = 7$, as follows from

$$(1, 2, 3) + (4, 5, 6, 7) \simeq (4, 5, 6, 7) + (1, 2, 3) \simeq (1, 2, \ldots, 7).$$

These statements, and generally $m + n = n + m$ for any finite types m, n, may be inferred also, instead from Definition IV, from § 6 and the one-to-one correspondence between finite types and finite cardinals. Hence, though the order of the terms essentially enters Definition IV (as in contrast with the addition of cardinals), the addition of two finite types is commutative and yields a finite sum. The same applies to the addition of *finitely many* finite types in the sense of Definition V, below.

2. In contrast herewith we have

$$\omega + 1 \neq 1 + \omega \, (= \omega).$$

For, using the sequence of increasing positive integers as representing ω, we obtain

$$\omega + 1 = \overline{(1, 2, 3, \ldots 0)},$$

i.e. the type of a set with a last member, while

$$1 + \omega = \overline{(0, 1, 2, 3, \ldots)} = \omega.$$

By induction we obtain $n + \omega = \omega$ and $*\omega + n = *\omega$ for every finite n, while $\omega + m \neq \omega + n$ and $m + *\omega \neq n + *\omega$ for different finite values m, n. Likewise we have $\omega + \omega \neq \omega$. In general, then, the addition of two types is *non-commutative* [1]), and a type may be changed by the addition of a finite or a denumerable type, in contrast with the cardinal equalities $\aleph_0 + n = \aleph_0 + \aleph_0 = \aleph_0$.

THEOREM 3. *The addition of ordered sets and of types according to Definition IV is associative*, i.e.

$$(S + T) + U = S + (T + U), \quad (\sigma + \tau) + \upsilon = \sigma + (\tau + \upsilon).$$

Proof. It suffices to prove the statement for sets. Since forming the union of plain sets is an associative operation (§ 6, 4), only the coincidence of order in the left-hand and right-hand sets has to be shown. If x_1 and x_2 belong to *the same* of the sets S, T, U then it is trivial that $x_1 \prec x_2$, if valid in one set, is valid in the other. Else, if $x_1 \prec x_2$ in $(S + T) + U$, either x_1 belongs to S and x_2 to T or U, or x_1 belongs to T and x_2 to U. In the first case we have $x_1 \prec x_2$ in $S + (T + U)$, in the second $x_1 \prec x_2$ in $T + U$, hence in $S + (T + U)$. The transition from right to left is verbally the same.

In view of Theorem 3, the common value of the sums of types may be written $\sigma + \tau + \upsilon$.

As examples we take

$$n + (\omega + \omega) = (n + \omega) + \omega = \omega + \omega = \omega + (n + \omega) = (\omega + n) + \omega$$

for any finite n; while these sums are independent of n, $\omega + \omega + m$ and $\omega + \omega + n$ are different for $m \neq n$.

---

[1]) Aronszajn 53 investigates the cases in which the addition is commutative, a task which is not simple at all. For the same question regarding *ordinal numbers* see the end of § 10, 4.

$*\omega + \omega$ is the type of the set of all integers arranged according to magnitude; for finite n we have

$$(*\omega + n) + \omega = *\omega + (n + \omega) = *\omega + \omega,$$

whereas the sums $n + *\omega + \omega$ and $*\omega + \omega + n$, different from one another if $n \neq 0$, are also dependent on the value of n.

6. General Addition of Order-Types.

DEFINITION V. Assume that to every member t of a non-empty ordered set T a type $f(t) = \varrho_t$ is uniquely assigned. To form the ordered sum of the ϱ_t, replace each ϱ_t by a set-representative R_t $(\overline{R}_t = \varrho_t)$ such that R_{t_1} and R_{t_2} are disjoint for $t_1 \neq t_2$. The union of the sets R_t shall be ordered by the following rule:

a) if x_1 and x_2 belong to the same R_t then $x_1 \prec x_2$ holds in the union if holding in R_t;

b) if $x_1 \in R_{t_1}$ and $x_2 \in R_{t_2}$ then $x_1 \prec x_2$ holds in the union if $t_1 \prec t_2$ holds in T.

This rule transforms the union into an ordered set K whose type κ is called *the ordered sum of the given types*; K is called *the ordered sum of the sets R_t*. One writes

$$\kappa = \sum_{t \in T} \varrho_t.$$

In short, the ordered sum of types is the type of the ordered sum of corresponding disjoint ordered sets. (Cf. Definition III of § 6.)

The remarks 1) to 4) added to Definition IV apply also to Definition V, which includes IV as a particular case. 4) now refers to the symbol $\sum$, instead of $+$. As to 5), κ is uniquely determined in view of the analogue to Theorem 1 of § 6, which states in the terminology of our definition: if R_t and R_t^* are representatives of ϱ_t, hence $R_t \simeq R_t^*$, then the ordered sum of the sets R_t is similar to the ordered sum of the sets R_t^*; accordingly the sum κ is independent of the chosen representatives. This is proven analogically as in § 6, 2 with the supplement given on p. 91; by means of Axioms I–VI one proves that, with respect to similar disjoint sets R_t and R_t^*, there exists the set of all similar mappings between them (which may be finite or infinite for infinite R_t, in contrast with mappings between plain sets), and even that the set exists whose members are all such sets of similar mappings while t ranges over T; however, to obtain a single mapping for each t as required for our purpose, here also the axiom of choice is required in general.

By comparing Definition V with Definition III of § 6 one easily extends the remark 6) of **5** to the statement that *the cardinal of an ordered sum of types equals the sum of the cardinals of the single types*; i.e.,

$$\overline{\overline{\sum_{t \epsilon T} \varrho_t}} = \sum_{t \epsilon T} \overline{\overline{\varrho_t}}.$$

The ordered sum of types as defined here is also independent of the auxiliary set T; it only depends on *the type of* T. In a more elaborate form: if $T \simeq T^*$ and the image of $t \epsilon T$, in view of a fixed similar mapping, is denoted by t^*, then by assigning ϱ_t to t^*, instead of to t, the sum κ is not changed. This is obvious because the new ordered sum-set with the same representatives is (not only similar but) equal to the original one.

While Definition IV yields examples of non-commutative addition only if one of the terms is transfinite, in the present case addition need not be commutative even if all terms are finite, as shown below in example 2. However, associativity also holds in the general case; just as in the case of cardinals, the problem is rather the *formulation* of the associative law than its proof which is quite simple.

In § 6, **4** the formulation was simplified by the use of the operator U for sum-sets. In order not to complicate the symbolism excessively we shall here use an operator *ad hoc*, S, to denote the ordered sum of an ordered set of sets, and the symbol $+$ of Definition IV also for more than two set-terms.

Let A be the ordered set of all sets R_t introduced in Definition V and

(1) $$A = \ldots + K + \ldots + L + \ldots + M + \ldots$$

an arbitrary ordered decomposition of A into complementary disjoint non-empty subsets (cf. (1) on p. 85); the members of the ordered subset K, for instance, precede those of L, according to the order fixed in A by the set T. Then the associative law for the ordered sum SA should be formulated (cf. (2) on p. 85) as

(2) $$SA = \ldots + SK + \ldots + SL + \ldots + SM + \ldots.$$

It was proven in § 6, **4** that the left-hand and right-hand sides of (2) contain the same members. Hence it only remains to show that they appear on both sides in the same order, which is done in analogy to the proof of Theorem 3 (p. 143). With respect to different members x_1 and x_2 of SA we distinguish between three cases:

A) x_1 and x_2 belong to the same $R_t \epsilon A$;

B) $x_1 \in R_{t_1}$ and $x_2 \in R_{t_2}$ with $t_1 \neq t_2$, but R_{t_1} and R_{t_2} belong to the same term on the right-hand side of (1), say both to K;

C) $x_1 \in R_{t_1}$ and $x_2 \in R_{t_2}$, where R_{t_1} and R_{t_2} belong to different terms of (1), say $R_{t_1} \in K$ and $R_{t_2} \in L$.

In each case the succession between x_1 and x_2 is the same on both sides; in A), on account of a) in Definition V; in B), on account of b) in Definition V, applied to SA and to the respective term on the right (SK); in C), on account of the succession in (1) of the respective terms on the right, i.e. because the members of K precede those of L.

Since (2) implies the corresponding associative law for types, we have

THEOREM 4. *The ordered addition of sets and types according to Definition V is associative, in the sense of the equalities (1) and (2) and their analogues for types. It is, however, not commutative in general, except for the addition of finitely many finite types.*

Theorem 4 includes Theorem 3 with the qualification that now finite sums are defined independently; while in view of Theorem 3 $\sigma + \tau + \upsilon$ is *defined* as the common value of $(\sigma + \tau) + \upsilon$ and $\sigma + (\tau + \upsilon)$, here the equality of the three expressions is a *proven statement*.

Examples. 1. Let T be an enumerated set, hence $\overline{T} = \omega$, and assign $f(t) = \omega$ to each $t \in T$. The sum $\sum_{t \in T} \omega = \omega + \omega + \omega + \dots$ is accordingly the type of a sequence of sequences. (In contrast with (1) and (2) above, dots appear here only at the end because every term has a sequent.) According to Cauchy's diagonal method (p. 101) we may obtain a representative of our sum by first writing the positive integers in the array

$$
\begin{array}{cccccccccc}
1 & 2 & 4 & 7 & 11 & 16 & . & . & . \\
3 & 5 & 8 & 12 & 17 & . & . & . & . \\
6 & 9 & 13 & 18 & . & . & . & . & . \\
10 & 14 & 19 & . & . & . & . & . & . \\
15 & 20 & . & . & . & . & . & . & . \\
21 & . & . & . & . & . & . & . & . \\
. & . & . & . & . & . & . & . & . \\
. & . & . & . & . & . & . & . & . \\
. & . & . & . & . & . & . & . & . \\
\end{array}
$$

and then arranging them according to successive rows.

If $f(t) = \omega + \omega$ is assigned to each $t \in T$ then the sum clearly remains unchanged in view of the associative law.

2. Let T be an arbitrary non-empty ordered set and $\overline{T} = \tau$. By assigning the type 1, and as its representative the unit-set $\{t\}$, to each $t \in T$, we obtain just the sum τ according to Definition V. Hence *any type $\tau \neq 0$ can be represented as an ordered sum of unities* 1, according to the cardinality and order of τ. (Cf. Theorem 5 of § 6.)

If, instead of 1, the type 2 is assigned to each $t \in T$ then the sum will change not only for finite T but in general also for infinite T. (In certain cases, e.g. for $\overline{T} = \omega$, it does not change.) For example, if T is the set R of all rationals r between 0 and 1 ordered by magnitude, and if $\overline{T}$, as usual, is denoted by η, then the function $f(r) = 1$ produces the "dense" sum η (cf. § 3, 3 and § 9, 1 and 3), while in the sum corresponding to $f(r) = 2$ each member has a neighbor. For the representative of $f(r) = 2$ we may, for instance, take the ordered pair $(r, 1 + r)$; the corresponding ordered sum shall be denoted by Q.

Yet if, instead of R, we consider the ordered set R' of all rationals between 0 and 2 except for 1 (in § 9, 3 we shall prove $R' \simeq R$) then a one-to-one correspondence between the members of Q and of R' is formed by relating to $r \in R'$ and $(1 + r) \in R'$ respectively the (equal) members of the pair $(r, 1 + r)$. Thus R' differs from Q by its order only. Since R' is dense, the types of Q and R' are different; this is, then, an example of non-commutativity in a case where all terms added are finite, namely unit-sets or the unity.

The rearrangement of R (with the type η) to a sequence (see § 3, 3) is another example.

Now we are in a position to essentially improve the result contained in Theorem 2 (in 4) for $c = \aleph_0$, namely to prove

THEOREM 5. *The set $T(\aleph_0)$ of all denumerable types has the cardinal $\aleph$ of the continuum.*

Proof.[1]) Since Theorem 2 states that the cardinal in question is $\leqslant 2^{\aleph_0^2} = 2^{\aleph_0} = \aleph$, it will be sufficient to prove that it is also $\geqslant \aleph$. This shall be done by presenting a subset of $T(\aleph_0)$ which has the cardinal $\aleph$. (That $T(\aleph_0)$ is not empty is shown by $\omega \in T(\aleph_0)$.)

Writing for short $*\omega + \omega = \zeta$, we assign to every *sequence* of positive integers $N = (n_1, n_2, \ldots, n_k, \ldots)$ the denumerable type

$$\tau_N = n_1 + \zeta + n_2 + \zeta + \ldots + n_k + \zeta + \ldots .$$

---

[1]) See Bernstein 05 (partly due to Cantor). Cf. Hausdorff 14, pp. 97 f., also Eyraud 40. — For the problem of all types of the cardinal of the continuum see Cuesta 45, Sierpiński 46a.

First we show that different types τ_N correspond to different sequences N, i.e. that

(3) $$N \neq N' \text{ implies } \tau_N \neq \tau_{N'}.$$

To prove (3) we use the following

LEMMA. *If R_1, R_2, S_1, S_2 are non-empty ordered sets and if one of the assumptions* (a) *and* (b) *is fulfilled*

(a) $R_1 + S_1 \simeq R_2 + S_2$, R_1 *and* R_2 *finite*, S_1 *and* S_2 *without first members*,

(b) $S_1 + R_1 \simeq S_2 + R_2$, $\overline{S}_1 = \overline{S}_2 = \zeta$,

then $R_1 \simeq R_2$ and (in case (a)) $S_1 \simeq S_2$.

In fact, a similar mapping of $R_1 + S_1$ onto $R_2 + S_2$ according to (a) cannot relate an $r \in R_1$ to an $s \in S_2$ since the latter is preceded by infinitely many members, the former only by finitely many; hence $R_1 \simeq R_2$ and $S_1 \simeq S_2$. The same impossibility subsists in the case (b), because every $r \in R_1$ is then preceded by a subset of the type ζ, i.e. without a last member, while every $s \in S_2$ is preceded only by subsets with last members, namely by proper non-empty initials of S_2; hence $R_1 \simeq R_2$, which completes the proof of the lemma.

Now (3) follows from the lemma by mathematical induction with respect to the sums

$$\tau_N = n_1 + \zeta + n_2 + \zeta + \ldots, \quad \tau_{N'} = n_1' + \zeta + n_2' + \zeta + \ldots.$$

$\tau_N = \tau_{N'}$ implies, according to (a) and the associativity of addition, $n_1 = n_1'$ and $\zeta + n_2 + \zeta + \ldots = \zeta + n_2' + \zeta + \ldots$. From the latter equality likewise follows $n_2 + \zeta + \ldots = n_2' + \zeta + \ldots$ by (b). Thus we obtain $n_k = n_k'$ for each k; i.e. $\tau_N = \tau_{N'}$ implies $N = N'$, as maintained by (3).

On account of (3), the cardinal of the set $T(\aleph_0)$, which in addition to types of the form τ_N certainly contains other types, is equal to or greater than the cardinal of the set $\mathbf{N}$ whose members are all sequences N of positive integers. Now a definite N is an insertion of integers into a denumerable set (§ 7, 2); hence $\mathbf{N}$ is an insertion-set of the cardinal $\aleph_0{}^{\aleph_0} = \aleph$. Accordingly, the cardinal of $T(\aleph_0)$ is $\geqslant \aleph$; since by Theorem 2 this cardinal is $\leqslant \aleph$, Theorem 5 has been proven.

7. On the Multiplication of Order-Types. The reason why in § 6, 5 and 6 the usual method of defining multiplication as repeated addition was abandoned is here missing, because we shall have to restrict ourselves to a finite number of factors. Therefore we define in analogy to arithmetic

DEFINITION VI. If in Definition V to every $t \in T$ the same type $f(t) = \varrho$ is assigned then the sum $\kappa = \sum_{t \in T} f(t)$ is called the product of ϱ and of the type $\tau = \overline{T}$ in this succession: $\kappa = \varrho\tau$.

To include the case $T = O$ we define $\varrho \cdot 0 = 0$ for every ϱ. In view of the representation of a type τ as an ordered sum of unities 1 (example 2 in 6) one may interpret Definition VI to mean that through replacing 1 by ϱ one obtains the sum $\varrho\tau$ instead of τ.

The remarks added to Definition V mean for the present case that $\varrho\tau$ is not dependent on the nature of T but on its type only and that $\overline{\varrho\tau} = \overline{\varrho} \cdot \overline{\tau}$ (cf. Theorem 5 of § 6). This is expressed in Theorem 6, below, in a generalized form.

Examples. If T is a pair to each of whose members the type ω is assigned, we have $\omega \cdot 2 = \omega + \omega$. Yet if to each member of a sequence T $(\overline{T} = \omega)$ the type 2 is assigned then the product $2 \cdot \omega$ evolves which may be represented by the enumerated set

$$(a_1, b_1, a_2, b_2, \ldots, a_k, b_k, \ldots);$$

hence $2 \cdot \omega = \omega \neq \omega \cdot 2$. The multiplication of two types is in general non-commutative — except for the multiplication of two finite types.

Therefore, the distinction between multiplicand and multiplier (see p. 94) becomes here essential. To regard the first factor ϱ as the multiplicand is, of course, an arbitrary convention; it was adopted by Cantor finally (originally he had considered the first factor to be the multiplier) and is now generally accepted.

As to the factor 1, we have for every ϱ

$$\varrho \cdot 1 = 1 \cdot \varrho = \varrho;$$

$\varrho \cdot 1 = \varrho$ follows from Definition V, while $1 \cdot \varrho = \varrho$ is another expression of example 2 on p. 147.

The type introduced in example 1 on p. 146 will now be written as

$\omega \cdot \omega$. Many other examples of products of types will appear in the following sections.

As to *formal laws*, we saw that multiplication is not commutative. The distributive law

$$(1) \qquad \varrho \, (\sigma + \tau) = \varrho\sigma + \varrho\tau, \text{ or more generally } \varrho \sum_{t \varepsilon T} \sigma_t = \sum_{t \varepsilon T} (\varrho\sigma_t)$$

holds true, for in view of Definition VI it is nothing but a particular case of the associative law of addition. However, the "second" distributive law, which in arithmetic runs $(a + b)c = ac + bc$, is here not valid in general, as shown by most simple instances; we have, in view of the associativity of addition,

$$(\omega + 1) \, 2 = \omega + 1 + \omega + 1 = \omega + \omega + 1 = \omega \cdot 2 + 1,$$
$$\omega \cdot 2 + 1 \cdot 2 = \omega \cdot 2 + 2;$$
$$(\omega + \omega) \, \omega = \omega + \omega + \omega + \omega + \ldots = \omega \cdot \omega,$$
$$\omega \cdot \omega + \omega \cdot \omega = (\omega \cdot \omega) \, 2.$$

But obviously $\omega \cdot 2 + 1 \neq \omega \cdot 2 + 2$ and $\omega \cdot \omega \neq (\omega \cdot \omega) \, 2$; these inequalities are simple cases of a general theorem (14 of § 10).

The associative law holds for the multiplication of types, but it shall be proven in the more general form corresponding to Definition VII below.

In § 6 the definition (IV) of multiplication for two plain sets yielding the Cartesian product was merely preparatory to its definition for any number of factors. As will presently turn out, here we have to restrict ourselves to a *finite* number of factors, no matter whether the method of Definition VI or another is adopted. For three and more factors it is simpler to define the product of types by means of the Cartesian product; we shall do so (Definition VII) and then state the equipollence to Definition VI as a theorem.

The problem, of course, is to introduce an *order* into the Cartesian product, a task in which we are guided by Definition VI. To define a product of two types $\varrho\tau$ we shall, analogically to § 6, start from disjoint ordered sets R, T with $\overline{R} = \varrho, \overline{T} = \tau$ and form at first the plain Cartesian product $R \times T$ whose members are all pairs $\{r, t\}$ for which $r \in R, t \in T$. To obtain the order provided by Definition VI we must produce sets of the type ϱ that succeed one another according to the type τ. Hence for a fixed t, the ordered pairs (r, t) have to be arranged according to the order of the members r in R, and these ordered sets shall succeed one another in the order of different t's in T; in other words, the succession of ordered pairs (r_1, t_1) and (r_2, t_2) is determined first by the succession of t_1 and t_2, and afterwards, namely for $t_1 = t_2$, by the succession of r_1 and r_2.

A more convenient arrangement according to "*first differences*" is made possible by inverting the order in the pairs, i.e. by expressing $\varrho\tau$ through the set of all ordered pairs (t, r) which now are arranged just as are two-letter words in a dictionary (*lexicographic order*); that is to say, all pairs with the same first component t are joined together and arranged according to the order of the second component r in R, while these ordered sets, serving as representatives of the type ϱ, succeed one another according to the order of t in T. This procedure clearly produces a set of the type $\varrho\tau$.

Now this method can be generalized without change to the case of any *finite* number of factors; the "complexes" (p. 89) which are the members of the Cartesian product must then be ordered inversely to the given order of the factors, to produce the desired ordered product of types by lexicographic order. Thus we arrive at

DEFINITION VII. To form the ordered product $\varrho_1 \varrho_2 \dots \varrho_{n-1} \varrho_n$ of finitely many given, not necessarily different types, replace the types ϱ_k by pairwise disjoint ordered set-representatives R_k (i.e. $\overline{R}_k = \varrho_k$) and arrange the ordered complexes

$$(r_n, r_{n-1}, \dots, r_2, r_1),$$

where r_k ranges over R_k, in *lexicographic order* (order by first differences) [1]), that is to say by the rule

$$(r_n, r_{n-1}, \dots, r_2, r_1) \prec (r'_n, r'_{n-1}, \dots, r'_2, r'_1),$$
$$\text{if } r_n \prec r'_n \text{ in } R_n$$
$$\text{or if } r_n = r'_n \text{ and } r_{n-1} \prec r'_{n-1} \text{ in } R_{n-1}$$

$$\cdot \qquad \cdot$$
$$\cdot \qquad \cdot$$
$$\cdot \qquad \cdot$$

$$\text{or if } r_n = r'_n, r_{n-1} = r'_{n-1}, \dots, r_2 = r'_2, r_1 \prec r'_1 \text{ in } R_1.$$

---

[1]) Had we ordered the members of the complexes in the given succession of the factors then we ought to arrange the complexes in "anti-lexicographic" order, i.e. by last differences. — A general examination of lexicographic order and "lexicographic functions" is contained in J. Schmidt 55a; this subject is closely connected with Birkhoff's researches mentioned at the end of subsection 1 above.

The type κ of the ordered set of complexes produced by this rule (sometimes named "the ordered Cartesian product $R_1 \times R_2 \times \ldots \times R_{n-1} \times R_n$") is called *the (ordered) product of the types* $\varrho_1, \varrho_2, \ldots, \varrho_{n-1}, \varrho_n$ in this succession; one writes

$$\kappa = \varrho_1 \varrho_2 \ldots \varrho_{n-1} \varrho_n.$$

If all ϱ_k are equal $= \varrho$ then one writes

$$\kappa = \varrho^n \text{ (the } n\text{th } power \text{ of the type } \varrho).$$

THEOREM 6. *For* $n = 2$, *Definition VII conforms to Definition VI. Generally the product* κ *depends only on the factors* ϱ_k *and not on the chosen representatives* R_k. *The cardinal of the ordered product of finitely many types equals the product of the cardinals of the factors, i.e.*

$$\overline{\overline{\varrho_1 \varrho_2 \ldots \varrho_n}} = \overline{\overline{\varrho_1}} \cdot \overline{\overline{\varrho_2}} \cdot \ldots \cdot \overline{\overline{\varrho_n}}.$$

All statements of this theorem follow immediately from earlier remarks. In accordance with the introduction to Definition VII, the first statement expresses that for $n = 2$ the product can be conceived as a sum every terms of which equals ϱ_1. The second and the third statements are (inductive) extensions of the remarks following Definition VI.

To prove the associative law for the multiplication of finitely many types it is sufficient to consider the case of a decomposition into two factors, from which it can be extended inductively to more factors — in contradistinction to the associative law of addition (Theorem 4) where decompositions into infinitely many terms had to be considered. We shall prove

(2) $$\varrho_1(\varrho_2 \ldots \varrho_n) = \varrho_1 \varrho_2 \ldots \varrho_n;$$

for the $n - 2$ other possible decompositions into two factors (without changing the order), viz. $(\varrho_1 \varrho_2) (\varrho_3 \ldots \varrho_n)$ etc., the proof is the same.

Proof of (2). First, the plain Cartesian products of set-representatives $R_1, R_2, \ldots, R_n$ corresponding to the factors are equivalent (though not equal); this is shown by the mapping which relates the complex $((r_n, \ldots, r_2), r_1)$ to $(r_n, \ldots, r_2, r_1)$, where $r_k \in R_k$. Secondly, if $((r'_n, \ldots, r'_2), r'_1)$ and $(r'_n, \ldots, r'_2, r'_1)$ are another pair of related members, the latter complexes will respectively either both precede the former or both succeed them, as follows from Definition VII; hence the mapping defined is similar. Since the types of similar sets are equal, (2) holds true.

Resuming (1) on p. 150 and the remarks appended, we have

THEOREM 7. *The multiplication of finitely many types is associative and, in connection with the addition of types, distributive in the sense of* (1). *On the other hand, except for finite types, it is in general neither commutative, nor distributive in the inverse sense.*

Products of two types, as well as general sums of types, were already introduced by Cantor [1]. But only his successors, in particular Hausdorff, did become aware that the extension to products of infinitely many types meets with enormous and in general insuperable difficulties regarding the introduction of an appropriate *order* into the Cartesian product. Such order should, of course, constitute a reasonable generalization of the order defined for the product of finitely many factors by Definition VII.

To understand the difficulty it suffices to consider the supposedly simple case that the factor-types are given as members of a sequence $(\varrho_1, \varrho_2, \ldots, \varrho_k, \ldots)$. Then, extending Definition VII, we should have to deal with complexes of the form $r = (\ldots, r_k, \ldots, r_2, r_1)$ where $r_k \in R_k$ and $\bar{R}_k = \varrho_k$. The lexicographic order between r and another complex $r' = (\ldots, r'_k, \ldots, r'_2, r'_1)$ must be based on the order in R_k of the *first* pair of corresponding *different* members r_k and r'_k, i.e. on the *greatest* k for which $r_k \neq r'_k$. But in general such a greatest k will not exist; for instance, if $r_k \neq r'_k$ for each k, or for each k greater than a certain n, or for each *even* k. In fact, a closer examination reveals that, except for certain particular orders of the infinitely many factors, *there exists no suitable arrangement of the complexes contained in the Cartesian product*. This includes the impossibility of an appropriate definition of *powers* of types with a transfinite exponent, e.g. with the exponent ω.

It is obvious that this difficulty is not caused by the stipulation made in the beginning of the present subsection regarding the rôles of multiplicand and multiplier; a permutation of these rôles would psychologically complicate, and materially not change, the difficulty inherent in infinite products and powers of types such as 2^ω or ω^ω.

In 1904 Hausdorff [2] began to develop an ingenious theory of what may

---

[1]   Cantor 1895, § 8.

[2]   Hausdorff 04, 06–07, 08, 14 (Chapter VI). For other questions of the theory of ordered sets and order-types (besides the problems treated in §§ 10 and 11) see, in addition to the more comprehensive textbooks (p. 11), the papers Mahlo 11 and 17 (rich in interesting material), Lindenbaum-Tarski 26 (§ 3), Wrinch 29 and 29a, Kurepa 34, Gleyzal 40–41. See also P. S. Alexandroff 56.

be called pseudo-products and pseudo-powers of types. The purpose is to replace the respective Cartesian product by a maximal subset such that a suitable order of its complexes can be defined (cf. p. 204). The result of these complicated investigations is meagre enough, for in general the pseudo-product has a *cardinal less than the full Cartesian product*. The exceptions do not possess much practical significance; for instance, if the factors are given in the order $*\omega^1$), i.e. $\ldots, \varrho_k, \ldots, \varrho_2, \varrho_1$, then the ordered complexes have the form $(r_1, r_2, \ldots, r_k, \ldots)$, for which always a first r_k with a given property (here, $r_k \neq r_k'$) exists.

While we do not enter into the theory of pseudo-products in general, we shall from a quite different viewpoint arrive at the (pseudo-) powers (§ 11, 3) in an important case, namely if the base and the exponent are *ordinals* (§ 10). The inadequacy of the pseudo-operation will then emerge most painfully; for instance, the power ω^ω has the cardinal $\aleph_0$ and not $\aleph_0{}^{\aleph_0} = \aleph$. Hence the last statement of Theorem 6 does not hold for those infinite products.

Exercises

1) Complete in detail the proof of similarity in example 5) of 3.

2) Elaborate the proofs that the sum of sets according to Definition V and the product of sets according to Definitions VI and VII are *ordered* sets.

3) What other types, instead of $\zeta = *\omega + \omega$, might be used to prove Theorem 5?

4) Complete the proof of the associative law of multiplication, and prove the (first) distributive law *on account of Definition VII*.

5) The analogue of the equivalence theorem (§ 5, 4) in the theory of similarity would run: if each of two ordered sets is similar to a subset of the other then the sets are similar. Give a few examples showing that this statement is false.[2]

6) What are the inverse types of $a + \beta$ and of $a\beta$, a and β being any types? Give a few examples.

7) Show that $\omega + \omega^2 = (\omega + \omega)\,\omega$ and that $\omega^2 \cdot 2 \neq \omega^2$.

8) Prove the theorem [3]: The set of all ordered sets of the cardinal **c** is equivalent to its subset containing those sets whose type is not changed

---
[1] More generally, in an "anti-well-ordered" succession; see § 10, 6.

[2] For a partial analogue, see Lindenbaum–Tarski 26, § 3, and Lindenbaum 27. Cf. Kurepa 48.

[3] See Chajoth 30.

by the removal of finitely many members. (For general c, the proof requires well-ordering and properties of well-ordered sets, see § 11, **5** and **6**.)

9) Let S be a partly ordered set (p. 131) with an order-relation R, and c and d different members of S which are not connected by R. Prove that R can be extended to a relation R^* (which includes R) such that c and d are connected by R^* in a given sense ($c \prec d$ or $d \prec c$).[1] — By combining this result with a method of Kuratowski's and using the axiom of choice one can infer that *any partial order of a set can be extended to a total order.*

10) On p. 135 the relation $\underset{G}{\sim}$, meaning equivalence of sets with respect to a non-empty class G of functions, was introduced. G is called a *group* if it satisfies the conditions: a) together with f also the inverse function f^{-1} is contained in G; b) if the functions f_1 and f_2 are contained in G then the same applies to the compound function $f_1 \times f_2$, i.e. f_1 performed upon f_2. Prove that $\underset{G}{\sim}$ is symmetrical and transitive if G is a group.

§ 9. LINEAR SETS OF POINTS.

The notions and theorems of this section are beyond the range of the present book inasmuch as we here deal with sets of points (numbers) and not with abstract sets. In particular, in subsections **1–4** ordered *linear* point sets, i.e. sets of real numbers, are our subject. In **5** and **6**, instead of order certain concepts peculiar to *spaces*, hence also transcending abstract sets, are used.

This digression originates from the wish to exhibit the power of set-theoretical methods as applied to well-known notions of elementary mathematics, whose full analysis is made possible only through the subtle tools introduced by Cantor. This especially applies to **1–4** where the restriction to linear sets of points is rather a matter of easy expression and convenience than of principle; essentially only the concept of (simple) order and not that of (linear) space is required here.

The contents of § 9 are not used in the following sections and may be disregarded by readers familiar with topology and related branches.

1. Dense or Continuous Ordered Sets.

In subsections **1–4** we deal with ordered sets of *real numbers* or — which is the same in view of a similar mapping of the set of all real numbers, ordered according to magnitude, onto the ordered set of all points of a straight line [2]) — with ordered

---

[1]) Szpilrajn 30. The method in question is contained in Kuratowski 22.

[2]) Roughly such a mapping was introduced in example d) of § 1. There are different ways of a more penetrating analysis. For instance, starting with an arithmetical introduction of real numbers (cf. example 4 in **2**) one may *define* the points of the line

sets of *points of a line*. We denote by L the ordered set of *all* these numbers or points and by $\prec$ the order relation in L. In general we speak of "points" and of "linear sets of points" but frequently denote the points by the corresponding numbers. Every definition or statement may be understood in the arithmetic-analytical as well as in the geometrical sense.

The preceding section has shown that abstract ordered sets are by no means restricted to subsets of L. Neither are ordered sets *of points* necessarily subsets of L; this is not the case, for instance, for multidimensional point-sets (cf. example 5) on p. 137/8) or for sets of "points" of a non-Archimedean straight line. Another example is a set of "decimal (dual) fractions" in which the sequence of digits (a_β) proceeds according to transfinite ordinal numbers (§ 11) restricted by $\beta < a$ for a given $a > \omega$ [1]). On the other hand, the points of a closed curve such as an ellipsa in one of the two natural arrangements cannot be taken as an example because they do not satisfy the conditions of an ordered set (§ 8, 2).

Throughout **1-4** the expression "set of points" means *a subset of L with at least two members*, and "two points of a set" always means *different* points.

DEFINITION I. A set of points K is called everywhere dense, or simply *dense*, if between any two points p_1, p_2 of K there is another $p_3 \in K$.

Hence no member of a dense set has a neighbor (§ 8, 2). From $p_1 \prec p_3 \prec p_2$, $p_1 \prec p_4 \prec p_3$ etc. we conclude inductively that between any two points of a dense set there are *infinitely many* points of the set; a dense set, then, is always infinite. A set which is similar to a dense set is also dense.[2])

---

as similarly related to the numbers; or else one may proceed from an axiomatic foundation of the points of a line in the classical sense, ensuring continuity by the axiom of Dedekind–Cantor or by the axiom of Archimedes (Eudoxos) and Hilbert's postulate of completeness, and then prove that there is a similar one-to-one correspondence between these points and the real numbers.

There exists a vast multitude of literature on this subject. We mention Dedekind 1872, Cantor 1872, Hilbert 1899/1930 of the original sources, Courant–Robbins 43 (chapter II) as a fine specimen of a modern elementary exposition.

[1]) See Cuesta 42 and 43; cf. Maximoff 40.

[2]) For an important logical property of open dense abstract sets see Skolem 20; Langford 27; Tarski 35–36II, p. 293; for an application to dense continuous sets (Definition III), Langford 39 (cf. Lewis–Langford 32, pp. 405 ff.).

DEFINITION II. If K_1 and K_2 are non-empty (disjoint) subsets of a set of points K such that $K_1 + K_2 = K$ in the sense of ordered addition (Definition IV, § 8, 5), one speaks of a *cut* $(K_1 \mid K_2)$ in K.[1])

Hence every point of K belongs either to K_1 or to K_2, and each point of K_1 precedes each of K_2. K_1 is an initial and K_2 a remainder of K (§ 8, 2). To determine $(K_1 \mid K_2)$ it suffices to specify, besides K, either K_1 or K_2.

By logical disjunction we obtain four mutually exclusive cases which cover all kinds of cuts, namely

a) K_1 has a last member k_1 and K_2 has a first k_2,
b) K_1 has a last member k_1 but K_2 has no first,
c) K_1 has no last member but K_2 has a first k_2,
d) K_1 has no last member and K_2 has no first.

In **2** we shall see that each of these logically possible cases can be realized mathematically. In the cases a), b), c) the cut $(K_1 \mid K_2)$ may simply be described as follows: K_1 is the initial of K that contains k_1 and all its predecessors, or K_2 is the remainder of K that contains k_2 and all its successors. Hence the cut is determined by k_1 or by k_2 or (in the case a)) by either.

DEFINITION III. k_1 in cases a) and b) and k_2 in cases a) and c) are said to *produce* the cut $(K_1 \mid K_2)$. In case a) the cut is called a *jump*, in case d) a *gap*, while in cases b) and c) the cut is called *continuous*. K is said to be a *continuous set* [2]) if *every* cut in K is continuous, i.e. if there are neither jumps nor gaps in K.

2. Examples. We begin with easy examples which show the use of the concepts introduced in **1**. In **3** and **4** more intricate examples are given.

1. Given two points p_1 and p_2 of L, let K be the *open interval* (p_1, p_2), i.e. the set of all points between p_1 and p_2. K is dense and retains this property if one of the points p_1 and p_2 or both are added; in the latter

---

[1]) The concept of cut (or section, in German *Schnitt*) was introduced in Dedekind 1872 (cf. 30–32II, pp. 356–370) where the theory of irrational and real numbers is based on cuts in sets of rationals, see below. (Cantor (1872), Méray, Weierstrass and others based real number on *sequences* of rationals.) Modern expositions are given, for instance, in Perron 21/47 and Graves 46/56.

[2]) For a reduction of this concept to the relation of inclusion (subset) see Foradori 33.

case we have the *closed interval* $\langle p_1, p_2 \rangle$. The set L itself is also dense.

2. p being any point of L, we form the cut $(L_1 \mid L_2)$ in L for which L_1 contains p and all preceding points, hence L_2 all other points. This cut is continuous and produced by p. The same holds true if p is allotted to L_2.

If, however, p is neither allotted to L_1 nor to L_2 then $(L_1 \mid L_2)$ is a cut in the subset $L' \subset L$ obtained by dropping p, and this cut is a gap since clearly L_1 has no last member and L_2 no first. Hence L' is dense but not continuous. On the other hand, according to our conception of a line (footnote [2]) on p. 155/6), L itself as well as any open or closed interval of L are continuous sets; any cut in L is produced by one and only one member of L.

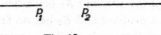

Fig. 12

3. Let $p_1 \prec p_2$ (cf. fig. 12) and K be the subset of L which contains, besides p_1 and p_2, the points preceding p_1 and the points succeeding p_2. The cut $(K_1 \mid K_2)$ for which p_1 is the last member of K_1, hence p_2 the first of K_2, is a jump in K (which set "jumps" from p_1 to p_2). K is not dense, and it is obvious that no set with a jump is dense; hence a dense set has no jumps, whereas every set without jumps is dense.

However, if we remove p_2 from K and call the new set K', then the cut $(K_1' \mid K_2')$ in K' for which K_1' is defined as K_1 above, is continuous. K' is a dense set and similar to L, as shown by the mapping which relates each point of $K_1' = K_1$ to itself and the points of K_2' to the points of L that succeed p_1.

To avoid shocking the readers who are acquainted with the concept of space, let us already here stress that, according to the attitude taken below in 5 and 6, K' is not dense because density then is a *relative* property, referring to the space L. Yet according to the purely ordinal attitude adopted here, there is no difference between the set L and its subset K'.

The same holds, of course, if p_2 is retained and p_1 removed.

4. Let R be the set of all rational points r of L, which clearly is dense, and $(R_1 \mid R_2)$ be the cut in R whose remainder R_2 contains all positive rationals $\frac{m}{n}$ for which $\frac{m^2}{n^2} > 2$. *This cut is a gap in R.* To prove this we shall show that $(R_1 \mid R_2)$ is not produced by any member of R. Since this is obvious for $r \leqslant 0$ we restrict ourselves to positive rationals r.

As is well known there is no r with $r^2 = 2$ [1]); hence a positive r producing the cut ought to satisfy either $r^2 < 2$ or $r^2 > 2$. But in the first case there are in R_1 rationals $r' > r$, in the second in R_2 rationals $r' < r$. One may prove this by utilizing the irrational point $\sqrt{2}$ (which belongs to L though not to R) and the fact that between any two real numbers there is a rational [2]); hence in the first case there is a rational r' such that $r < r' < \sqrt{2}$, in the second an r' such that $\sqrt{2} < r' < r$, which means $r' \,\epsilon\, R_1$ or $r' \,\epsilon\, R_2$ respectively. In neither case, then, does r produce the cut $(R_1 \mid R_2)$, which therefore is a gap.

In the same way as by $\sqrt{2}$, a gap in R is created by every irrational point of L, while the cuts in R produced by the members of R are clearly continuous. — If R is replaced by the set of all rationals between two fixed points the situation is not changed.

Comparing the examples 2 and 4 we find that a dense set *always* has continuous cuts and *may* have gaps, but certainly no jumps; it may be continuous (as 1) or not (as 4). On the other hand, every continuous set is dense.

The gap $(R_1 \mid R_2)$ defined above may be *filled*, i.e. transformed into a continuous cut by adjoining the point $\sqrt{2}$ to R, allotting it either to R_1 or to R_2. By adjoining *all* irrational points to the rationals, R is transformed into a continuous set. (The same may be achieved for any abstract dense set; see exercise 3) at the end of this section.) The attitude here taken

---

[1]) This fact, discovered by the Pythagoreans and referred to by Aristotle, is proved by Euclid along the following lines. If m and n are positive integers without a common divisor then the assumption $r^2 = \left(\dfrac{m}{n}\right)^2 = 2$, i.e. $m^2 = 2n^2$, implies that m is even, hence n odd. But this means that m^2 is divisible by 4 while $2n^2$ is not (since n^2 is odd); the contradiction shows that $\sqrt{2}$ is not rational.

This result is easily generalized to the theorem that $\dfrac{m^2}{n^2}$ cannot be an integer if $n > 1$. The importance attributed to this subject by the Greeks is illustrated by Plato's report (in the dialogue *Theaitetos*) that his teacher Theodoros had proved the irrationality of $\sqrt{k}$ for all k from 3 to 17 (except, of course, 4, 9, 16).

[2]) This theorem, used also in 4, is proven most easily for beginners by expanding the real numbers into decimals. If A and B are, say, positive real numbers between which there is no integer and if $A < B$, let B be expanded into an infinite decimal (see § 4, 2) and A, if possible, into a terminating decimal, otherwise into an infinite one. Then, for instance, the terminating decimal which results by stopping the expansion of B after the first digit that differs from the corresponding digit of A, is a rational greater than A and smaller than B.

In a more elegant way the theorem is proven by the method indicated in exercise 11) at the end of § 3.

presupposes an appropriate foundation of irrational numbers; incidentally, these *may just be defined as the gaps in R.* Since the set of the irrational numbers has the cardinal $\aleph$, in our case the set of the gaps in R has a greater cardinal than R itself; this phenomenon is not surprising since the cuts are essentially subsets and not members of the set. By mere spatial intuition or classical geometrical attitudes without set-theoretical methods, the phenomenon can neither be stated nor comprehended.

3. The Type η of the Set of Rationals. The concepts introduced in **1** are sufficient to completely characterize some of the most important and widely used types. While for ω (or $*\omega$) and $*\omega + \omega$ the (rather simple) proofs shall be left to the reader (see exercises 1) and 2) below) we deal in the present subsection with the *type of all rationals ordered by magnitude,* which type is (after Cantor) denoted by η.

The ordered set R of all rational points of L clearly has the following properties (cf. § 3, **3**):

    a) R is denumerable,

    b) R is dense,

    c) R is open, i.e. has no first and no last member.

The set of all rational points between two arbitrary (rational or irrational) points a and b of L has the same properties a)–c). We now prove

THEOREM 1. *The properties a) — c) together completely determine the order-type of R.* In other words, any abstract ordered set S which satisfies these properties is *similar* to R.

The proof, accordingly, will not presuppose S to be a subset of L.

Proof.[1]) Let S be any ordered set with the properties a)–c) and let

$$(r_1, r_2, r_3, \ldots, r_k, r_k + 1, \ldots)$$

be an arbitrary enumeration of R; for instance, that of § 3, **3**. In view of a) there is a sequence

$$(s_1, s_2, s_3, \ldots, s_k, s_k + 1, \ldots)$$

which contains just all members of S. Naturally there is no connection

---

[1]) See Cantor 1895, § 9. Extensions (in different directions) are given in Skolem 20 (§ 4) and Fraïssé 53. For a remarkable metamathematical result inferred from the theorem see Vaught 54.

between the succession of the r_k (and s_k) in these sequences and their order in the sets R (and S).

To establish a similar mapping of R onto S we use mathematical induction along the sequence (r_k) and begin with relating s_1 to r_1. The second step, then, consists in relating a suitable $s_m \epsilon S$ to $r_2 \epsilon R$. We have either $r_1 \prec r_2$ or $r_2 \prec r_1$ in R, and since s_1 is neither the first nor the last member of S (property c)) there are members of S preceding and succeeding s_1. If $r_1 \prec r_2$ we relate to r_2, among the successors of s_1, the s_m with the *least index* m, and if $r_2 \prec r_1$, the predecessor with the least index; in either case we denote by $s^{(2)}$ the (uniquely determined) image in S of r_2. For the sake of uniformity we also write $s^{(1)}$ for s_1. Hence $s^{(1)} \prec s^{(2)}$ or $s^{(2)} \prec s^{(1)}$ holds in S according as $r_1 \prec r_2$ or $r_2 \prec r_1$ holds in R.

For the third step we notice that between the members r_1, r_2, r_3 of R six different orders are possible; if $r_1 \prec r_2$ we have

$$r_3 \prec r_1 \prec r_2 \quad \text{or} \quad r_1 \prec r_3 \prec r_2 \quad \text{or} \quad r_1 \prec r_2 \prec r_3,$$

and three analogous cases if $r_2 \prec r_1$. Now there exist members of S, even infinitely many, which stand in the same order to $s^{(1)}$ and $s^{(2)}$ in which r_3 stands to r_1 and r_2; if r_3 precedes both r_1 and r_2 or succeeds them, this follows from c), whereas it is a consequence of b) if r_3 is between r_1 and r_2. In each case we denote, among the appropriate s_m's, the one with the least index m by $s^{(3)}$ and relate $s^{(3)}$ to r_3. Then the order of $s^{(1)}$, $s^{(2)}$, $s^{(3)}$ in S is the same as that of r_1, r_2, r_3 in R.

For the inductive procedure we assume that for a certain k we have already related "suitable" images $s^{(1)}$, $s^{(2)}$, ..., $s^{(k)}$ to the first k members r_1, r_2, ..., r_k of the enumeration of R, i.e. biunique images such that the orders of these members $s^{(n)}$ in S conforms to the order of the respective r_n in R. We show that to r_{k+1}, too, a suitable image can be chosen in a well-defined way. r_{k+1} *either* precedes or succeeds all r_1, r_2, ..., r_k, *or else* r_{k+1} intervenes between two of them, say between r_l and r_m, so that none of the members r_1, r_2, ..., r_k is between r_l and r_m. There are, in view of the properties c) and b), infinitely many members of S which stand in the same order to $s^{(1)}$, $s^{(2)}$, ..., $s^{(k)}$ as r_{k+1} stands to r_1, r_2, ..., r_k; the one with the least index among those members shall be denoted by $s^{(k+1)}$ and related to r_{k+1}. Then the subset of R containing r_1, r_2, ..., r_k, r_{k+1} is similar to the subset of S containing $s^{(1)}$, $s^{(2)}$, ..., $s^{(k)}$, $s^{(k+1)}$.

Hence, by mathematical induction, *to any n first members of the sequence (r_k), n images, namely members of the sequence (s_k), are related* in a similar one-to-one correspondence, and for a given n these s_k include those chosen in the preceding steps. Accordingly there exists a sequence

$$(s^{(1)}, s^{(2)}, \ldots, s^{(k)}, s^{(k+1)}, \ldots)$$

which contains the images of *all* r_k, namely the union of the denumerably many sets of n members $s^{(k)}$ for each n. (Cf. the corresponding argument in proof A of Theorem 4 in § 3, **5**; yet here our method is strictly constructive without using the axiom of choice.) [1])

However, the reader should not think that hereby the proof of Theorem 1 is finished. It is *a priori* evident that this cannot be, for we have not yet exhausted our presuppositions; while we utilized the properties a)–c) of S, regarding R so far a) only has been used. In fact, what has been proved by now is that there is a similar mapping of R *into* S; it has still to be shown that our construction *exhausts* the set S, i.e. yields a mapping of R *onto* S. (One might save this second half of the proof by applying the above inductive procedure alternately to R and to S; but this would impair its lucidity.)

The member $s_1 (= s^{(1)})$ of S has been used in our mapping; we shall now prove that, if the members $s_1, s_2, \ldots, s_k$ are used, also s_{k+1} is being used.

Of course, in general more than k steps of our process are required to reach s_k, say l steps; that is to say, $s_k = s^{(l)}$, where $l \geqslant k$. s_{k+1} may accidentally occur among the members $s^{(1)}, \ldots, s^{(l)}$, in which case nothing is left to prove. Else we contemplate the order relations which subsist between s_{k+1} and the l members just mentioned; as above, s_{k+1} may precede or succeed all of them or may intervene just between two of them.

Now the properties b) and c) *of the set R* guarantee that there are members r_n which stand in the same relations to $r_1, \ldots, r_l$ as s_{k+1} stands to $s^{(1)}, \ldots, s^{(l)}$. Let r_{l+p} with $p \geqslant 1$ be the r_n with *the least index* that satisfies those relations. Then automatically its image $s^{(l+p)}$ (which will prove to be s_{k+1}) stands in the same relations even to the $l + p - 1$ members

$$s^{(1)}, \ldots, s^{(l)}, \ldots s^{(l+p-1)}$$

in which r_{l+p} stands to $r_1, \ldots, r_l, \ldots, r_{l+p-1}$; that is to say, none of the members $s^{(l+1)}, \ldots, s^{(l+p-1)}$ occurs at that place between

---

[1]) On a much higher level, with transfinite instead of mathematical induction, a corresponding argument is used in § 10, **2**.

$s^{(1)}, \ldots, s^{(l)}$ which is taken by $s^{(l + p)}$. For otherwise, in view of the similar correspondence between the r_n and $s^{(n)}$, already some of the members $r_{l+1}, \ldots, r_{l+p-1}$ ought to stand in those order-relations to $r_1, \ldots, r_l$ in which r_{l+p} was found to stand, and r_{l+p} was just supposed to be the one with the least index.

Therefore, according to the first half of our proof, s_{k+1} is the image of r_{l+p}, i.e. $s_{k+1} = s^{(l+p)}$; this shows that, together with $s_1, \ldots, s_k$, also s_{k+1} participates in our process of mapping R into S. Hence *all* s_n participate, i.e. $S \simeq R$, as maintained in Theorem 1.

From Theorem 1 we draw a number of conclusions which are not evident at all and manifest the strength of the theorem.

First, $\eta = \overline{R}$ is as well the type of the set of the rationals between two arbitrary points of L as pointed out above. But, according to Theorem 1, also sets resulting from R by dropping a single point, or a finite number of points, or an entire closed or semi-closed "interval" of R (producing subsets of R which are analogous to fig. 12 on p. 158), have the type η as well.

Furthermore, according to Theorem 1, we have

$$\eta = \eta + 1 + \eta = \eta + \eta = \eta \cdot n \text{ (for finite } n \neq 0) = \eta \cdot \omega = \eta \cdot \eta;$$

for the last two statements we are using $\aleph_0 \cdot \aleph_0 = \aleph_0$. (Cf. exercise 4) at the end of § 9.) [1]

The three properties indicated in Theorem 1 are obviously *independent*. Hence the question arises what results evolve if one of the properties is dropped.

Dropping c) causes no difficulty; we then obtain the four *dense denumerable types*

$$\eta, 1 + \eta, \eta + 1, 1 + \eta + 1.$$

Yet dropping a) or b) while retaining or not retaining c) yields the difficult problems of all dense or all denumerable types. (To the latter cf. Theorem 5 in § 8, **6**; regarding dense sets cf. exercise 5) at the end of § 9.)

4. The Type λ of the Linear Continuum. With respect to the historical and philosophical importance, the types ω and η are surpassed by the

---

[1]   In Franklin 25 mappings between different sets of the type η are constructed by means of continuous monotonic, or even analytic, functions. This paper also deals with the analogous task regarding Theorem 2 in **4**. – As to generalizations of $\eta^2 = \eta$, cf. Davis–Sierpiński 52.

type of the *linear continuum*, i.e. of the ordered set L of all points on a straight line, or of a finite interval of these points. As in 3, in the latter case we shall exclude the ends of the interval.

The importance of the continuum in analysis and geometry is obvious. Even before its mathematical significance was emphasized philosophers and theologians had been trying to reveal the nature of the (linear) continuum which seems to constitute continuity in spatial and temporal sense. Yet all attempts to analyse its structure remained unsuccessful, and even mathematicians were inclined to assume that the concept of continuum was *primitive* and not capable of an exhaustive logico-mathematical analysis. Some philosophical and also mathematical schools endeavored to base the continuum on the (extramathematical and extralogical) concept of *time*, and tendencies towards shifting the problem into mystical ground were not missing.

Characteristic of the situation at the time when Cantor attacked the problem is his own description of 1883. After a sketch of the development throughout antiquity and the middle ages he continues: [1] "We here perceive the *medieval-scholastic* origin of the view that the continuum is an indivisible concept or, as others express it, a pure aprioristic intuition which would hardly be capable of a definition by other concepts; any attempt *to determine this mystery* by arithmetical methods is considered an illicit intrusion and emphatically rejected. People of a timid disposition thus get the impression that the continuum constitutes rather a *religious dogma* than a logico-mathematical concept."

"Far be it from me to renew these controversies, the more since in the present limited frame I should not be able to discuss them in sufficient detail; I only feel bound to develop the concept of continuum in the logical sobriety required for its conception in the theory of aggregates, in utmost brevity and with respect to *mathematical* set theory only. This attitude has not been easy for me since among the mathematicians to whose authority I like to refer none has treated the continuum in the sense which I here need." [2]

The following treatment of the problem in its general lines follows

---

[1]   Cantor 1879–84V, § 10. (Translation from the German original.)

[2]   Naturally, to a great extent the ground for Cantor's treatment was prepared by the methods introduced into analysis by Cauchy, Bolzano, Weierstrass, and others. By 1880 these methods had been generally accepted.

For the connection between continuity and empiric knowledge cf. Russell 14/26, chapter V.

Cantor, except for an important detail stressed below (property a)) and for the use of (Dedekind's) cuts instead of (Cantor's) fundamental sequences. It should be pointed out that the problem is conceived, by Cantor as well as in the present treatment, in the frame of the theory of abstract ordered sets and types, just as the problem of η in **3**; that is to say, a full *description* only of the linear continuum is intended. This altogether differs from a *construction* of the continuum, one of the most intricate (and in a certain sense unsolvable) problems of foundations of mathematics; in fact we take for granted the *existence* of the set of all points of a line, or of all real numbers. (See p. 72 and *Foundations*, in particular chapter IV, e.g., pp. 247ff.)

At first sight, density might seem to be the characteristic of the continuum. That this property is not sufficient shows the type η which is dense but, in contrast with the continuum, denumerable. Continuity of a set in the sense of Definition III in **1** comes certainly nearer the object; between the 1860's when continuity in this sense was first formulated, and Cantor's discovery nobody seems to have doubted that this was the best possible characterization of the linear continuum. We shall point out the error of this belief, amended by Cantor through postulating β) of Theorem 2, at the end of this subsection.

As in the beginning of **3**, we start with stating three simple properties of the open linear continuum I (bounded or not). First, no cut in I is a gap (which is included in its being continuous, see example 2 in **2**); secondly, I contains the denumerable subset R of all rationals, and between any two points of I there is a rational point (footnote [2]) on p. 159); thirdly, I is open, i.e. without ends. We shall show that these properties, which to some extent are analogical to the properties a) – c) of Theorem 1 in **3**, *completely characterize* the type of the linear continuum.

THEOREM 2. *Any abstract ordered set C of the following properties*
  a) *no cut in C is a gap,*
  β) *C has a d e n u m e r a b l e subset D such that between every two members of C there is a member of D* (in short, a denumerable subset D is dense in C),
  γ)   *C is open,*
is similar to the open linear continuum I, for instance to the set of all real x with $a < x < b$ ordered by magnitude, a and b being arbitrary numbers.

  Hence the properties a) – γ) determine a type, the type λ of the open linear continuum.

Remarks. The theorem includes that λ is independent of the choice of a and b and is also the type of the entire set L. As to a), C has no jumps either, as follows from β), namely from the density of C; hence a) ensures that C is a *continuous* set. Cantor [1]) had determined the type λ (in fact, the type $1 + \lambda + 1 = \theta$) by demanding C to be "perfect" instead of continuous, a property introduced below in 5 in a somewhat different sense; in this matter he was guided partly by his own theory of irrationals, but continuity and Dedekind's theory used in the following proof are preferable.

As to β), the following remark is important. It is easily seen (cf. exercise 11) at the end of § 3) that in an ordered set with the property β) there are at most denumerably many non-overlapping intervals (in the sense of mere order). In 1919 M. Souslin raised the question [2]) whether the latter property, in addition to a) and γ), also determines the type λ; in spite of pursued efforts devoted to this *problem of Souslin* since the early 30's it has not been solved so far [3]).

Proof of Theorem 2. It will be sufficient to sketch the proof, which presents no actual difficulty after Theorem 1 has been proven. First we show that any subset D of the kind β) has the type η. By taking, for the members of C mentioned in β), members of the subset D we see that D is dense, and since D is also open (by β) and γ)) D has the three properties of Theorem 1. Hence $D \simeq R$. Let φ be an arbitrary fixed mapping of D onto the set R of all rationals of I.

It now remains to relate similarly the gaps in D to the gaps in R. If c is a member of C that does not belong to D, let D_1 be the set of those $d \, \epsilon \, D$ which precede c in C, and D_2 the set of the other members of D. $(D_1 \mid D_2)$ clearly is a gap in D, and by the mapping φ we obtain a corresponding cut $(R_1 \mid R_2)$ in R which is also a gap. But a gap in the set R of rationals

---

[1]) Theorem 2, in the modified form, is stated and proven in Cantor 1895, § 11; cf. already 1879–84V, § 10. Cf. Kuratowski 22a, Webber 31.

A detailed elementary exposition of the types ω, η, λ is given in Huntington 05–06; cf. Veblen 05.

[2]) Souslin 20.

[3]) In particular Kurepa (see 35 [especially p. 124 and §§ 9, 11, 12], 48a, 50a and the papers cited there) examined this problem in various directions and stated a number of equipollent assertions. Denjoy 53 (cf. 46–54III) can hardly be considered to constitute a solution. A remarkable progress was recently made by Ésénin-Vol'pin 54 who shows that the problem cannot be answered in the affirmative without using the axiom of choice.

For certain other problems regarding λ, partly also unsolved, see the profound and comprehensive paper Erdös-Rado 56.

uniquely determines a real, more exactly an irrational number i in I which fills the gap, as shown in example 4 of subsection **2**; the existence of i is a consequence of the continuity of I. i *shall be related to* $c \in C$. Evidently this rule establishes a one-to-one correspondence between all members of $C - D$ and members of $I - R$ (i.e. irrational numbers). By inverting the direction one realizes without difficulty that the correspondence even comprehends *all* members of $I - R$; hence by supplementing it with φ we obtain a mapping of C onto I.

Finally, this mapping is *similar*, as follows from the nature of the above rule. In fact, each member of C (not only of $C - D$) which precedes $c \in C$, i.e. which belongs to the initial of the cut in C produced by c, has an image in I which precedes the image of c; this ensures the similarity and completes the proof.

From Theorem 2 we infer that $1 + \lambda + 1 = \theta$ is the type of the continuum as represented by a closed intervall $\langle a, b \rangle$. Obviously types such as $\lambda \cdot n$ (for $n > 1$) and $\lambda \cdot \omega$ are different from λ and from each other, for different finite values of n; for instance, $\lambda \cdot 2$ has a gap" in the middle". It is not difficult to see that $\lambda \cdot \lambda$ has also gaps. On the other hand, $\theta + \theta$ has a jump in the middle. In contrast with η, by dropping a single member from the linear continuum one creates a gap, thus altering the type.

Regarding the *independence* of the system of properties $a) - \gamma)$, $\gamma)$ is insignificant, whereas $\beta)$ and $\gamma)$ without $a)$ are clearly satisfied, for instance, by the type η. The interesting point, then, is dropping $\beta)$, the property which constitutes Cantor's peculiar discovery. The following example of a (simply) ordered set (not a subset of L!) shows that $\beta)$ is not redundant. Conceive the square $OXZY$ in figure 11 (§ 8, 3) as the set of all its points including the points of the sides, with the exception of O and Z; order the set as done in § 8 by arranging them according to increasing abscissae, and for equal abscissae according to increasing ordinates. The set is open and, as is easily seen, also continuous, but does not satisfy $\beta)$. For even if to each subset, containing the points with a fixed abscissa, but a single member of D belonged, then D would have the cardinal $\aleph$ and not $\aleph_0$.

5. Accumulation Point and Related Concepts.

While the subsections **1–4** virtually deal with abstract ordered sets and the restriction to subsets of L was merely a matter of convenience, in this subsection we introduce a subject which is altogether outside the scope of the present book and belongs to the applications of set theory to sets of points or to topology. The reasons for briefly including this subject are twofold. First, it seems desirable to give the reader who is not yet acquainted with such applications of set theory at least a glimpse of some extremely simple concepts and problems of this domain. The second reason is rather historical. The concepts and examples introduced here were also contemplated by Cantor himself, but chiefly in the frame of abstract sets; this in particular applies to the terms occurring in Definition VI. Then, to be sure, the respective notions have an "absolute" meaning with respect to the set considered, whereas here, in accordance with the attitude prevailing to-day which is most useful in the applications, they are conceived *relative to the space* in which the sets are imbedded. Most simply we may grasp this difference through example 3 of 2; while the set K' defined there is dense and even continuous, it is not dense-in-itself or perfect in the sense of Definition VI below. Cf. the last paragraph of 5.

The concept of order does not enter the following considerations; instead we need a specific new concept, transcending the membership relation which is sufficient for abstract sets. It would be most suitable to define our concepts in a topological (n-dimensional) space and to take, for instance, *neighborhood* as the characteristic primitive concept.[1]) Yet since we only wish to give an idea of the attitude mentioned, it seems preferable to appeal to notions well-known to everybody; therefore we restrict ourselves to one-dimensional metric space and instead of neighborhood use the concept of *distance* in the ordinary sense, which is alien to topology.

With this restriction to one dimension we might even imbed the following in the frame of abstract ordered sets, in view of Theorem 2.[2]) Yet we shall not proceed in this way, for the reasons given above and also to enable the reader to interpret the concepts introduced in Definitions IV–VI in the (Euclidean) plane or three- or n-dimensional metric spaces S; the "points" of the latter are ordered n-tuples $(x_1, x_2, \ldots, x_n)$ where x_k stands for a real number. The term "a set K" in the following definitions then means a subset K of S.

Though the examples given in 6 are taken, for the sake of simplicity and brevity, from a one-dimensional space S, the reader is recommended to conceive the following definitions with respect to, say, a plane S.

---

[1])   The chief classical source is Hausdorff 14, chapter VII. Instead of Definition IV below, a neighborhood of p would then mean an open interval containing p.

[2])   Cf. Haar–König 11.

DEFINITION IV. Given a point p of S, the subset of S that contains the points whose distance from p is less than a positive number d is called the *d-neighborhood* of p.

DEFINITION V. Given a set K, a point p of S (not necessarily of K) is called an *accumulation point of K* if in *every* d-neighborhood of p — for short, in *the* neighborhood of p — there is a point $\neq p$ of K. The set of all accumulation points of K is called the *derivation K'* of K. A point of K which is not an accumulation point of K is called an *isolated point of K*.

In the neighborhood of an accumulation point p of K — i.e. an open linear interval if S is one-dimensional, a circle without its boundary if S is two-dimensional, etc. — *there are infinitely many points of K*. For, if $p_1 \epsilon K$ is in the d_1-neighborhood of p and if $d_2 = | p - p_1 | < d_1$ is the distance between p and p_1, then by definition there is a point $p_2 \epsilon K$ ($p_2 \neq p_1$) in the d_2-neighborhood of p; generally, if $d_k = | p - p_{k-1} |$, the d_k-neighborhood of p contains a $p_k \epsilon K$ which differs from all p_n with $n < k$, in view of $d_n < d_{n-1}$. Hence all points p_k with $k = 1, 2, 3,$ ... lie in the d_1-neighborhood of K.

(The statement may as well be proven indirectly by supposing that only finitely many points were in the neighborhood of p and contemplating the d-neighborhood with d being the minimum of the distances of p from those points.)

If K is a set of rational points, i.e. points with rational coordinates, then in the neighborhood of any point of S there are *at most denumerably many* points of K. In other cases, for instance in that of an open interval (circle, sphere, etc.) K, there are *non-denumerably many* points in the neighborhood of an accumulation point of K, which in this case is also called a *condensation point of K*. The ends of an open interval are accumulation (and even condensation) points of the interval; this example confirms that an accumulation point of K need not be a point of K. Another example is the set $K_0 = \{1, \frac{1}{2}, \frac{1}{3}, \ldots, \frac{1}{k}, \ldots\}$; it has the accumulation point 0 which does not belong to K_0. Every point of K_0 is an isolated point of K_0.

Obviously, an isolated point of K may also be characterized by its having a d-neighborhood in which no other point of K is contained.

DEFINITION VI. A (non-empty) set K is called *dense-in-itself*[1]

---

[1] After Hausdorff we use hyphens in order to avoid confusion with a current terminology which refers to the density of a set *in another*.

if every $k \in K$ is an accumulation point of K, i.e. if $K \subseteq K'$; it is called *closed*[1]) if every accumulation point of K belongs to K, i.e. if $K' \subseteq K$; it is called *perfect* if it is both dense-in-itself and closed, i.e. if $K' = K$.

Not every set has one of these properties; for instance, not the set K_0 defined above.

It should again be stressed that these definitions differ *in principle* from those given in **1**. For instance, the set containing the points x satisfying $0 < x < 1, 3 < x < 4$, and $x = 2$, within the one-dimensional space S, has according to Definitions V and VI the isolated point 2 and is neither dense-in-itself nor closed. In the sense of Definitions I and III, however, i.e. in the sense of abstract ordered sets, it is not only dense but even continuous and of the type λ. Cf. also example 4 in **6**.

6. Examples. In the following examples the space S shall be one-dimensional, i.e. S is the set of all points of a straight line.

1. If K is the open interval between the points p_1 and p_2 then every point of K is an accumulation point of K, hence K is dense-in-itself; but K is not closed because p_1 and p_2, though accumulation points, do not belong to K, hence $K \subset K'$. Yet the closed interval $\langle p_1, p_2 \rangle$ is closed and perfect.

From the geometrical point of view, the closeness of $\langle p_1, p_2 \rangle$ is a consequence of the (axiomatic or otherwise) conception of the notion "points of a line"; cf. the footnote [2]) on pp. 155/6.

2. The set R of all *rational* points between two arbitrary points p_1 and p_2 of S is dense-in-itself because in the neighborhood of a rational point there are others. However, an accumulation point of R "in general" does not belong to R; more precisely (cf. example 4 in **2**), R has $\aleph$ accumulation points of which only $\aleph_0$ (the points of R) belong to R. Hence R, also after the addition of p_1 and p_2, is not closed. The term *closed* explains itself similarly as "filling the gaps" in **2**; by adding to R all its accumulation points we obtain a closed set.

3. Let H be the set $\{0, \pm 1, \pm 2, \ldots\}$ of all integral points of S or, which amounts to the same, any infinite set of equidistant points. H is certainly not dense-in-itself, all its points being isolated, but it is

---

[1]) There is no danger of confusion with a "closed interval" (subsection **2**). For the connection between both terms cf. examples 1 and 2 below.

closed; for $H' = O$, and O is a subset of every set. For the same reason (having no accumulation point) every finite set is closed, in contrast with the set K_0 (p. 169) which does not contain its (only) accumulation point 0 — though all points of K_0, like those of H, are isolated.

4. Finally we consider a famous and widely used example, called *Cantor's discontinuum* (or perfect and nowhere-dense set), though it had been introduced by H. J. S. Smith some years before Cantor.[1]) A set of points will be called *nowhere-dense* ("dense" taken similarly as in 1) if between every two points of the set there is an (open) interval — at least one — of the space S which contains no point of the set. We shall content ourselves with briefly sketching a few interesting properties of the set.

Fig. 13

Let us take a special type C of Cantor's set, from which more general ones are easily gathered. Starting with the closed interval $\langle 0, 1 \rangle$ (see fig. 13) we "mark" the middle third $\langle \frac{1}{3}, \frac{2}{3} \rangle$ as the first step. Of the two thirds which remain unmarked, viz. from 0 to $\frac{1}{3}$ and from $\frac{2}{3}$ to 1, we mark the middle thirds $\langle \frac{1}{9}, \frac{2}{9} \rangle$ and $\langle \frac{7}{9}, \frac{8}{9} \rangle$ as the second step. The third step then consists in marking four closed intervals $\langle \frac{1}{27}, \frac{2}{27} \rangle$ etc., and after the kth step 2^k unmarked open intervals will remain, in each of which the middle third shall be marked.

C shall contain, first, *the ends of all marked intervals*, i.e. $\frac{1}{3}, \frac{2}{3}, \frac{1}{9}, \ldots$, including the ends 0 and 1 of the original interval $\langle 0, 1 \rangle$, and in addition all points of $\langle 0, 1 \rangle$ *which are not contained in any marked interval*. The points of the latter kind may also be described as the members of the intersection of *all* sets $C^{(k)}$ where $C^{(k)}$ contains the points which at the kth step do not belong to a marked interval.

C is nowhere-dense. In fact, two given points c_1 and c_2 of C may be the ends of the same marked interval, in which case no point of C is between them. Otherwise at least one marked interval (one end of which may be c_1 or c_2) lies between them, and in point of fact even infinitely many marked intervals. Since the corresponding *open* intervals contain no point of C, our statement is true.

Nevertheless, *C is dense-in-itself*. For a given point c of C is either an

---

[1]) Smith 1875; Cantor 1879–84 V (1883), p. 590.

end of a marked interval or does not belong to a marked interval. On the side opposite to that interval in the first case, and on both sides of c in the second, there are in the neighborhood of c certainly marked intervals, according to the definition of C, and their ends belong to C. In the neighborhood of c, then, are even points of the denumerable subset of C which contains the ends of marked intervals only; hence c is an accumulation point of C.

The fact, surprising at first sight, that C contrives to be dense-in-itself and nowhere-dense at the same time is easily explained. For those points which do not belong to a marked interval it follows from the presence of marked intervals in every neighborhood, and for the ends of marked intervals the same still holds *in one direction*, which is sufficient for the property of being dense-in-itself (though not for density).

Finally, *C is closed, hence perfect.* Any accumulation point of the original interval $\langle\, 0, 1\,\rangle$, all the more of the set C, belongs to $\langle\, 0, 1\,\rangle$. Hence, to prove that every accumulation point a of C belongs to C we have only to show that a is not an interior point of a marked interval; but this is evident since in a certain neighborhood of such interior points there is no point of C at all.

To prove further properties of Cantor's discontinuum it is convenient to represent the members of C arithmetically, namely as *triadic* (instead of decimal or dual) fractions (cf. § 4, 3). The digits admitted are, then, 0, 1, 2. But the above definition of the points of C means that the middle digit, 1, is excluded by the successive steps and only 0 and 2 are admitted. Hence C can be conceived as *the set of all those* (infinite and terminating) *triadic fractions beginning with* 0. *in which the digit* 1 *does not occur*. This duly includes the ends of the marked intervals and the points 0 and 1; for the corresponding real numbers, save for 0, admit two triadic expansions, one infinite and one terminating (§ 4, **2**), and the left-hand end of every marked interval (see figure 13) can be written as an infinite fraction without the digit 1, the right-hand end as a terminating one. For instance, in triadic expansion,

$$1 = 0.222\ldots, \quad \tfrac{1}{3} = 0.0222\ldots, \quad \tfrac{2}{3} = 0.2, \quad \tfrac{1}{9} = 0.00222\ldots, \quad \tfrac{2}{9} = 0.02.$$

From this representation we easily infer that *C has the cardinal* $\aleph$ — which is surprising for a set which is nowhere dense and which has the property stated in the following paragraph.[1]) For if in each

---

[1]) For a remarkable mapping of C onto the set of all denumerable types, which has the cardinal $\aleph$ (Theorem 5 of § 8), see Kuratowski 37.

triadic fraction of C we replace the digit 2 by 1, we formally obtain the set of all infinite and terminating *dual* fractions which has the cardinal $\aleph + \aleph_0 = \aleph$.[1])

Another surprising fact is that the sum of the lengths of all marked intervals is

$$\tfrac{1}{3} + \tfrac{2}{3^2} + \tfrac{2^2}{3^3} + \ldots + \tfrac{2^{k-1}}{3^k} + \ldots = \tfrac{1}{3}\left(1 + \tfrac{2}{3} + \left(\tfrac{2}{3}\right)^2 + \ldots\right) = \tfrac{1}{3}\cdot 3 = 1.$$

That is to say, the sum *equals* the length of the original interval $\langle 0, 1 \rangle$. Hence, in accordance with the usual generalization of the elementary concept of length (or area, etc.) to that of measure, C *has the measure* 0 (though the cardinal $\aleph$).

The "ordinal" subjects of **1–4** and the "spatial" subjects of **5** and **6** give but a hint of the wealth of applications which the theory of sets of points has found in the theory of functions, in topology, and in many other fields of analysis and geometry. (Cf. § 12.) For these applications [2]), as well as for the theory of sets of points itself, the reader is referred to the great number of textbooks, comprehensive treatises, and encyclopedic expositions of these subjects.

Exercises

1) Prove that the type ω is determined by the following properties of a corresponding set

   a) it has a first but no last member,

   b) every cut is a jump.

2) Prove that the type $*\omega + \omega$ is determined by the following properties of a corresponding set [3])

   a) it has neither a first nor a last member,

   b) every cut is a jump.

---

[1])　$\overline{\overline{C}} = \aleph$ is a particular case of the statement that every perfect set P of points has the cardinal $\aleph$. The proof is quite easy for a one-dimensional P. Then P may include an interval, in which case the statement is trivial. Otherwise the set is nowhere-dense; then it is not difficult to show that P or a subset of it is similar, all the more equivalent, to C.

[2])　For applications in metamathematics see Beth 59, part VII.

[3])　Among the methods of determining this type by Peano's relation of sequent, Devidé 56 may be mentioned. On the other hand, Ohkuma 54 shows that the following property is *not sufficient* to determine $*\omega + \omega$: a and b denoting any two members of a corresponding set, there exists a single mapping $f(x)$ of the set onto itself for which $f(a) = b$.

3) Show that every (abstract) dense set can be rendered continuous by filling its gaps [1]) (cf. the end of **2**).

4) Prove that $\eta \cdot a = \eta$ for every denumerable type a [2]).

5) Prove that, given a dense set D and a denumerable (ordered) set A, A is similar to a subset of D. (Hence every dense set has a subset of the type η.) [3])

6) A set S of sets is called *monotone* (or a *chain*; cf. § 11, **7**) if of any two members of S one is a subset of the other. A monotone set S can be regarded as an ordered set by interpreting $s_1 \subset s_2$ as $s_1 \prec s_2$. Prove the following theorem [4]): If and only if a is a subtype of λ (i.e. the type of a subset of the open linear continuum) then there exists a monotone set of the type a the members of which are sets of positive integers.

7) Examine the properties of the types $(\lambda + 1)(1 + \lambda + 1)$ and $(1 + \lambda + 1)^2$.

8) (Cf. exercise **5**)) Show that every continuous set has a subset of the type λ.

9) Ascertain the derivation K' and the second derivation $K'' = (K')'$ of the sets

a) $K = \{0, \pm \frac{1}{2}, \pm \frac{2}{3}, \ldots, \pm \frac{k-1}{k}, \ldots\}$,

b) K = the set of all terminating decimal fractions.

10) Examine the examples of **6** in the light of the concepts introduced in **1**.

§ 10. GENERAL THEORY OF WELL-ORDERED SETS. FINITE SETS

1. The Concept of Well-Ordered Set. The well-ordered sets, introduced in this subsection in various ways, constitute a kind of ordered sets which is remarkable for its simplicity and for its generalizing certain properties of finite sets. The order-types of well-ordered sets will in fact prove to be similar to integers in many respects; the most important ones are *comparability* and *applicability of induction*.

The significance of the well-ordered sets is enhanced by the fact (see

---

[1]) A generalization of this method is given in Cuesta 54.

[2]) Cf. Słupecki 54.

[3]) For more far-reaching results, including a generalization from $\aleph_0$ to any transfinite cardinal, see Shepherdson 51, p. 304; Ginsburg 53, p. 522; Mendelson 58. Cf. Gillman 58 and the literature given there. — For an analogous but far profounder problem see Erdös–Rado 53 (where, however, the generalized continuum hypothesis (§ 11, **7**) and inaccessible numbers are involved).

[4]) See Sierpiński 32a.

§ 11, **6** and **7**) that the well-ordering theorem, one of the most important and most useful achievements of modern mathematics, allows to transfer the properties of well-ordered sets to any (ordered or plain) sets. From the beginning Cantor took the possibility of well-ordering for granted, without seriously attempting to prove it. One of the consequences is an enormous simplification of the arithmetic of cardinals (but not of order-types).

In § 8 we introduced ordered sets and order-types by refraining from the second act of abstraction that in § 4 led us to the concept of cardinal, namely abstraction from the order in which members succeed one another. Hereby we seemed to obtain *counting*: first, second, etc. Yet general order-types do not resemble the process of counting; this process always begins with a first object to be counted, and every object counted is followed by a next one, whereas in an ordered set there is in general no first member and no sequent to a given member.

To obtain closer resemblance to counting we have, then, to add to the conditions of § 8, **2** a further one. It cannot be merely beginning with a first member and providing each member save possibly the last with a sequent, for this would yield only sequences and their subsets. The additional condition was introduced by Cantor [1]) from 1883 on in various forms, notably those of Theorem 2 or Definition I; he also coined the terms "well-ordered" and "ordinal number" (see Definition III in **4**). More than any other single step in the development of set theory has the theory of well-ordered sets influenced mathematics in its entirety since the turn of the century.

DEFINITION I. An ordered set W is called *well-ordered* if every non-empty subset of W has a *first member*. For practical reasons also the null-set is called well-ordered.

Hence a well-ordered set has itself a first member, in accordance with the first feature of counting stated above.

This definition has become customary though it is not the simplest one in principle. In fact, the transitivity of the order relation (Definition I of § 8) becomes redundant if every subset is required to have a first member. There are two preferable ways of defining a set W as well-ordered:

a) *either* to require the relation $\prec$ in W to be irreflexive and to connect every two different members w_1, w_2 by a single of the relations $w_1 \prec w_2$ and $w_2 \prec w_1$, in addition to which every non-empty subset of W shall have a first member;

---

[1]) Cantor 1879–84IV, and V, §§ 2, 3, 11; 1897, § 12.

b) *or* to require W to be an ordered set and to add the condition of Theorem 2, below (cf. the *Remark* on p. 177).

Originally Cantor had taken the second way, replacing it later by Definition I. We shall mostly use Definition I which is the usual one.[1])

From the definition we conclude

THEOREM 1. *Every subset of a well-ordered set, and every ordered set which is similar to a well-ordered set, is also well-ordered.*

The simplest instances of well-ordered sets are the finite ordered sets (cf. **6**) and the *enumerated* sets, i.e. those of the type ω. (A *denumerable* set need not be ordered and, if it is, not be well-ordered; for example, the set of all integers or the set of all rationals, ordered according to magnitude.) Examples of infinite well-ordered but not enumerated sets are (cf. also p. 146)

$$(0, 1, 2, 3, \ldots -1, -2, -3, \ldots)$$

$$(1, 2, \bar{3}, \ldots \tfrac{1}{2}, \tfrac{3}{2}, \tfrac{5}{2}, \ldots \tfrac{1}{3}, \tfrac{2}{3}, \tfrac{4}{3}, \ldots \tfrac{1}{4}, \tfrac{3}{4}, \tfrac{5}{4}, \ldots \ldots).$$

More intricate examples are given in § 11, **3**; non-denumerable well-ordered sets, however, will explicitly appear only in § 11, **5**.

We shall now give three additional definitions of the concept of well-ordered set. To show that they are equipollent to Definition I we formulate them as theorems of the form "a set is well-ordered if and only if —".

While the first feature of counting (p. 175) is stressed by Definition I the second is emphasized in

THEOREM 2. *An ordered set W is well-ordered if and only if every subset W_0 which is not confinal with W has a* s e q u e n t *in W.* (For "confinal" see d) at the end of § 8, **2**.)

For $W = O$ the condition is satisfied vacuously. For $W_0 = O$ the sequent is the first member of W. If the subset is a unit-set (a), either a is the last member of W in which case no condition is imposed, or the condition requires a to have a sequent which is the second feature of counting mentioned above. The condition of Theorem 2, then, is a generalization of this feature.

Proof of Theorem 2. a) If W is well-ordered let $\overline{W}_0$ be the set of all $y \in W$ which succeed *every* $x \in W_0$. By assumption $\overline{W}_0 \neq O$; hence,

---

[1]) For recent generalizations of the concept of well-ordered set, notably with a view to partly ordered sets (§ 8, **2**), cf. J. Schmidt 55 and the literature given there.

according to Definition I, $\overline{W}_0$ has a first member which evidently is the sequent of W_0.

b) Let the condition of the theorem be satisfied by the ordered set W and let W' be a non-empty subset of W; we have to show that W' has a first member. If W_0 is the subset of W that contains those $y \in W$ which precede *every* $x \in W'$, then W_0 has a sequent s; s clearly belongs to W' and is its first member. Hence W is well-ordered.

Remark. Theorem 2 characterizes well-order by the property that *every non-empty remainder* of W, defined as the set of those $y \in W$ which succeed all members of a subset not confinal with W, has a first member, namely the sequent of the subset. This weakens the condition of Definition I which requires the same property of *every non-empty subset* of W. Hence the characterization of Theorem 2 is preferable in principle.

Here we insert an almost evident theorem on ordered sets which might have been formulated as well in § 8, **2** after the definition of *section*. However, only in the following does the theorem gain importance.

THEOREM 3. *A section of a section of an ordered set S is a section of S, and conversely, of two different sections of S one is a section of the other.*

Proof. The first statement is trivial. To prove the second let x_1 and x_2 be different members of S which determine the sections X_1 and X_2 respectively; then according as $x_1 \prec x_2$ or $x_2 \prec x_1$, X_1 is a section of X_2 or X_2 a section of X_1.

While every section of S is an initial (§ 8, **2**), the converse is not true. For instance, if the positive integers are ordered in the succession

$$(1, 3, 5, 7, \ldots \quad \ldots 8, 6, 4, 2)$$

then the ordered subset of the odd integers is an initial but not a section. If S is the ordered set of the points of a line, the same applies to the subset which contains a definite point and all points that precede it.

For well-ordered sets W, however, there is no distinction between initials and sections, save for W itself which is an "improper" initial of W. For we have

THEOREM 4. *An ordered set W is well-ordered if and only if every proper initial of W is also a section of W.*

W is an initial of itself but not a section because it has no sequent.

Proof (by Theorem 2). a) Since an initial which has a sequent in W is the section determined by this sequent we have to show that every proper initial of a well-ordered set does have a sequent. This follows from Theorem 2.

b) Assuming that the condition of Theorem 4 is satisfied by the ordered set W, let W_0 be any subset of W which is not confinal with W. To prove that W_0 has a sequent in W we replace W_0 by the set I which, in addition to the members of W_0, also contains all predecessors in W of any $x \in W_0$. I is a proper initial of W, hence a section by our assumption; the member that determines this section is then the sequent of (I and) W_0, which by Theorem 2 expresses that W is well-ordered.

THEOREM 5. *An ordered set W is well-ordered if and only if it has no subset of the type $*\omega$.*

Proof (by Definition I). a) If W is well-ordered then every non-empty subset has a first member, hence has not the type $*\omega$.

b) If no subset of W has the type $*\omega$ then every non-empty subset has a first member. For otherwise it would include a sequence (a_k) such that $a_{k+1} \prec a_k$ for every k, i.e. it would include a subset of the type $*\omega$.

Definition I and Theorems 2, 4, 5 are explicitly unilateral (asymmetrical) with respect to order; "first" cannot be replaced by "last" nor "sequent" by "immediate predecessor", "initial" by "remainder", $*\omega$ by ω. Of course, by introducing ordered sets each non-empty subset of which has a *last* member one would obtain a completely analogous theory, yielding nothing new. As to requiring both a first and a last member, see subsection **6**.

Finally, as well as the theory of ordered sets also the general theory of well-ordered sets can be based upon our axioms, and for the definition of well-order the detour via order (§ 8, **2**) can be somewhat curtailed. (See *Foundations*, pp. 128–134.) Existential statements, however, such as those occurring in § 11, require not only the axioms of infinity and of choice but mostly an additional axiom of "substitution" (see § 11, **2**).

2. Transfinite Induction. In this and the following subsection we deal with the two most important subjects of the *general* theory of well-ordered sets — in contrast to existential subjects and to ordinal numbers, treated in § 11. The proofs of Theorem 7 and 8 are not easy. Beginners are therefore advised to postpone the former until they arrive at § 11 where (in **3**) Theorem 7 is referred to for the first time. As to Theorem 8, its proof is not essential altogether, for in § 11, **2** another proof of this theorem, easier though less direct and typical, will be given.

As is well known, the characteristic method of proving and defining in arithmetic is *mathematical induction*, i.e. the method of generally proceeding from n to $n + 1$, provided that the case $n = 1$ (or $= 0$) is separately dealt with.[1]) After the order between the positive integers n has been introduced it is often more convenient to deal with $n + 1$ on the assumption that *all preceding* values (from 1, or 0, to n) are dealt with; this is the form analogous to Theorems 6 and 7. Some authorities on mathematics and philosophy maintain that mathematical induction is the very root of mathematics. (Cf. *Foundations*, chapter IV.)

Obviously mathematical induction is not sufficient to serve (ordered) sets which are neither finite nor sequences as the sequence of the positive integers. Yet there is a far-reaching generalization, called "transfinite induction", which is fit for all *well-ordered* sets and their types (ordinals) and can, by means of the well-ordering theorem (§ 11, 6), be transferred to infinite sets in general.[2])

In the applications of set theory to analysis and other branches of mathematics no tool has proved as important and powerful as transfinite induction.[3])

The simplest aspect of transfinite induction, namely its use for *proving*, is contained in

THEOREM 6 *(Proof by Transfinite Induction). Let be given a well-ordered set W and a condition (predicate, property) $\mathfrak{P}(x)$ defined for all members x of W; if the truth of $\mathfrak{P}$ for the members of every section of W implies its truth for the member which determines the section, then $\mathfrak{P}$ is true for all members of W.*

An equipollent formulation is: given a well-ordered set W and a set S (not necessarily ordered) which contains, together with the members of any section of W, also the member which determines that section, then S contains all members of W.

---

[1]) Occasionally we leaned upon proofs by mathematical induction, for instance in § 2, 5; § 3, 5; § 9, 3. After its partial use by Euclid (book IX, prop. 8), Gersonides (Levi ben Gerson), and others, the general formulation originates with Blaise Pascal. Cf. Freudenthal 53.

[2]) For more general inductive procedures (which include mathematical and transfinite induction) see Bell 20, Bennett 22, Blumberg 36; for induction in the (linear) continuum Khintchine 23 and Perron 26, cf. Duren 57 (see footnote [3]) below); for induction in partly (well-)ordered sets, J. Schmidt 53 and 55.

[3]) For some branches, notably algebra and topology, alternative methods (equipollent to transfinite induction) were recently introduced. Cf., for instance, Tukey 40, Birkhoff 42 and 48. For Zorn's principle see *Foundations*, pp. 68–70; cf. J. Schmidt 57.

According to the assumption, $\mathfrak{P}$ *is true for the first member* w_0 *of* W (or S contains w_0); for the section determined by w_0 is empty, hence the assumption is vacuously fulfilled by w_0.

For the concept of a condition [1]) (predicate, property) $\mathfrak{P}(x)$ cf. *Foundations*, p. 27 (and 38–41); for its use here, however, no logical analysis is needed. ("$\mathfrak{P}(x)$ is true" is just another expression for "x satisfies the condition $\mathfrak{P}$".)

The (indirect) *proof* of Theorem 6 is almost trivial. If the theorem were not true there ought to exist members x of W which do not satisfy $\mathfrak{P}$, and these members constitute a non-empty subset of W which has a first member x_0. But then the members of the section of W determined by x_0 satisfy $\mathfrak{P}$, hence by assumption also x_0. This contradiction shows that the theorem is true.

For the task of indirect procedure in this and other proofs of the present section see the end of subsection **5**.

A far more intricate problem than proving is *defining* by transfinite induction. The situation is to a great extent analogous to that in the realm of positive integers [2]); yet there the definition by mathematical induction involves the additional problem of ordering the integers whereas in a well-ordered set the order is presupposed.

While definitions by transfinite induction had been naively used by Cantor [3]) to introduce powers of ordinal numbers, only in the twenties did von Neumann [4]) discover and fill up this gap in the theory of well-ordered sets and ordinals, and only during the last decade did a rigorous treatment enter the textbooks of set theory. The nature of the gap becomes evident

---

[1])   The term is adopted from Rosser 53, p. 200; cf. above, p. 16.

[2])   The definitions of addition and of other operations were for the first time strictly based in Dedekind 1888, § 9; cf. Bernays 37–54II, p. 11 and Wang 57. Peano's procedure (from 1889 on, cf. Peano 1895) is not sufficient as long as it is not supplemented by a new primitive symbol for addition or by an appropriate primitive rule of inference; otherwise one has, as here in Theorem 7, to prove that *a function exists* which satisfies Peano's recursive definition. Cf. Landau 30, Lorenzen 39, Kalmár 40, Church 52, and the comprehensive analysis given in Felscher–Schmidt 58 and in Beth 59 (chapter 6).

[3])   Cantor 1897, pp. 231ff.; cf. Schoenflies 00–07I, p. 45 and Hausdorff 06–07I, pp. 127ff.

[4])   Von Neumann 23 and 28. — A method of rendering inductive definitions, in the sense of both mathematical and transfinite induction, *explicit*, is given in Kleene 44 (cf. 38). This is a question of principle, because inductive definitions cannot simply be eliminated as can explicit definitions (cf. above, § 4, 6); therefore, in a proof of non-contradiction for a deductive theory (*Foundations*, chapter V) inductive definitions must be considered separately (cf. Hilbert–Bernays 34, p. 294).

from Theorem 7 and its proof; previously one had assumed that Theorem 6 was sufficient for defining, too.

We precede Theorem 7 with a definition which has the only purpose of formulating the theorem in a simple way.

> DEFINITION II. A rule which uniquely assigns values to all functions defined on sections of a well-ordered set W, is called a *recursive rule on W*. A function f defined on W is said *to satisfy a recursive rule* $\mathfrak{p}$ *on W* if, for each $x_0 \in W$, $f(x_0)$ equals the value assigned by $\mathfrak{p}$ to the restriction of f to the section determined by x_0.

THEOREM 7 (*Definition, or Construction, by Transfinite Induction*). *For any recursive rule* $\mathfrak{p}$ *on a well-ordered set W, there exists one and only one function defined on W which satisfies the rule* $\mathfrak{p}$. In short, *a recursive rule uniquely defines a function on W.*

Remarks. $f(x)$ is accordingly defined for the first member of W by the recursive rule, just as in the case of Theorem 6. There are various ways of defining functions on W by recursive rules; a fixed rule from among them is assumed to be given.

A recursive rule $\mathfrak{p}$ on W is, then, a function $\psi(x_0, g)$ where $x_0 \in W$ and g ranges over functions defined on the set of all $x \in W$ which satisfy $x \prec x_0$. Given a function f defined on W, let us denote by $C(f, x_0)$ the restriction of f to the section of W determined by x_0. Thus $C(f, x_0)$ is the set of all ordered pairs $(x, f(x))$ where $x \in W$ and $x \prec x_0$. That a function f satisfies the recursive rule $\mathfrak{p}$ requires that $f(x_0) = \psi(x_0, C(f, x_0))$ for all $x_0 \in W$.

Instead of saying "f satisfies the recursive rule $\mathfrak{p}$" we also say "f has the recursive property $\mathfrak{p}$".

Proof of Theorem 7. We start with proving that *if* there exists a function satisfying the recursive rule then there exists *one only*. This follows immediately, just as in the proof of Theorem 6.

In fact, let $f_1(x)$ and $f_2(x)$ be two functions satisfying the rule. If there were an $x \in W$ for which f_1 differs from f_2, then the subset of W that contains all such x would have a first member x^*. But $f_1(x^*) \neq f_2(x^*)$, together with $f_1(x) = f_2(x)$ for all $x \prec x^*$, contradicts the assumption of recursiveness.

To show the *existence* of a function satisfying the recursive rule, we first arrange all *sections* of W according to the order in which the *members* that determine the sections appear in W. This ordered set of all sections is similar to W, hence well-ordered, and it retains this property if to the sections, succeeding them, W itself is added; hereby, according to Theorem 4, the well-ordered set I of all *initials* of W is obtained. (This transition from the members of W to its initials is natural because the recursive rule connects the function value at a definite place x_0 with the values on the whole section [initial] determined by x_0.)

To construct the function desired we use the following

LEMMA. *Under the assumption of Theorem 7, for every initial i of W there exists a function $f_i(x)$, defined for all $x \in i$, which satisfies the recursive rule* p.

To prove this statement we use transfinite induction in the well-ordered set I of all initials of W. (For the first initial, namely the null-set, the statement is trivial.) We assume the statement to be true for all initials (sections) which precede a particular initial i_0. To show that it is also true for i_0 we distinguish between two cases.

a) i_0 *has a last member* z. By assumption there exists a function $f_{i_0'}(x)$ satisfying the rule p, which is defined on the section i_0' of i_0 determined by z. But according to the nature of p, the function value v for $x = z$ is uniquely defined by the totality of values $f_{i_0'}$ on i_0'. Therefore we may define the function f_{i_0} as coinciding with $f_{i_0'}$ on i_0' and as equalling v for $x = z$; then $f_{i_0}(x)$ is a function satisfying the rule p and defined for all $x \in i_0$.

b) i_0 *has no last member*. Then *each* member of i_0 belongs to a section i_0' of i_0, and by assumption a function $f_{i_0'}$ defined on i_0' exists which satisfies the rule p. It does not matter which section i_0' is taken, for all such functions coincide for the same argument; in fact, if i_0' and i_0'' are different sections of i_0 and if i_0' is a section of i_0'' (Theorem 3), both $f_{i_0'}$ and $f_{i_0''}$ are defined on i_0' and coincide there in view of the uniqueness of any function satisfying the rule p, as proven above. We can therefore define $f_{i_0}(x)$ on i_0 by the rule: if $x \in i_0$ belongs to the section i_0' of i_0 then $f_{i_0}(x) = f_{i_0'}(x)$; this f_{i_0} also satisfies the rule p.

Hereby the lemma is proven, and at the same time Theorem 7 since W is an initial of itself.

Theorem 7 deals with functions of a single argument x. The extension to functions of any finite number of arguments involves no difficulty of principle; in this case, instead of the rule $f(x_0) = \psi(x_0, C(f, x_0))$ (see above), we shall use a rule of the form

$$f(a_1, \ldots, a_{n-1}, x_0) = \psi(a_1, \ldots, a_{n-1}, x_0, C(f, x_0))$$

where $a_1, \ldots, a_{n-1}, x_0$ belong to the same well-ordered set.

In contrast to the *successive* steps of inductive procedure at many junctures in arithmetic, Theorem 7 gives a simultaneous construction. This difference, to be sure, is mainly of a psychological nature (cf. § 11, **6**) and is connected with certain problems of principle hinted at below (p. 191/2).

As to the terms "mathematical" and "transfinite" induction, the former (as well as the term "complete induction" used instead in most continental languages) of course contrasts not with the latter but with the "incomplete" induction of natural science. On the other hand, mathematical induction, while referring to an infinite (enumerated) set, is distinguished by the fact that every single member of the set is preceded by finitely many members only. The situation is different for transfinite induction where in general a member is preceded by infinitely many members — more precisely, by a set with a transfinite ordinal number (below, subsection **4**).

Definition by transfinite induction occurs explicitly in § 11, for instance in **3**. Implicitly it is already used, and based without reference to Theorem 7, in the proof of the following Theorem 8.

3. Comparability of Well-Ordered Sets.[1]) At the end of § 5 the fundamental problem of the theory of equivalence was *left open*, viz. the question whether every two (plain) sets can be compared in respect of their cardinals. Regarding similarity instead of equivalence, i.e. order-types instead of cardinals, the corresponding problem for ordered sets was raised and *settled in the negative* in § 8, **4**. In contrast, the most important property of *well-ordered* sets, next to the applicability of transfinite induction, is that they can be compared indeed. In § 11, **5** and **7** this affirmative answer will be utilized also for equivalence, i.e. for comparing cardinals.

THEOREM 8 (COMPARABILITY OF WELL-ORDERED SETS). *Of two well-ordered sets which are not similar, one is similar to a section of the other.*

In contrast with the situation in § 5, here the case of similarity has to be singled out because a well-ordered set cannot be similar to a section of itself (Theorem 14).

Proof.[2]) We begin with a heuristic remark. If *A* and *B* are *similar*

---

[1]) Beginners are referred to the introductory remark of **2**, p. 178.

[2]) The earliest proofs of comparability are those of Cantor 1897, Baire 05, Hessenberg 06, Young–Young 06. The proof of Hausdorff 14 (pp. 103–105), which makes the detour via ordinal numbers, excels in lucidity; it is displayed in § 11, **2** without using the present proof (which, as that of § 11, **7**, chiefly leans on suggestions made to the author by A. Plessner in 1927).

well-ordered sets then a similar mapping [1]) relates the first member of A to the first of B, the second to the second, etc.; if the sets are infinite, also the members that determine sections of the types ω, $\omega + 1$, etc. correspond to each other. This fact leads to the conjecture that a similar mapping φ between A and B which relates $a \in A$ to $b \in B$, also relates the section of A determined by a to the section of B determined by b, in the sense that the latter section contains just the images by φ of the members of the former.

This shall serve as our guiding principle for constructing a rule of correspondence between members of *any* two well-ordered sets. The rule will be defined along the lines of Theorem 7 and our proof virtually follows that of this theorem.

If V and W are non-empty well-ordered sets we shall, *as far as possible*, attach to every $v \in V$ a uniquely defined image $w \in W$ by the following rule:

(*) Let x be an arbitrary member of V and X the section of V determined by x. Assuming that to every member of X an image in W has been related, denote the set of these images by Y, hence $Y \subseteq W$. If W contains members which succeed all members of Y then *the sequent y of Y in W shall be related to $x \in V$*. We write $y = \varphi(x)$.

According to (*) the first member of W is related to the first of V because either determines the null-set as section.

The rule may fail to relate an image to $x \in V$, viz. when Y is not succeeded by any member of W. Anyhow, the members of V that do have an image in W on account of (*) constitute an initial of V, for (*) defines an image for $x \in V$ only if all $v \in V$ with $v \prec x$ have images.

Let us first form a rough idea of the nature of our rule by contemplating its application to the first few members of V. If v_0 is the first member of V and w_0 the first of W we have $w_0 = \varphi(v_0)$ as mentioned above. The second member v_1 of V determines the section $X_1 = (v_0)$; since the corresponding subset (initial) $Y_1 \subseteq W$ is (w_0), the image of v_1 is the sequent of (w_0) in W, i.e. the second member w_1 of W (if W has more than one member). Analogically we find that the image of the nth member v_{n-1} of V is the nth member w_{n-1} of W, provided neither set is exhausted before. If V is neither finite nor of the type ω then the initial $(v_0, v_1, \ldots, v_k, \ldots)$ of V is the section determined by its sequent v_ω;

---

[1])   Theorem 13 states that there is a single similar mapping only between them.

hence, if W is also comprehensive enough, $\varphi(v_\omega) = w_\omega$ is the sequent of the subset (initial) $(w_0, w_1, \ldots, w_k, \ldots)$ of W.

After this introduction we are going to prove two fundamental properties of the rule (*). For this purpose only (Lemmata I and II), an initial X of V all members of which have images in W on account of (*), shall for short be called "imageable", and the subset Y of W that contains the images of the members of X shall be called the "image-set" of X. (We shall not later use these terms.)

LEMMA I. *If x_1, x_2 are members of an imageable initial X of V and y_1, y_2 their images in Y respectively, then $x_1 \prec x_2$ in X (and V) implies $y_1 \prec y_2$ in Y (and W). Hence (*) defines a s i m i l a r mapping of any imageable initial of V onto its image-set.*

Proof. If $x_1 \prec x_2$ then by (*) the image y_2 of x_2 succeeds all $y \in Y$ that are images of the members of the section of X determined by x_2; y_1 certainly is among these images because y_1 is related to x_1 which precedes x_2, i.e. $y_1 \prec y_2$. Hence different members of Y are related to different members of X; accordingly we have a similar one-to-one correspondence.

LEMMA II. *The image-set Y of any imageable initial X of V is an initial of W.*

Proof. Let y_1 be a member of $Y \subseteq W$ and y_0 any member of W which precedes y_1; we have to show that $y_0 \in Y$.

$y_1 \in Y$ expresses the existence of an $x_1 \in X$ such that $y_1 = \varphi(x_1)$, and $y_0 \prec \varphi(x_1)$ shows that there exist members x of X such that $y_0 \preceq \varphi(x)$ in W. Let x_0 be *the first of all these* $x \in X$; we shall show that $y_0 = \varphi(x_0)$.

By the definition of x_0, all members $\overline{x}$ of X (or V) for which $\overline{x} \prec x_0$, satisfy $\varphi(\overline{x}) \prec y_0$ in W. But by the definition of φ in (*), $\varphi(x_0)$ is the *first* member of W that succeeds these $\varphi(\overline{x})$; therefore $y_0 \prec \varphi(x_0)$ is impossible, hence $y_0 = \varphi(x_0)$, and this means $y_0 \in Y$, as our lemma states. (If y_0 is the first member of W then x_0 is the first member of V (and X), and $y_0 \in Y$ becomes evident.)

From the lemmata we easily infer the comparability of the well-ordered sets V and W by means of the rule (*). As noted above, the subset $X \subseteq V$ of those members which have an image in W is an initial of V, and by Lemma II the set Y of their images is an initial of W.

Accordingly we have the following alternative:

1) $X = V$. Then (*) yields a similar mapping of V onto an initial Y of W which either coincides with W (*first case*) or, by Theorem 4, is a

section W' of W (*second case*). In the first case we have $V \simeq W$, in the second $V \simeq W'$. In the latter, while every member of V is related by (*) to a certain member of W there are members of W to which no member of V corresponds, namely all $w \in W$ that succeed the section W'.

2) $X \subset V$, i.e. X is a proper initial, hence a section V' of V (*third case*). In this case the set Y of the images of the members of V' must *coincide with W*, i.e. $V' \simeq W$; for if Y were a section of W then the rule (*) would relate the member of W which determines the section Y to the member of V which determines the section $X = V'$ — contrary to the definition of $X = V'$ as the initial of *all* $x \in V$ which have images in W.

In analogy to the scheme of possible cases regarding equivalence between plain sets and their subsets given in § 5, **4**, we here present a scheme of cases regarding similarity between well-ordered sets and their sections.

	$Y = W$	Y a section of W
$X = V$	first case: $V \simeq W$	second case: V similar to a section of W
X a section of V	third case: W similar to a section of V	fourth case

In § 5 we were unable to deal with the fourth case. Yet here we have succeeded in showing its *impossibility*; hence there remain only the three cases specified in Theorem 8, the proof of which is now completed. (Why it is called the comparability theorem will become obvious when an order between the types of well-ordered sets is defined in § 11, **1**. Moreover, in § 11, **5** we shall show that hereby also the comparability of the *cardinals* of well-ordered sets is ensured.)

4. Addition and Multiplication. Ordinals. The operations with ordered sets introduced in § 8 shall now be specialized to well-ordered sets. We shall not use Theorems 7 and 8 in the following; as to Theorem 6, we do not explicitly refer to it although the simple argument which is at its bottom will be frequently used in **5**.

Addition and multiplication of well-ordered sets and their types are subsumed under Definitions IV–VII of § 8. The obvious question here is how far the operations, when applied to well-ordered sets, yield again such sets; that the answer is not *generally* in the affirmative follows from example 2 on p. 147 which shows that *any* ordered set can be obtained by addition of unit-sets — which, as every finite ordered set, are well-ordered. However, we shall prove

THEOREM 9. *If T is a well-ordered set whose members are pairwise disjoint well-ordered sets, then the ordered sum K (Definition V of § 8) of the members of T is well-ordered. Hence the addition of any f i n i t e number of well-ordered sets yields a well-ordered sum, however the terms are ordered.*

In contrast with the formulation in § 8 which starts with types, here no advantage is gained by assigning the terms (sets) of the sum to the members of an auxiliary set.

Proof. We show that every non-empty subset $K_0 \subseteq K$ has a first member. Those members of T which contribute to K_0, i.e. members of which are contained in K_0, form a non-empty subset of T; its first member shall be denoted by t_0. t_0, then, contains at least one member of K_0 while no predecessor of t_0 in T does. Hence the first member of the well-ordered intersection $t_0 \cap K_0$ is also the first member of K_0, which completes the proof.

Beginners are advised to facilitate the comprehension of this proof by first assuming T to be an ordered *pair*.

DEFINITION III. The type of a well-ordered set is called an *ordinal number*, or simply an *ordinal*; if the set is infinite, a *transfinite ordinal*.

The dignified title of *number*, attributed to cardinals with some reservations (§ 4, **5**) and denied to general order-types (§ 8, **4**), is here conferred on the types of well-ordered sets owing to their comparability (Theorem 8, more explicitly Theorem 3 of § 11).[1]) The ordinal of a well-ordered set is shared by all similar sets and by these only. In accordance with the introduction to § 10, ordinals constitute a most natural generalization of non-negative integers beyond the domain of finiteness; this will show particularly in § 11, **3**.

Since for finite sets cardinal, type, and ordinal virtually coincide

---

[1]) We shall not dwell upon the distinction made by Denjoy 41, 46, and 46–54 between "types of well-ordered sets" and "ordinal numbers" (meaning "rank"), which has not been generally accepted.

(§ 8, **4**; cf. below, subsection **6**) the symbols denoting the positive integers, including 0, may be maintained for finite ordinals. Transfinite ordinals, however, are distinct from cardinals just as are transfinite types in general. It will turn out — most generally in § 11, **6** — that there are always (infinitely many) ordinals among the types which correspond to a given transfinite cardinal.

In § 8, **6** we found that $2^{\aleph_0} = \aleph$ different types correspond to $\aleph_0$; how many ordinals are among them is discussed in § 11, **5** and **7**. Among the examples given in § 8, **1** which order the set of all integers in various ways, b) and c) have the ordinals ω and $\omega + \omega$ respectively while the types of a) and d) are not ordinals. Neither are η, λ, and generally the types of dense sets which, according to Theorem 2, are not well-ordered.

Theorem 9 may now be formulated as

THEOREM 10. *An ordered sum of ordinals taken in well-ordered arrangement, i. e. as assigned to the members of a well-ordered set, is an ordinal. Hence the same applies to a product of two (or of a finite number of) ordinals. In particular, a sum of finitely many ordinals is an ordinal, however the terms of the sum are ordered.*

The statement about products follows from the first statement by taking *equal* terms in the sum and applying Definition VI of § 8. Therefore the power σ^n for any ordinal σ and finite $n > 0$ is an ordinal too. Yet the cases of a product with infinitely many factors or of σ^τ with transfinite τ are not included; see § 8, **7** and § 11, **3**.

Whereas for the validity and invalidity of formal laws governing the addition and multiplication of ordinals nothing need be added to Theorems 4 and 7 of § 8 [1]), there is an elaborate system of arithmetic (including subtraction and division) of ordinals; see § 11, **4**.

---

[1]) For ordinals, particular questions have been raised and partly been answered. For instance, the pairs a, β of different transfinite ordinals which satisfy the equations $a + \beta = \beta + a$ or $a\beta = \beta a$ or $a^\beta = \beta^a$ (the latter is, among finite integers, satisfied only by the pair 2, 4) are investigated in Jacobsthal 07 (cf. 09a and Sierpiński 56); a comprehensive survey is given in H. Bachmann 55, § 22. (It is easily seen that the equation $x^y = y^x$ is satisfied by infinitely many pairs of *cardinals*; see Sierpiński 28, p. 221.)

For the second distributive law for ordinals see Zakon 53.

Given a set of ordinals, one may ask what well-ordered arrangements of its members yield a minimal, or maximal, ordered sum; the interesting answers are given in Rado 54. – Erdös 50 (cf. the literature annexed in the present book's Bibliography) ascertains the number of different sums that originate from a finite number of ordinal-terms according to their arrangements.

5. Elementary Properties of Well-Ordered Sets. Theorem 4 of § 3 states that every plain infinite set S has a denumerable subset; its proof was not simple and partly non-constructive. The analogue for well-ordered sets, where „denumerable" is replaced by "enumerated", is far simpler and fully constructive. By Theorem 2 of the present section an infinite well-ordered set W contains a first member w_0, a second w_1, and generally an nth member w_{n-1} for every positive integer n; w_{n-1} is the sequent of the finite subset $(w_0, w_1, \ldots, w_{n-2})$ of W. Hence we conclude (cf., for instance, § 9, 3) that the uniquely defined enumerated set $W_0 = (w_0, w_1, \ldots, w_k, \ldots)$ is a subset, and even an *initial*, of W. Thus we have

THEOREM 11. *Every infinite well-ordered set W has a subset of the ordinal ω. More precisely, W can be represented uniquely as an ordered sum of the form*

$$(1) \qquad\qquad W = W_0 + W_1$$

where $\overline{W_0} = \omega$ (while W_1 may be empty, finite, or infinite).

Hence every transfinite ordinal σ has a unique additive decomposition of the form

$$\sigma = \omega + \sigma_1$$

where the ordinal σ_1 equals 0 if and only if $\sigma = \omega$.

The almost evident fact that the decomposition is unique has not been stressed in the proof because it is a consequence of Theorem 12 (or 13), in whose proof Theorem 11 is not utilized.

We use Theorem 11 to give an example which facilitates the understanding of Theorem 12. Every infinite well-ordered set can, in view of (1), be similarly mapped onto a proper subset as follows. If w_k ($k \neq 0$) is an arbitrary member of $W_0 = (w_0, w_1, \ldots)$ and if $W_0' = (w_k, w_{k+1}, \ldots)$ then the subset $W_0' \subset W_0$ is similar to W_0; a similar mapping (the only one by Theorem 13) is obtained by relating $w_n \in W_0$ to $w_{k+n} \in W_0'$. Writing W in the form (1) and using the identical mapping of W_1 onto itself we obtain a similar mapping of W onto its proper subset $W_0' + W_1$, which has the following property: there are members w of W — namely all members of W_0 — which are related to an image w' in the subset that *succeeds* w, i.e. $w \prec w'$ in W. Of course there may also be members of W which are related to *themselves*, as are in our case the members of W_1 if $W_1 \neq O$.

Naturally the question arises whether the third case may also happen, namely that the image *precedes* the original in W. The (negative) answer is given by the following theorem due to Zermelo,[1]) which may serve as the keystone for the general theory of well-ordered sets, including comparability.

THEOREM 12. *A similar mapping of a well-ordered set W onto a subset never relates to a member w of W an image that precedes w in W.*

Two equipollent formulations are:

a) If W is well-ordered and $f(x)$ a single-valued function defined on W, assuming values of W, and such that $x_1 \prec x_2$ implies $f(x_1) \prec f(x_2)$, then for no $x \in W$ can $f(x) \prec x$ hold true.

b) On account of a similar mapping of a well-ordered set W onto a subset, the image of a $w \in W$ either coincides with w or succeeds w in W.

Proof. Let φ be a similar mapping of W onto $W' \subseteq W$ and let the image of $w \in W$ in W' be denoted by $\varphi(w)$. If there were at least one $x \in W$ such that $\varphi(x) \prec x$ then there would be a *first* such x, say x_0; we write $\varphi(x_0) = x_1$. In view of the similarity of φ we have, in addition to $\varphi(x_0) \prec x_0$, also $\varphi(x_1) \prec x_1$. Since $x_1 \prec x_0$, this contradicts the assumption that x_0 is the *first* x satisfying $\varphi(x) \prec x$; hereby Theorem 12 is proven.

A more obvious if less elegant form of the proof consists in taking *any* x_0 with the property $\varphi(x_0) \prec x_0$ and successively proceeding to members x_1 (as above), x_2, ..., thus producing a sequence of members of W which has the type $^*\omega$, contrary to Theorem 5.[2])

Postponing an analysis of the method of our proof to the end of this subsection, we draw two important conclusions from Theorem 12.

THEOREM 13. *Between two similar well-ordered sets there exists a single similar mapping only. Hence a well-ordered set can be similarly mapped onto itself only identically, by relating each member to itself.*

Proof. The second statement, seemingly a particular case of the first, is actually equipollent to it. In fact, if φ_1 and φ_2 are similar mappings of a well-ordered set V onto another W, let $\varphi_1(v) = w_1$ and $\varphi_2(v) = w_2$ be the images in W of the same $v \in V$. Since similarity is a transitive relation we

---

[1]) Published in Hessenberg 06, see p. V.

[2]) For denumerable sets one can invert Theorem 12 in the sense that a denumerable ordered set with the property of the theorem is well-ordered. This inversion does not remain true for non-denumerable sets, cf. Dushnik–Miller 40.

hereby obtain a similar mapping ψ of W onto itself which relates w_1 to w_2. Hence, if φ_1 and φ_2 did not coincide, i.e. if there existed a $v \in V$ for which $w_1 \neq w_2$, then ψ would be non-identical. This shows that the first statement also follows from the second.

To prove the second statement we assume that there existed a $w_1 \in W$ whose image w_2, by a similar mapping of W onto itself, were $\neq w_1$. Then either $w_1 \prec w_2$ or $w_2 \prec w_1$, but each case contradicts Theorem 12.

The property expressed by Theorem 12 pertains to well-ordered sets but is not *characteristic* of them. For instance, every ordered set of the type $\omega + 1 + {}^*\omega$ has clearly the same property. In contrast, cf. exercise 6) at the end of § 10.

THEOREM 14. *A well-ordered set W is not similar to any section of itself nor to a section of any subset of W. Different sections of W are not similar to one another.*

Of course, W may have proper *subsets* similar to W, and an infinite W always has (p. 189).

Proof. The first statement is the important one, but as it is a particular case of the second (referring to a section of a subset) we prove this second. If X is a section, determined by $x \in W'$, of $W' \subseteq W$, then we show that $X \simeq W$ cannot hold. Any similar mapping of W onto X would relate x to a member y of the section X, which implies that $y \prec x$ in W'; but this contradicts Theorem 12 since $X \subset W'$.

The last statement of Theorem 14 follows from the first in view of Theorem 3.

Remark. By means of Theorem 8 — which, however, we proposed not to use for the time being — it follows from Theorem 14 that *a subset W' of W is similar either to W or to a section of W.* For otherwise W ought to be similar to a section of W' which contradicts Theorem 14.

We conclude this subsection with some methodical remarks on the proof of Theorem (6 and) 12, which is the base of Theorems 13 and 14. We there used the *indirect method* of proving (*reductio ad absurdum*) [1]

---

[1] We shall not dwell here upon the general problems of indirect proof in their logical and didactic-psychological aspects. In the first direction it will suffice to refer to Löwenheim 46 and Goodstein 48. In the second, the puzzling question arises why an indirect proof of a theorem is often more easily grasped than a direct proof though it distorts the mind towards an impossible assumption. As examples we refer to the diagonal method, e.g. in § 4, to the remark on p. 169, and also to the proof B on p. 44 and to the proof of IV on p. 227 (which might as well be conducted – but less readily comprehended – in a direct way).

which is typical of the theory of well-ordered sets (and of parts of arithmetic, cf. the proof of Theorem 5 of § 2). To prove a certain property $\pi(x)$ for all members x of a well-ordered set W one assumes the contrary, namely that at least one $w \in W$ has the property non-π; then the set of all such w, being a non-empty subset of a well-ordered set, has a first member w_0. Either the peculiar nature of this w_0 or — which is more characteristic of the theory — the fact that all predecessors of w_0 in W do have the property π yields then the contradiction required for the proof. In particular, w_0 may be the first member of W. In short, the property of well-ordered sets expressed in Definition I enables us to replace *any* $w \in W$ by a *definite one* w_0 in order to refute the assumption.[1])

On the other hand, instead of making use of indirect procedures in each individual case as in the proof of Theorem 12, one may generally rest upon its use in the proof of Theorem 6; this is what is called "proof by transfinite induction". The situation is analogous for the proof by mathematical induction in arithmetic; the property of Definition I is then replaced by the property, satisfied by every set of positive integers, of containing a least number.[2])

6. On Finite Sets and their Ordinals. The asymmetric character of the definition of well-ordered sets was pointed out above at the end of **1**; in addition to Theorems 2, 4, 5, this asymmetry of well-order shows particularly in Theorem 12. Imposing the inverse asymmetry (last member instead of first, "anti-well-ordered sets") yields nothing new, and the condition that every non-empty subset should contain a first *or* a last member leads only to a slight generalization of well-order.[3]) Yet the question suggests itself: what emerges if both a first *and* a last member are postulated?

The expectation that these "double-well-ordered sets" might constitute a new interesting kind of ordered sets is not fulfilled, for the new kind is too simple: they are the *finite* sets. By applying Theorem 5 in both directions we conclude that a double-well-ordered set contains neither subsets

---

[1]) For induction in the continuum (see footnote [2]) on p. 179), the greatest lower bound takes the part of the first member w_0. (Cf. also Kurepa 54a.)

[2]) Lebesgue 04 (2nd ed., 1928, p. 329) gives a penetrating analysis of the parallelism and the difference between mathematical and transfinite induction and of the rôle of indirect proof, distinguishing between the cases where either a bounded number of steps, or a finite but indefinitely great number, or transfinitely many steps are required.

[3]) See Steckel 28 and exercise 4) at the end of this section. Another generalization proposed by Hausdorff in 1901 has not gained much significance either.

of the type $*\omega$ nor of the type ω, which implies its finiteness in view of Theorem 11. Another method of showing this is using Theorem 12 in both directions; then such sets prove to have no proper similar subsets and also no proper equivalent subsets, which means finiteness in the sense of non-reflexiveness (Definition VII of § 2). (The converse statement, namely that every finite [inductive] ordered set is double-well-ordered, is almost trivial.) Moreover, as Tarski has shown (see below), the definition of finiteness in the sense of double-well-ordered is *elementary* in the sense that it proves equipollent to inductiveness (Definition VI of § 2) without the use of the axioms of choice and of infinity — in contra-distinction to non-reflexiveness ([1] from which inductiveness can be derived only by means of the axiom of choice (§ 2, **5** and § 6, **5**).

The new definition has the merit of imbedding the theories of finite sets and of integers in the general theory of well-ordered sets. This merit is especially significant in the eyes of those who share Zermelo's opinion that finite sets, integers, and arithmetic can totally be based on set theory.[2] This is not a thesis of the present book, and readers interested in this controversy are referred to *Foundations* (chapters II–IV); but also if arithmetic is considered to be based independently one might find interest in its re-development in the frame of set theory, a direction implicitly taken by great thinkers from Descartes to Peirce, Dedekind, Frege, and Russell.

True, Poincaré [3] ridiculed those who explore the realm of sets by means of general concepts and methods with disregard of integers, to discover, at a late stage of their excursion, the finite sets and numbers in a remote corner of the huge realm. Yet this is a psychological and didactic rather than a logico-mathematical argument; how far set theory can be used as a basis or a frame for arithmetic is a serious and profound problem, except for intuitionistic attitudes (*Foundations*, chapter IV).

From the 1880's up to these days many different definitions for the

---

[1]   This is what usually is called "Dedekind's definition of finiteness", see Dedekind 1888. However, in the preface to the second edition (1893) of this classical booklet Dedekind mentions another definition of finiteness, originating from 1889, which Dedekind considered complicated and unfit for a basis of arithmetic; yet actually it is just elementary in the above sense.

Cf. Dedekind 30–32III, pp. 450–458; Tarski 25; Cavaillès 32.

[2]   Of course, this does not exclude the use (and the independent introduction) of a few of the smallest non-negative integers. It is the general concept of integer whose foundation is under discussion.

[3]   For instance, Poincaré 08, livre II; cf. 09.

finiteness of a set were given and a more or less comprehensive part of arithmetic was derived from them. These definitions may be classified according to various points of view; for instance, to the complexity of the concepts entering the definition, such as mapping (Dedekind's first definition), order (double-well-ordered), etc., or to the psychological simplicity and obviousness. From our point of view preference should be given to definitions which allow to derive arithmetic without using principles that are alien to finite sets, particularly without the axioms of choice and of infinity. Tarski and others [1]) introduced and classified such definitions systematically. An important question is the interdependence of different definitions without, or by means of, the axiom of choice; in particular, how far the equipollence of different definitions constitutes an assumption from which the axiom of choice can be derived. Accordingly, a hierarchy of definitions with respect to this axiom may be given. For these and related problems see *Foundations*, especially pp. 53, 62ff., 118, where further literature references are given.

Exercises

1) Prove that in every set that satisfies the conditions a) of p. 175 the relation $\prec$ is transitive, hence constitutes an order relation.

2) Let V and W be similar well-ordered sets and w be the image in W (see Theorem 13) of $v \in V$. Prove that the section of V determined by v is similar to the section of W determined by w. (This is at the bottom of the proof of Theorem 8.)

3) Prove that if to every section of the well-ordered set V there corresponds a similar section of the well-ordered set W and vice versa, then $V \simeq W$. (Cf. Theorem 8.)

4) Prove that every non-empty subset of an ordered set S has a first or a last member if and only if S can be written as an ordered sum $S = S_1 + S_2$ such that S_1 is well-ordered and S_2 "anti-well-ordered" (see the beginning of 6). Is this representation of S unique?

5) Prove that every well-ordered set W (but not every ordered set; give a counter-example!) has the following property: every set T of

---

[1]) The most comprehensive research is Tarski 25 (cf. 38a); in the *Annexe* of 25 the problems connected with the axiom of choice are outlined. Of earlier investigations we only mention Zermelo 09 and Grelling 10, where for the first time the theory of finite sets and numbers is derived from set-theoretical axioms *without assuming the existence of an infinite set* (which was assumed by Dedekind); cf. Wang 53 and 57.

sections of W contains a *least* section, namely the intersection of all members of T.

6) In contrast with the property of well-ordered sets expressed by Theorem 13, ordered sets of types such as $*\omega + \omega$, η, etc. admit infinitely many similar mappings onto themselves. Prove this and look for the source of the contrast.

7) A member s of an ordered set S shall be called a *fixed* member of S if *every* similar mapping of S onto itself relates s to itself. According to Theorem 13, each member of a well-ordered set is fixed; the same holds, for instance, for each member of sets of the type $\omega + n + *\omega$ with finite n. On the other hand, a set of the type $*\omega + \omega$ has no fixed member, a set of the type $*\omega + \omega + n + *\omega + \omega$ has n fixed members (those "in the middle").

Prove the theorem [1]): If the disjoint ordered sets S and T have the fixed points s_0 and t_0 respectively, then s_0 or t_0 is a fixed point of the ordered sum $S + T$.

8) Prove Theorems 13 and 14, instead of by Theorem 12, by means of the fact that the rule (*) of **3** is satisfied by every similar mapping between well-ordered sets.

9) Starting from each of the three definitions of a finite set pointed out in **6** (double-well-ordered, inductive, non-reflexive), try to prove the two others as criteria, i.e. in the form: a set is finite if and only if —.

10) Discern the intrinsic difference between these definitions of finiteness by proving, in view of each of them, the statement that the power-set of a finite set is also finite.

§ 11. ORDINALS AND ALEPHS. WELL-ORDERING AND COMPARABILITY

1. The Arrangement of Ordinals by Magnitude. While the equality between ordinals is settled by its definition for types in general, their order is established by

> DEFINITION I. If τ and υ are the ordinals of the well-ordered sets T and W respectively and if T is similar to a section of W, then τ is called *less* than υ. In symbols, $\tau < \upsilon$.

This *term* coincides with the one introduced in § 5, **1** for ordering

---

[1]) Ginsburg 54, p. 554.

cardinals by magnitude, but no confusion will arise owing to the distinct notations used for cardinals and ordinals (except for *finite* numbers for which the respective statements in both cases prove to concur, see below). Obviously the truth of $\tau < \upsilon$ does not depend on the choice of the representatives T and W; therefore one may choose them so that T is itself a section of W.

We show that $<$ is an order relation in the usual sense (§ 8, **2**). $<$ is irreflexive because W is not similar to a section of itself, according to Theorem 14 of § 10, **5**. $<$ is also transitive because a section of a section of W is itself a section of W. Hence $<$ is asymmetrical; for the conjunction of $\tau < \upsilon$ and $\upsilon < \tau$ would imply $\tau < \tau$, contrary to irreflexivity.

This involves the need of a new symbol $>$ for expressing $\tau < \upsilon$ by starting with υ, just as in § 5, **1**; $\upsilon > \tau$ is read "υ is *greater* than τ".

So far the properties of the order relation are based chiefly on Theorem 14 of § 10. For types in general the situation is different because an ordered set S may be similar to a section of S; $\overline{S} = {}^*\omega + n$ and $\overline{S} = \eta$ are simple instances.

What is still missing is the *connexity* of $<$, i.e. the comparability of ordinals: either $\tau < \upsilon$ or $\upsilon < \tau$ for $\tau \neq \upsilon$. This follows from Theorem 8 of § 10, but we shall not use it until we prove it by a new method (Theorem 3, below).

Definition I clearly settles the succession of *finite ordinals* in the ordinary sense, hence also in conformity with the order of finite *cardinals*. Therefore it does not matter for the truth of the statement $m < n$ whether the finite numbers m and n are conceived as cardinals or ordinals. Furthermore, we easily obtain without using comparability

THEOREM 1. $\sigma + \upsilon > \sigma$ *holds for every* σ *and every* $\upsilon \neq 0$. *Conversely, if* $\tau > \sigma$ *there exists a* $\upsilon \neq 0$ *such that* $\tau = \sigma + \upsilon$. $\sigma + 1$ *is the s e - q u e n t of* σ; *that is to say, there is no ordinal* υ "*between*" σ *and* $\sigma + 1$ (*i.e. such that* $\sigma < \upsilon < \sigma + 1$). ω *is the least transfinite ordinal and every other transfinite ordinal is of the form* $\omega + \upsilon$ *with* $\upsilon \neq 0$. *Every finite ordinal is less than every transfinite ordinal.*

Proof. (Cf. Theorem 1 of § 5.) If $S + W$ is a representative of $\sigma + \upsilon$ then the first member of W determines the section S, which means $\sigma < \sigma + \upsilon$. On the other hand, if $\tau > \sigma$, i.e. if the well-ordered set T of the ordinal τ has a section of the ordinal σ, then T can be written as an ordered sum $T = S + W$ with $\overline{S} = \sigma$, $\overline{W} = \upsilon \neq 0$, hence $\tau = \sigma + \upsilon$; if in particular W is a unit-set we have $\tau = \sigma + 1$, and in general $\tau > \sigma$ implies $\tau \geqslant \sigma + 1$, as follows through considering the first member of W, i.e. the member of T which determines the section S.

Furthermore, by Theorem 11 of § 10 every transfinite ordinal σ can be written as $\omega + \sigma_1$; hence either $\sigma = \omega$ or $\sigma > \omega$, i.e. ω is the least transfinite ordinal. Finally, $n < \omega$ (n finite) follows from Definition I, and the conjunction of $n < \omega$ and $\omega \leqslant \sigma$ gives $n < \sigma$, which completes the proof.

While every ordinal has a uniquely fixed sequent, ordinals such as ω, $\omega \cdot 2$, $\omega \cdot \omega$ are not sequents of ordinals. Yet if $n \neq 0$ is finite then each of the ordinals n, $\omega + n$, $\omega \cdot 2 + n$, etc. has an immediate predecessor whose sequent it is; if v is the sequent of τ we write $\tau = v - 1$ (without hereby defining an operation of subtraction), hence $(v - 1) + 1 = v$.

DEFINITION II. An ordinal v which is the sequent of an ordinal τ is called an *isolated* ordinal, or of the *first kind*; one writes $\tau = v - 1$. Other ordinals $v \neq 0$ are called *limit-numbers*, or of the *second kind*.

Accordingly, a given ordinal a is either 0 or isolated or a limit-number. In the latter case a is the sequent of a non-empty set S of ordinals β in which there is no maximum; one writes $a = \lim \beta$. However, S is not determined by a; for instance, if $a = \omega$ we may take for S the set of all finite ordinals or of all even or of all prime numbers, etc. Additional illustrations and precision are given in **2** (Theorems 2, 4, 6) and **3**.

2. The Comparability of Ordinals. Without using Theorem 8 of § 10 we prove the fundamental

THEOREM 2. *The set of all ordinals which are less than a given ordinal a can be ordered after the magnitude of its members (Definition I). This ordered set, denoted by $W(a)$, is well-ordered and has the type (ordinal) a.*

First we illustrate the theorem by a few instances. $W(0) = O$ since no ordinal is less then 0, and in fact $\overline{O} = 0$. $W(1) = (0)$, and $\overline{(0)} = 1$. If n is any finite ordinal we have $W(n) = (0, 1, \ldots, n - 1)$, which set has the ordinal n. The ordered set of all finite ordinals, i.e. of all ordinals $< \omega$ (Theorem 1), is the sequence $(0, 1, 2, \ldots)$ and has the ordinal ω. The set of all ordinals less than $\omega + 1$ is $W(\omega + 1) = (0, 1, 2, \ldots \omega)$, and $\overline{W(\omega + 1)} = \omega + 1$.

As the first instances show, for finite a the simple form of the theorem depends on the admission of the null-set, which was not yet introduced by Cantor.

Proof of Theorem 2. Let A be any well-ordered set of the ordinal a. By Definition I, $\mu < a$ means that A has a section of the ordinal μ — incidentally one section only (Theorem 14 of § 10). Therefore, if μ_1 and μ_2 are different ordinals $< a$, they are the types of different sections of A; by the (almost trivial) Theorem 3 of § 10 one of these sections is a section of the other, hence $\mu_1 < \mu_2$ or $\mu_2 < \mu_1$. (This result, reached without comparability, is due to the assumption that both ordinals are less than the same ordinal a.) The transitivity of this order also follows from Theorem 3. Hereby we have obtained the ordered set $W(a)$ of all ordinals $< a$.

We are now going to establish a similar mapping of $W(a)$ onto the well-ordered set A. To any $\mu \epsilon W(a)$, i.e. to any $\mu < a$, we relate the $a \epsilon A$ that determines the section of A which has the ordinal μ; this correspondence is biunique, for according to Definition I a given $a \epsilon A$ determines a section of A whose ordinal is less than $a = \overline{A}$. Finally, the correspondence is similar. For let a_1, a_2 be different members of A, say $a_1 \prec a_2$, and μ_1, μ_2 their respective images in $W(a)$; then $\mu_1 < \mu_2$ (hence $\mu_1 \prec \mu_2$ in $W(a)$) holds true because the section of A determined by a_1 is a section of the section determined by a_2.

Thus we have shown that $W(a) \simeq A$; since A is well-ordered and of the ordinal a the same applies to $W(a)$, as Theorem 2 maintains.

Readers who have gone over the proof of Theorem 8 of § 10 will notice the intrinsic analogy between that proof and the present one, though the latter is much easier. In fact Theorem 2 will yield comparability by providing *standard sets* of a given ordinal.

Theorem 2 allows to write all members of a well-ordered set A in the form a_μ where the index μ assumes all ordinals less than $\overline{A} = a$; μ is the member of $W(a)$ which in our proof was related to a_μ. This notation is a natural generalization of writing *sequences* as (a_k) where k ranges over the non-negative integers, i.e. over the ordinals less than ω.

An important consequence of the theorem is the possibility of *directly defining ordinals*, viz. of conceiving an ordinal a as the well-ordered set $W(a)$ of all ordinals less than a. (Hitherto ordinals, as a particular kind of types, were only defined by a process of abstraction as outlined in § 8, **4**.) Hence it is sufficient to introduce a single symbol for the least ordinal 0; this may be denoted by the null-set O. Hereby ordinals, i.e. numbers, are represented as *sets*, as implied in the beginning of § 2. For instance, the ordinals 0, 1, 2, 3, 4, ... are then written in the form

$$O$$
$$\{O\}$$
$$\{O, \{O\}\}$$
$$\{O, \{O\}, \{O, \{O\}\}\}$$
$$\{O, \{O\}, \{O, \{O\}\}, \{O, \{O\}, \{O, \{O\}\}\}\}$$
·
·
·

The set containing all (denumerably many) sets of this kind is ω, and $\omega + 1$ is the set which, besides the members of ω, also contains ω itself as a member.

These plain sets may also be regarded as (well-)ordered sets; ordering them by magnitude is easy since, of any two different ordinals, one is both a member and a proper subset of the other. Moreover, any ordinal $\mu < a$ (i.e., $\mu \epsilon a$) is just the section of a determined by μ. However, this theory of ordinals, developed first by J. von Neumann in 1923 [1]), requires, in addition to the definition by transfinite induction (Theorem 7 of § 10), a further "axiom of infinity" which may roughly be formulated as

Axiom of Substitution or of Replacement (VIII). **For any set S and any single-valued function f with a free variable x there exists the set that contains just the members $f(x)$ with $x \epsilon S$.**

For a stricter formulation and for the use of the axiom in set theory see *Foundations*, chapter II, §§ 5–8 (especially p. 85). The axiom fulfils many other purposes, all of a more specific character than those fulfilled by Axioms I–VII. In the following we shall not explicitly refer to its use.

To derive comparability from Theorem 2, let a and β be two ordinals. Instead of comparing *any* well-ordered sets of the ordinals a and β as done in § 10, 3, we now compare the *particular* sets of ordinals $W(a)$ and $W(\beta)$. Either "begins" with the members 0, 1, 2, etc. and we are going to show that this coincidence of the members continues as far as possible, namely until at least one of the sets is exhausted.

Let V be the well-ordered intersection of $W(a)$ and $W(\beta)$. V is an *initial* of both sets because, for any $v \epsilon V$, every member of $W(a)$ preceding v belongs to $W(\beta)$ and vice versa, hence also to V. We distinguish between the cases $V = W(a)$ and $V \subset W(a)$.

In the first case $W(a)$ is either $= W(\beta)$, i.e. $a = \beta$, or a proper initial — hence a section — of $W(\beta)$, which means $a < \beta$.

If $V \subset W(a)$ then V is a section of $W(a)$. Since $V \subseteq W(\beta)$, it would seem as if again there arose an alternative between $V = W(\beta)$ and $V \subset W(\beta)$. $V = W(\beta)$ means that $W(\beta)$ is a section of $W(a)$, hence $\beta < a$. But $V \subset W(\beta)$ is *impossible*, for then V were also a section of $W(\beta)$, i.e. the ordinal v of V were $< a$ *and* $< \beta$, hence $v \epsilon V$, while $V = W(v)$

---

[1]) Von Neumann 23; also 25, 28, 28a. Cf. Quine 41, Stein 60. — For an axiomatic introduction of ordinals, independently of ordered sets and types, see Tarski 25b and Lindenbaum–Tarski 26.

contains only ordinals less than v. (Cf. the corresponding impossibility in the fourth case of the scheme at the end of § 10, 3.) Hence

THEOREM 3 (COMPARABILITY OF ORDINALS). *Of two different ordinals one is less than the other.*

This theorem coincides with Theorem 8 of § 10. In the terminology of § 10 our theorem says: if $W(a)$ and $W(\beta)$ are not similar then one of them is similar to a section of the other. With the present notation the scheme used in § 10, **3** assumes the form:

1) $v = a$, $v = \beta$, hence $a = \beta$;
2) $v = a$, $v < \beta$, hence $a < \beta$;
3) $v < a$, $v = \beta$, hence $\beta < a$;
4) $v < a$, $v < \beta$: impossible.

For the following, a few additional theorems on *sets of ordinals* are needed.

THEOREM 4. *Any set of ordinals the members of which are ordered by magnitude is well-ordered. Hence every set of ordinals contains a least ordinal.*

Proof. Let R be such an ordered set, R_0 a non-empty subset of R, and ϱ an arbitrary member of R_0. The (ordered) intersection I of R_0 and $W(\varrho)$ is empty only if ϱ is the *first* member of R_0. Otherwise I, being a subset of the well-ordered set $W(\varrho)$, has a first member which is also the first member of R_0. Hence in either case R_0 has a first member, which proves the theorem.

THEOREM 5. *Given a set R of ordinals ordered by magnitude, the ordered sum of the members of R is either greater than each member of R or equal to a member of R, namely to the greatest among its members.*

Proof. Otherwise, in view of comparability, there ought to be in R an ordinal ϱ greater than the sum σ, which itself is an ordinal (by Theorem 4, and Theorem 10 of § 10). Thus, by passing from ordinals to suitable set-representatives, we would have a set of the ordinal σ which is similar to a section of a set of the ordinal ϱ, while the latter set is a subset of the former. But this contradicts Theorem 14 of § 10.

Remarks. First, if the sum equals one of its terms, this clearly is the maximum among the terms; hence, if R contains no maximum, the sum exceeds each ordinal of R. (Cf. Theorem 7 of § 6; here the situation is simpler because the members of R are known to be comparable.) Moreover, Theorem 5 clearly remains true if the terms of the sum are given not as the members of a set but as assigned to the members of a well-ordered auxiliary set T (cf. Definition V of § 8); this slight generalization leaves room for equal terms in the sum.

THEOREM 6. *To every set R of ordinals there exist still greater ordinals, in particular a sequent, i.e. the least of all ordinals that exceed those of R.*

Proof. R either contains a greatest ordinal (maximum) μ, or else for each $\varrho \in R$ there is a greater one in R. In the first case $\mu + 1$ is the sequent. In the second case let σ be the ordered sum of the members of R ordered by magnitude; then σ is greater than each member of R. If, among the members of $W(\sigma + 1)$, σ_0 is the least that exceeds all members of R, then σ_0 is the sequent of R.

We use Theorem 6 to illustrate Definition II (end of subsection 1). One easily sees that the sequent of R is a limit-number if and only if R contains no maximum. In the notation $a = \lim \beta$ for limit-numbers the set S of ordinals β was not fixed. A universal method is choosing $S = W(a)$, hence writing $a = \lim_{\beta < a} \beta$; yet from Theorem 6 we infer that any set S of increasing ordinals without maximum does as well, a denoting the sequent of S. In other words, every set of ordinals which is confinal with $W(a)$ may replace $W(a)$. If β_ν ranges over such a set then we write for short $a = \lim \beta_\nu$, or simply $a = \lim \beta_\nu$.

In view of Theorem 6 we may express Theorem 2 also in the following form:

THEOREM 7 (COROLLARY TO THEOREM 2). *A set of ordinals that contains, besides any member v, also all ordinals $< v$, can be ordered by magnitude. This ordered set W is well-ordered and its ordinal a is the sequent of its members*: $W = W(a)$ with $a = \overline{W}$.

This form is more far-reaching than Theorem 2, for it does not *start* with a, which ordinal instead *emerges* from the given "initial". Besides the application made of the theorem in 3 for constructing Cantor's series of ordinals, it is also a suitable starting-point for von Neumann's inductive definition of ordinals outlined above.

It might seem as if Theorem 7 could simply be expressed in the form "any initial W of the ordered set of *all* ordinals is well-ordered...". However, Theorem 6 (or 7) reveals the shocking result:

The totality of all ordinals does not constitute a set.

In fact, if it were a set, by ordering its members according to magnitude we would obtain a well-ordered set whose ordinal were *greater than any ordinal*, hence including itself.

For the third time, after the antinomy of Russell (§ 5, 3) and the antinomy of the set of all cardinals (§ 6, 7), we have unintentionally arrived at a contradiction, *the antinomy of the set of all ordinals* called after *Burali–Forti*. (See *Foundations*, p. 9.) It is the earliest (1895/97) of the modern so-called logical antinomies and — like the antinomy of § 6, 7 to which it shows a remarkable analogy — derives from technical set-theoretical arguments, in contrast with Russell's antinomy which is based on logical arguments only. The contradictory character in these instances, particulary those of the sets of all cardinals and of all ordinals, arises from conceiving them as sets, which then may serve as members of other sets, and not as mere totalities or classes (see the end of § 1). However, the assumption that they constitute sets only leans on accepting Cantor's definition of set as the basis of set theory, to which definition the totalities mentioned conform. If, as in the present book, set theory is explicitly or implicitly based on axioms which restrict the extent of the set concept (for instance, the seven or eight axioms introduced here, or other axiom systems as described in chapters II and III of *Foundations*) then the totalities in question cannot be proven to constitute sets and assume the character of "classes" which are not available for membership. Hereby they cease producing mathematical contradictions.

When speaking of the totality of all ordinals in subsection 3 we shall call it not "set" but "series"; by this term we also hint at the succession of ordinals according to magnitude.

3. Exponentiation. The Series of Ordinals.

In § 8 (end of subsection 7) the difficulties connected with the multiplication of infinitely many order-types and with the exponentiation of types were outlined. The situation is in principle not different for ordinals, nevertheless their *exponentiation* must be considered here in detail. General products may be introduced in the same way, yet they have less practical importance.

We begin with a remark regarding definitions and proofs by transfinite induction, as far as ordinals are concerned. When the ordinals less than a fixed ordinal $a_0 \neq 0$ are considered it is often useful to distinguish between the cases that a_0 is of the first (isolated) or of the second kind (a limit number); see Definition II above. This is just the differentiation made in the proof of Theorem 7 of § 10 (about definition by transfinite induction); there we distinguished between the cases that the initial i_0 has a last member or not. To an isolated ordinal a_0 we proceed from its immediate predecessor $a_0 - 1$, to a limit-number a_0 from a set of increasing ordinals whose sequent is a_0. Hence, instead of generally defining σ^a ($a \neq 0$) as the least ordinal $\geq \sigma^\beta \cdot \sigma$ for $\beta < a$ [1]), we prefer the following formulation (which was introduced by Cantor without a justification of inductive definition).

DEFINITION III. If σ is a given ordinal > 1 the power $p(a) = \sigma^a$ is inductively defined by

a) $p(0) = \sigma^0 = 1$,

b) $p(a) = p(a - 1) \cdot \sigma = \sigma^{a-1} \cdot \sigma$ for isolated a,

c) $p(a) = \lim_{\beta < a} p(\beta) = \lim_{\beta < a} \sigma^\beta$ for limit-numbers $a = \lim \beta$.

In addition, $1^a = 1$, $0^a = 0$ for $a > 0$.

In c), $\beta < a$ means that β ranges over $W(a)$ or another set of increasing ordinals β whose sequent is a.

To illustrate this definition we remark: For finite $a = n$ the definition clearly concurs with the "elementary" definition valid for any types ϱ (VII of § 8), which conceives ϱ^n as obtained by repeated multiplication. If the base $\sigma = m$ is finite and > 1 then m^ω is, according to c), the sequent of the set of all finite ordinals m^n for $n < \omega$, hence $m^\omega = \omega$. Similarly ω^ω is defined as the sequent of the set of all powers ω^n ($n < \omega$); since $1 + \omega + \omega^2 + \ldots + \omega^n = \omega^n$ we may also write $\omega^\omega = 1 + \omega + \omega^2 + \ldots + \omega^k + \ldots$. Furthermore

$$n^{\omega + 1} = n^\omega \cdot n = \omega \cdot n, \quad \omega^{\omega + 1} = \omega^\omega \cdot \omega.$$

Definition III, which usually serves for introducing powers of ordinals (for another method see below), requires some additional explanation in view of our method of defining by transfinite induction (Theorem 7 of § 10). This theorem does not directly yield the existence of our function $p(a)$; for the rules b) and c) are based upon two conditions regarding which no provision is made in that theorem: b) makes sense only provided $p(a - 1)$ is an ordinal, and c) requires that, for a limit-number a, the values of $p(\beta)$ with $\beta < a$ form a set of increasing ordinals without a maximum; otherwise the expression $\lim_{\beta < a} p(\beta)$ would be meaningless.

To guarantee that a function $p(a)$ satisfying these conditions exists, we may introduce a Definition III* which determines a function in full accordance with Theorem 7 of § 10 and then prove that this $p(a)$ has indeed the properties stated in Definition III. For instance, we may stipulate that $p(a - 1) \cdot \sigma$ in b) means an arbitrary ordinal when

---

[1]) In just this form one can define a product of ordinals σ_λ which are assigned to the members λ of $W(\mu)$ with a fixed μ, the "exponent of the product".

$p(a-1)$ is not an ordinal, and that $\lim p(\beta)$ in c) means an arbitrary ordinal when the set of all $p(\beta)$ contains a maximum (or not ordinals). Then p is uniquely defined for any ordinal a provided it is defined for the ordinals $< a$, whatever the values for these ordinals may be.

Now the properties of p are easily established. All values of p prove to be ordinals and the expressions $p(a-1) \cdot \sigma$ and "the sequent of all $p(\beta)$ for $\beta < a$" have their ordinary meanings. Furthermore, p is a *monotonic function* (cf. below), i.e. the inequality $\gamma < \delta$ implies $p(\gamma) < p(\delta)$, as may be shown by induction with respect to δ. Hence p is in accordance with the rules of Definition III; the uniqueness of the function described by this definition follows from the fact that all values of *any* such function p' are ordinals and that p', accordingly, has the properties required by III* — which, by Theorem 7 of § 10, determines p' uniquely. This completes the proof that Definition III is admissible.

Definition III* may also be introduced in other ways; for instance, as defining $p(a)$ to equal 1, $\mu \cdot \sigma$, or the limit of the set of all $p(\beta)$ with $\beta < a$ respectively, according as the latter set is empty, contains a maximum μ, or contains ordinals without a maximum. That the function defined hereby is the function described by Definition III can be proven as above, except that the proof of the uniqueness must now use the monotony of any such function.

A more general and comprehensive treatment of definitions by transfinite induction, which includes general products of ordinals, was given by Kuratowski and Mostowski.[1])

Besides the inductive introduction of powers of ordinals originating from Cantor, Hausdorff and Hessenberg paved the way to a direct definition. In § 8, 7 we outlined the difficulty of defining products of infinitely many *order-types*, caused by the impossibility of lexicographically ordering the respective Cartesian products. The seemingly obvious device of instead considering the maximal orderable subsets of the Cartesian product is impracticable because there are different such subsets and their properties are unfit for the purpose. Nevertheless Hausdorff succeeded in defining quasi-products of types; in § 8, 7 it was pointed out that they remain short of the goal. Still the specialization to products of infinitely many *ordinals*, in particular to powers of ordinals,[2]) yields relatively simple results; it turns out that hereby one obtains just the powers (and products) defined above inductively. We refrain from entering into this rather involved subject and refer interested readers to the literature.[3])

Just as infinite products and powers of types in general, also powers

---

[1]) Kuratowski–Mostowski 52, in particular p. 198. The exposition of the subject in this Polish textbook is rendered in English in Sierpiński 58, notably chapter XIV, §§ 15–17. Cf. also Montague 55.

[2]) In this case one may also lean on the (slightly generalized) representation of ordinals in the normal form (Theorem 11 of § 11), as done by Hessenberg.

[3]) The theory originates from Hausdorff 06–07I, cf. Hessenberg 07 and Wrinch 20. Systematic expositions are found in the textbooks Hausdorff 14 (chapter VI) and Sierpiński 58 (chapter XIV).

(and products, too) of ordinals *cannot be interpreted cardinally*, no matter which way the power is defined; more presicely, if $\overline{\sigma} = s$ and $\overline{a} = a$, in general the cardinal of σ^a is less than s^a. As follows from previous remarks, this drawback is not due to transfinite induction or special properties of ordinals but derives from the intrinsic nature of ordered sets and their types which excludes comprehensive enough ordered products.

That in general $\overline{\sigma^a} < \overline{\sigma}^{\overline{a}}$ is shown by the examples given above. For 2^ω we have $\overline{\sigma}^{\overline{a}} = 2^{\aleph_0} = \aleph$ while $\overline{2^\omega} = \overline{\omega} = \aleph_0 < \aleph$. (Here the symbol 2 for the base denotes first the ordinal and then the cardinal.) As to ω^ω, we have $\overline{\omega}^{\overline{\omega}} = \aleph_0^{\aleph_0} = \aleph$; that nevertheless $\overline{\omega^\omega} = \aleph_0$ may be shown directly by arranging all positive integers after the type ω^ω, as follows.

1; 2, 3, 5, 7, 11, ...
4, 6, 10, 14, ...; 9, 15, 21, ...; 25, 35, 55, ...; ...
8, 12, 20, ...; 18, 30, 42, ...; ...; 27, 45, 63, ...; ...; 125, ...
16, 24, 40, ...; 36, 60, ...; ...; 54, ...; ...; 81, ...
. . . . .

After 1, the prime numbers follow according to magnitude, then all products of 2, 3, ... (equal or different) primes; to arrange the products of n primes among themselves we write the factors in the order of increasing magnitude and let the products succeed according to the magnitude of the first different corresponding factors. Since evidently the set of all integers preceding 2^k has the type (ordinal) ω^{k-1}, the entire set has the type

$$1 + \omega + \omega^2 + \ldots + \omega^k + \ldots = \omega^\omega.$$

By b) and c) of Definition III the function $p(a) = \sigma^a$, for $\sigma > 1$, has the properties
 A) $p(a_1) < p(a_2)$ for $a_1 < a_2$
 B) $p(\lim_\nu a_\nu) = \lim_\nu p(a_\nu)$.
A function $p(a)$ of ordinals with these two properties is called a *normal function*.[1]) (Disregarding A) we obtain the more general concept of a

---

[1])   For the early use of this concept, which was introduced by Veblen 08, see Jacobsthal 09 and 09a (cf. Sudan 31), Hausdorff 14, pp. 114ff. For recent developments and generalizations, cf. H. Bachmann 50, Ackermann 51, Neumer 51, Schütte 54. A comprehensive exposition of the theory of normal functions of ordinals is given in H. Bachmann 55, §§ 5 and 7.

continuous function of ordinals.[1])) The concept of normal function is to a large extent analogous to that of monotonic and continuous function in analysis and has won great significance for the arithmetic of ordinals. $\sigma + a$ and $\sigma \cdot a \, (\sigma \neq 0)$ are normal functions of a but not $a + \sigma$ (for $\sigma \neq 0$), $a \cdot \sigma$ (for $\sigma > 1$), a^2 (cf. Theorem 8 in **4**); for instance, $\lim_{n} n^2 = \omega$ and not $= \omega^2$. Every normal function $p(a)$ satisfies the inequality $p(a) \geqslant a$; cf. the proof of Theorem 11.

We conclude this survey of exponentiaton by proving, by means of transfinite induction, the *formal laws*

(1) $$a^\beta \cdot a^\gamma = a^{\beta + \gamma},$$

(2) $$(a^\beta)^\delta = a^{\beta\delta}.$$

Since the multiplication of (types and) ordinals is not commutative, no analogue to the arithmetical law $a^c \cdot b^c = (ab)^c$ and its generalization for cardinals (§ 7, **4**) can be expected; even in a case as simple as $a = \omega$, $b = c = 2$, we have $\omega^2 \cdot 2^2 \neq (\omega \cdot 2)^2 = \omega \, (2 \cdot \omega) \, 2 = \omega^2 \cdot 2.$[2])

We sketch the proofs, leaving slight completions to the reader. Incidentally, for $\gamma = 1$, (1) becomes the rule b) of Definition III.

Let in (1) a and β be fixed ordinals; we prove the equality by transfinite induction with respect to γ (where $\gamma \, \epsilon \, W(\overline{\gamma})$ for an arbitrary $\overline{\gamma}$), using a) – c) of Definition III.

(1) is true for $\gamma = 0$ since $a^0 = 1$ by a). We assume (1) to be true for all ordinals less than a given $\gamma_0 \neq 0$ and prove it for γ_0.

If γ_0 is isolated, hence $\gamma_0 = (\gamma_0 - 1) + 1$, then (1) holds by assumption for $\gamma = \gamma_0 - 1$; therefore, by the rule b) and the associative law,

$$a^\beta \cdot a^{\gamma_0} = a^\beta (a^{\gamma_0 - 1} \cdot a) = (a^\beta \cdot a^{\gamma_0 - 1}) a = a^{\beta + (\gamma_0 - 1)} \cdot a = a^{(\beta + \gamma_0) - 1} \cdot a = a^{\beta + \gamma_0};$$

for $\beta + \gamma_0$, too, is isolated and is the sequent of $\beta + (\gamma_0 - 1)$.

---

[1])   For their properties cf. Sierpiński 52.

[2])   In this context it is worth mentioning that Fermat's Last Theorem, constituting a still unsolved problem for integers (cf. § 2, **2**), can easily be *refuted* for ordinals; more precisely, the equation $\xi^\lambda + \eta^\lambda = \zeta^\lambda$ has, for every ordinal $\lambda \neq 0$, ordinal solutions ξ, η, ζ even above any given bound. See Sierpiński 50; the proof is given separately for λ being finite, transfinite of the first kind, and of the second kind. In the same paper Goldbach's conjecture is refuted for ordinals; $\omega + 10$ is the least even ordinal which is not the sum of two primes (see below p. 212).

Before we prove the truth of (1) for limit-numbers γ_0, let us remark that the following equalities are easily seen to hold true:

(3) $$\kappa + \lim_{\nu} \lambda_\nu = \lim_{\nu} (\kappa + \lambda_\nu), \quad \kappa \cdot \lim_{\nu} \lambda_\nu = \lim_{\nu} (\kappa \lambda_\nu).$$

Hence for a limit-number $\gamma_0 = \lim_{\nu} \gamma_\nu$, the assumption that (1) holds for all ordinals $< \gamma_0$ yields in view of the rule c):

$$a^\beta \cdot a^{\gamma_0} = a^\beta \cdot \lim a^{\gamma_\nu} = \lim (a^\beta \cdot a^{\gamma_\nu}) = \lim a^{\beta + \gamma_\nu} =$$
$$= a^{\lim (\beta + \gamma_\nu)} = a^{\beta + \lim \gamma_\nu} = a^{\beta + \gamma_0}.$$

Hereby the proof of (1) is completed, and (2) is proven quite analogically. Accordingly we have, for instance,

$$(\omega^\omega)^\omega = \omega^{\omega^2}, \quad (\omega^{\omega^n})^\omega = \omega^{\omega^{n+1}}.$$

Now we are sufficiently prepared for the *series of ordinals*, one of Cantor's most daring and most beautiful achievements, which constitutes his "continuation of the series of real integers beyond the infinite" (see p. 3) [1].

By Theorem 7, which is the basis for each single step in constructing the series of ordinals, the sequence of the integers is followed by the ordinal ω of this sequence. Similarly the set of all ordinals $\omega \cdot k + l$ with $k = 0, 1$ and $l = 0, 1, 2, \ldots$ is followed by ω^2, and the sequence $(\omega, \omega^2, \ldots, \omega^n, \ldots)$ by $\lim \omega^n = \omega^{\lim n} = \omega^\omega$. Thus, if k, l, m_k denote finite ordinals, the series begins with

$$0, 1, 2, \ldots, k, \ldots \omega, \omega + 1, \ldots, \omega + k, \ldots \omega \cdot 2, \omega \cdot 2 + 1, \ldots \omega \cdot 3,$$
$$\ldots, \omega \cdot k + l, \ldots \omega^2, \ldots, \omega^2 + \omega \cdot k + l, \ldots \omega^2 \cdot k, \ldots \omega^3, \ldots \omega^k,$$
$$\ldots, \omega^k \cdot m_k + \omega^{k-1} \cdot m_{k-1} + \ldots + m_0, \ldots \omega^\omega, \ldots \omega^\omega \cdot k, \ldots \omega^{\omega+1},$$
$$\ldots \omega^{\omega \cdot k}, \ldots \omega^{\omega^\omega}, \ldots \omega^{\omega^{\cdot^{\cdot^\omega}}}, \ldots$$

Like in arithmetic, ω^{ω^ω} means the power $\omega^{(\omega^\omega)}$, and not $(\omega^\omega)^\omega$ which equals ω^{ω^2}; it is the sequent of the sequence $(\omega, \omega^\omega, \omega^{\omega^2}, \omega^{\omega^3}, \ldots)$.

---

[1]   The constructive character of the process becomes still more obvious in the light of the *geometrical* construction of a comprehensive class of transfinite ordinals given by Haenzel 34.

The sequent of the set of all ordinals hinted at above is also the sequent of the confinal sequence

$$(1, \omega, \omega^\omega, \omega^{\omega^\omega}, \ldots, \omega^{\omega^{\cdot^{\cdot^{\cdot^\omega}}}}, \ldots);$$

it is usually denoted by ε_0. According to Definition III, c) we conclude that ω^{ε_0} is the sequent of the sequence $(\omega, \omega^\omega, \omega^{\omega^\omega}, \ldots)$, i.e. $\varepsilon_0 = \omega^{\varepsilon_0}$. Cantor called any solution ε of the equation $\omega^\varepsilon = \varepsilon$ an *epsilon-number* [1]); accordingly, ε_0 is the least epsilon-number [2]).

Contrary to what might be expected, we shall prove in subsection **5** that all ordinals mentioned here are types of *denumerable* sets.

Let us again survey the construction of the "series of ordinals". Owing to the comparability of ordinals (Theorem 3) and to the unique determination of the sequent of every "initial" (as the ordinal of the initial; see Theorem 7), the series can be continued according to a well-defined law without restriction and without danger of furcating into different incomparable directions. Thus Cantor's idea of continuing the process of counting beyond ω has been carried out in a completely rigorous way; instead of a hazy notion of infinity we have obtained distinct and comparable transfinite ordinals which, moreover, can be utilized to "enumerate" the members of any well-ordered set through the procedure exhibited in the proof of Theorem 2.

4. Arithmetic of Ordinals. Abundant material regarding the arithmetic of ordinals has accumulated from Cantor to our days, and it is still increasing. The reader interested in details is referred to more comprehensive sources [3]); we shall restrict ourselves to general inequalities and inverse operations, including a few results required for the following subsection.

THEOREM 8. (INEQUALITIES BETWEEN ORDINALS.)
A. (*Monotony laws.*) If a, σ, τ are ordinals and $\sigma < \tau$, then
1) $a + \sigma < a + \tau$,
2) $\sigma + a \leqslant \tau + a$,

---

[1])   For a related kind of ordinals, the "delta-numbers", see Sudan 46.

[2])   For a set of arithmetical functions with the type ε_0 see Skolem 57.

[3])   Besides Hausdorff 14 and 27 (English edition, 1957), H. Bachmann 55 and Sierpiński 58 (chapter XIV; for alephs, chapter XV) contain a great wealth of arithmetical statements.

3) $a\sigma < a\tau$ if $a \neq 0$,

4) $\sigma a \leqslant \tau a$.

B. (*Cancellation laws.*) *Conversely we have*

1) $a + \sigma < a + \tau$, *or* $\sigma + a < \tau + a$, *implies* $\sigma < \tau$,

2) $a + \sigma = a + \tau$ *implies* $\sigma = \tau$,

3) $a\sigma < a\tau$, *or* $\sigma a < \tau a$, *implies* $\sigma < \tau$,

4) $a\sigma = a\tau$ *implies* $\sigma = \tau$ *if* $a \neq 0$.

C. *If* $\kappa < \lambda$ *and* $\sigma < \tau$, *then*

1) $\kappa + \sigma < \lambda + \tau$,   2) $\kappa\sigma < \lambda\tau$.

Proof. To A. By Theorem 1, $\sigma < \tau$ means the existence of a $\xi \neq 0$ such that $\sigma + \xi = \tau$; hence 1) means $a + \sigma < a + \sigma + \xi$, 3) means $a\sigma < a(\sigma + \xi) = a\sigma + a\xi$, and both inequalities are true by Theorem 1. As to 2) and 4), let A, S, T be sets of the ordinals a, σ, τ respectively such that A and T are disjoint and S is a section of T. Then we have for the ordered sums and Cartesian products

$$S + A \subset T + A, \quad S \times A \subseteq T \times A.$$

(The equality refers to $A = O$.) But this expresses $\sigma + a \leqslant \tau + a$, $\sigma a \leqslant \tau a$ in view of comparability (cf. the Remark on p. 191).

One cannot improve 2) and 4) so as to obtain strict inequalities, as shown by the examples $0 + \omega = n + \omega$, $1 \cdot \omega = n \cdot \omega$ (n finite and $\neq 0$).

To B. 1) – 4) follow from A 1) – 4) in view of the comparability of ordinals (and of the properties of equality by which $\sigma = \tau$ implies $a + \sigma = a + \tau$, etc.). On the other hand, from $\sigma + a = \tau + a$, or $\sigma a = \tau a$, one cannot draw any conclusion regarding the order between σ and τ, as shown by the above examples.

To C. 1) follows from A1) and 2), 2) from A3) and 4). For instance, $\kappa + \sigma < \kappa + \tau \leqslant \lambda + \tau$. The assumption $\kappa \neq 0$ clearly becomes superfluous. (Note that the analogues to the multiplicative inequalities do not hold true in the arithmetic of integers, where negative integers exist.)

THEOREM 9. (SUBTRACTION.) *If* $\sigma < \tau$ *then the equation* $\sigma + \xi = \tau$ *has a uniquely determined solution* ξ *which is written as* $\xi = -\sigma + \tau$. *On the other hand, the equation* $\xi + \sigma = \tau$ *is not generally solvable.*

Proof. The first statement follows from Theorem 1 and (for the uniqueness) from B2) of Theorem 8. The second statement is evident for $\sigma > \tau$ and is, for $\sigma < \tau$, illustrated by instances such as $\xi + n = \omega$ with n finite $\neq 0$; more generally, the equality has no solution if one of the ordinals σ, τ is isolated and the other a limit-number. (The contrast derives from the fact that different ordinals always are "co-initial" but not "confinal".) If in the second equation $\sigma = 1$, its solvability means that τ is isolated and $\xi = \tau - 1$ (Definition II at the end of 1).

If the equation $\xi + \sigma = \tau$ *is* solvable then it is not uniquely solvable, except for finite τ. For instance, $\xi + \omega^2 = \omega^2 \cdot 2$ has the solutions ω^2, $\omega^2 + n$, $\omega^2 + \omega$, etc.

THEOREM 10. (DIVISION.) *For any given ordinals σ and δ ($\delta \neq 0$) there is a single pair of ordinals κ, ϱ such that*

(1) $$\sigma = \delta\kappa + \varrho \text{ with } \varrho < \delta.$$

Obviously $\kappa = 0$ if and only if $\sigma < \delta$.

In particular ($\delta = \omega$) there is a uniquely determined finite ordinal r such that

(2) $$\sigma = \omega\kappa + r.$$

This theorem is analogous to the arithmetical theorem, fundamental in multiplicative number theory, that states: if s and d are positive integers, there is a single pair of non-negative integers q, r such that $s = dq + r$ where the remainder r is less than the divisor d.

Proof of Theorem 10 [1]). Our first aim is to form a product with the left-hand factor (divisor) δ which exceeds the dividend σ; for this purpose the right-hand factor $\tau = \sigma + 1$ will do, for by $\delta \geqslant 1$ and A4) in Theorem 8

$$\delta\tau = \delta(\sigma + 1) \geqslant \sigma + 1 > \sigma.$$

Let D and T be disjoint well-ordered sets of the types δ and τ respectively. To obtain a set-representative of $\delta\tau$ we lexicographically order the Cartesian product whose members are the ordered pairs (t, d) with $t \in T$, $d \in D$ (see Definition VII of § 8) and denote this *well-ordered* set with $D \times T$; then $\overline{D \times T} = \delta\tau$. On account of $\sigma < \delta\tau$ there is a certain section S of $D \times T$ which has the type σ; the member determining this section shall be denoted by (t_0, d_0). According to the order in $D \times T$, S contains all pairs (t, d) with $(d \in D$ and) $t \prec t_0$ in T, and in addition the pairs (t_0, d) with $d \prec d_0$ in D.

---

[1])   Division for *general types* naturally is much more intricate than for ordinals. We refer the reader to Sierpiński 48, Ginsburg 55, and the literature cited in these papers.

Now let κ be the type (ordinal) of the section of T determined by t_0, ϱ the type of the section of D determined by d_0. In view of the properties of the section S of $D \times T$ we have

$$\overline{S} = \sigma = \delta\kappa + \varrho,$$

where $\varrho < \delta$.

This representation of σ, with the left-hand divisor δ and with $\varrho < \delta$, is *unique*. For assume

$$\delta\kappa_1 + \varrho_1 = \delta\kappa_2 + \varrho_2. \quad (\varrho_1 < \delta, \varrho_2 < \delta)$$

If $\kappa_1 \neq \kappa_2$, say $\kappa_1 < \kappa_2$ and accordingly $\kappa_1 + 1 \leqslant \kappa_2$, then on account of A3) and A2) in Theorem 8 we would obtain

$$\delta\kappa_1 + \varrho_1 = \delta\kappa_2 + \varrho_2 \geqslant \delta(\kappa_1 + 1) + \varrho_2 = \delta\kappa_1 + (\delta + \varrho_2),$$

which by B1) and B2) implies $\varrho_1 \geqslant \delta + \varrho_2$, contrary to our assumption. Hence $\kappa_1 = \kappa_2$, and by B2) $\varrho_1 = \varrho_2$.

The last statement of the theorem rests upon the fact that the ordinals $< \omega$ are finite. From this statement results

COROLLARY. *An ordinal is a limit-number if and only if it is leftwards divisible by ω, i.e. if in* (2) $r = 0$.

Theorem 10 deals only with left-hand division by δ. Right-hand division is certainly not unique, as shown by $1 \cdot \omega = 2 \cdot \omega = \ldots = \omega$. Cf. exercise 3) at the end of § 11.

By taking $\delta = 2$ in (1), we obtain a distinction between *even* and *odd* ordinals 2κ and $2\kappa + 1$. A limit-number is not only even but left-hand-divisible by *every* finite ordinal $\neq 0$ (and by ω), for otherwise it would be isolated according to (1).

Similarly as in arithmetic we derive from Theorem 10 the so-called *algorithm of Euclid*, whose availability for ordinals is not self-evident; the point is that the process terminates after a finite number of steps. Starting from the ordinals σ and δ ($\delta \neq 0$), the algorithm has the well-known form [1])

---

[1]) The "continued fraction" defined by the quotients $\kappa, \kappa_1, \ldots, \kappa_n$ is conceived by Hausdorff 06–07I, pp. 145ff. as representing the "rational ordinal" $\dfrac{\sigma}{\delta}$; the correspondence formed hereby is biunique. For a theory of rational ordinals see Zakon 55.

$$\sigma = \delta\kappa + \delta_1 \qquad (\delta_1 < \delta)$$
$$\delta = \delta_1\kappa_1 + \delta_2 \qquad (\delta_2 < \delta_1)$$

$$\cdot$$
$$\cdot$$
$$\cdot$$

$$\delta_{n-2} = \delta_{n-1}\kappa_{n-1} + \delta_n \qquad (\delta_n < \delta_{n-1})$$
$$\delta_{n-1} = \delta_n\kappa_n.$$

After finitely many steps a divisor δ_{n-1} must emerge which is divisible by the corresponding remainder δ_n, for otherwise we would obtain an infinite sequence of *decreasing* ordinals δ_k, contrary to Theorem 4.

An ordinal $\sigma > 1$ is called a *prime number* if it cannot be decomposed into a product of two ordinals each of which is less than σ. [1]). It is easily seen that every ordinal > 1 can be decomposed into a product of finitely many prime numbers. However, this decomposition is not unique; for instance, $\omega \cdot \omega = (\omega + 1)\,\omega$ although both ω and $\omega + 1$ are evidently prime.

As to divisors in general, an ordinal has only finitely many right-hand divisors [2]) but may have infinitely many left-hand divisors; cf. the example of p. 211 and exercise 3) at the end of § 11.

Another feature known from arithmetic, called by Cantor *the normal form of ordinals* [3]), shall be treated in detail because we are going to use it in the following subsection.

THEOREM 11. *Every ordinal* $\sigma \neq 0$ *can be uniquely represented in the form*

(3) $$\sigma = \omega^{\beta_1} \cdot \gamma_1 + \omega^{\beta_2} \cdot \gamma_2 + \ldots + \omega^{\beta_k} \cdot \gamma_k$$

where $k, \gamma_1, \gamma_2, \ldots, \gamma_k$ *are finite ordinals* $\neq 0$ *and the exponents satisfy the inequalities*

(4) $$\beta_1 > \beta_2 > \ldots > \beta_k \geqslant 0.$$

---

[1]) For a distinctive definition of "indecomposable" and "prime" ordinals (for the multiplicative decomposition of ordinals) see the comprehensive survey in H. Bachmann 55, §§ 19 and 20. For unique decompositions cf. Sieczka 24.

[2]) This is not the case for general types; for instance, the denumerable type η has $\aleph$ right-hand divisors (§ 9, 3 and exercise 4) on p. 174). While η has only five left-hand divisors, namely 1, η, $1 + \eta$, $\eta + 1$, $1 + \eta + 1$, Sierpiński 50a shows that there are denumerable types with even more-than-denumerably many left-hand divisors.

[3]) Cantor 1897, p. 237. In Zakon 54 the normal form is used for the concept of "similarity" between transfinite ordinals. For the rôle of epsilon-numbers in the normal form cf. Kaluza Jr. 50.

Obviously this representation is analogous to the decadic (or g-adic, for integers $g \geqslant 2$) representation of integers by the scale of 10 in arithmetic. For every number σ one has finitely many (k) terms, the exponents β_n are decreasing, and the coefficients γ_n are less than the base (here ω, in arithmetic 10 or g). β_1 is called the *degree* of σ; we shall see that the degree is $\leqslant \sigma$. (Contrary to arithmetic, $\beta_1 = \sigma$ can happen, e.g. for $\sigma = \varepsilon_0 = \omega^{\varepsilon_0}$, see p. 208.)

Theorem 11 holds also true, and is proven quite analogically, if the base ω is replaced by any transfinite or finite base $a \geqslant 2$, in which case $\gamma_n < a$; yet for applications the base ω is most important. For $a = 2$, already $\sigma = \omega$ equals its degree: $\omega = 2^\omega$.

Proof of Theorem 11. We begin with proving that for every β

(5)
$$\omega^\beta \geqslant \beta.$$

Using transfinite induction, we first see that (5) is true for $\beta = 0$. β_0 given, assume (5) to hold for all $\beta < \beta_0$. If β_0 is isolated and $\geqslant 2$ then we have

$$\omega^{\beta_0} = \omega^{\beta_0 - 1} \cdot \omega \geqslant (\beta_0 - 1)\, \omega > (\beta_0 - 1) + 1 = \beta_0, \text{ i.e. } \omega^{\beta_0} > \beta_0,$$

which is also true for $\beta_0 = 0, 1$. For limit-numbers $\beta_0 = \lim \beta_\nu$ we infer from c) of Definition III:

$$\omega^{\beta_0} = \lim \omega^{\beta_\nu} \geqslant \lim \beta_\nu = \beta_0, \text{ i.e. } \omega^{\beta_0} \geqslant \beta_0.$$

$\omega^{\varepsilon_0} = \varepsilon_0$ shows that here $\geqslant$ cannot be replaced by $>$. Hence (5) is true for all β. (5) holds also if ω is replaced by any base > 1. — The proof may also be conducted by using Theorem 12 of § 10.

Since, by (5), $\omega^{\sigma+1} \geqslant \sigma + 1 > \sigma$ there exists a *least* ordinal δ such that $\omega^\delta > \sigma$. This δ cannot be a limit-number since then $\xi < \delta$ implies $\xi + 1 < \delta$, hence $\omega^{\xi+1} \leqslant \sigma$ and $\omega^\xi < \sigma$, from which by c) of Definition III follows

$$\omega^\delta = \lim_{\xi < \delta} \omega^\xi \leqslant \sigma,$$

contrary to the assumption $\omega^\delta > \sigma$.

Hence δ is isolated and by the definiton of δ we have for $\beta_1 = \delta - 1$:

(6)
$$\omega^{\beta_1} \leqslant \sigma < \omega^{\beta_1 + 1}.$$

By Theorem 10 there are ordinals γ_1 (> 0) and σ_1 $(< \omega^{\beta_1})$ such that

$$(7) \qquad\qquad \sigma = \omega^{\beta_1} \cdot \gamma_1 + \sigma_1.$$

Hence by (6): $\omega^{\beta_1} \cdot \gamma_1 < \omega^{\beta_1 + 1}$, and by B3) of Theorem 8: $\gamma_1 < \omega$, i.e. γ_1 is finite and $\neq 0$.

If $\sigma_1 = 0$ then $\sigma = \omega^{\beta_1} \cdot \gamma_1$ is the representation desired. If $\sigma_1 > 0$ we deal with σ_1 in the same way as above with σ and thus obtain successive equalities of the form (7)

$$(8) \qquad\qquad \sigma_1 = \omega^{\beta_2} \cdot \gamma_2 + \sigma_2, \quad \sigma_2 = \omega^{\beta_3} \cdot \gamma_3 + \sigma_3, \ldots$$

where β_n is determined by σ_{n-1} as is β_1 by σ. Accordingly we have $\sigma \geqslant \omega^{\beta_1} > \sigma_1 \geqslant \omega^{\beta_2} > \sigma_2 \geqslant \omega^{\beta_3} > \ldots$, hence

$$\beta_1 > \beta_2 > \beta_3 > \ldots .$$

Since a sequence of decreasing ordinals is necessarily finite, the process terminates after finitely many steps by yielding a $\sigma_n = 0$; moreover, all γ_n are finite and $\neq 0$.

From (7) and (8) emerges the representation (3) of Theorem 11; it still remains to prove its uniqueness. The assumption

$$(\sigma =) \omega^{\beta_1} \cdot \gamma_1 + \ldots + \omega^{\beta_k} \cdot \gamma_k = \omega^{\overline{\beta}_1} \cdot \overline{\gamma_1} + \ldots + \omega^{\overline{\beta}_{\overline{k}}} \cdot \overline{\gamma_{\overline{k}}}$$

first implies $\overline{\beta}_1 = \beta_1$; for $\overline{\beta}_1 > \beta_1$, hence $\overline{\beta}_1 \geqslant \beta_1 + 1$, would mean $\sigma \geqslant \omega^{\beta_1 + 1}$, which is impossible in view of (6).

Secondly, $\overline{\beta}_1 = \beta_1$ implies $\overline{\gamma}_1 = \gamma_1$; for $\overline{\gamma}_1 > \gamma_1$, i.e. $\overline{\gamma}_1 = \gamma_1 + \gamma_1^*$ with $\gamma_1^* \neq 0$, would enable us, on account of B2) of Theorem 8, to suppress $\omega^{\beta_1} \cdot \gamma_1$ on both sides and to obtain

$$\omega^{\beta_2} \cdot \gamma_2 + \ldots = \omega^{\overline{\beta}_1} \cdot \gamma_1^* + \omega^{\overline{\beta}_2} \cdot \overline{\gamma_2} + \ldots$$

which is impossible because of $\beta_2 < \beta_1$. This argumentation can be continued up to the last conclusion $\overline{k} = k$, which completes the proof of Theorem 11.

The normal form of ordinals leads to the notion of *natural sum* introduced by Hessenberg.[1]) Let the ordinals σ and τ be represented as in Theorem 10

$$\sigma = \sum_n \omega^{\beta_n} \cdot \gamma_n, \quad \tau = \sum_n \omega^{\beta_n} \cdot \delta_n.$$

---

[1]) Hessenberg 06, Jacobsthal 09a; cf. the exposition in H. Bachmann 55, § 23. For recent applications in algebra see Carruth 42 (with the literature annexed) and Sikorski 50.

Since either sum contains finitely many terms only, we may use the same exponents β_n, admitting coefficients $\gamma_n = 0$ and $\delta_n = 0$. The natural sum of σ and τ is defined as

$$\mathfrak{S}(\sigma, \tau) = \sum_n \omega^{\beta_n}(\gamma_n + \delta_n).$$

Hence $\mathfrak{S}(\sigma, \tau) = \mathfrak{S}(\tau, \sigma)$ because the γ_n and δ_n are finite. In general, the natural sum coincides with neither of the ordered sums $\sigma + \tau$, $\tau + \sigma$. For instance, if $\sigma = \omega^3 + \omega$, $\tau = \omega^2$, we have

$$\mathfrak{S}(\sigma, \tau) = \omega^3 + \omega^2 + \omega, \quad \sigma + \tau = \omega^3 + \omega^2, \quad \tau + \sigma = \omega^3 + \omega,$$

which sums are different from each other.

In **5** we shall require the following property of natural sums: For a given ordinal ϱ, *there exist finitely many pairs σ, τ only such that* $\mathfrak{S}(\sigma, \tau) = \varrho$. To prove this let the normal forms of ϱ, and of some σ and τ, be

$$\varrho = \sum_n \omega^{\alpha_n} \cdot \lambda_n, \quad \sigma = \sum_n \omega^{\beta_n} \cdot \gamma_n, \quad \tau = \sum_n \omega^{\delta_n} \cdot \varepsilon_n.$$

It easily follows from Theorem 11 that $\mathfrak{S}(\sigma, \tau) = \varrho$ entails the equations $\lambda_n = \gamma_n + \varepsilon_n$, where the required solutions γ_n, ε_n are also finite (as is λ_n). But for a given n, this equation clearly has only a finite number of solutions γ_n, ε_n; since the number of equations is also finite the proof of our statement is completed.

5. Alephs, Number-Classes, Initial Numbers.

In this subsection we restrict ourselves to some fundamental theorems and a few others which are important for the applications; for additional material see the references at the beginning of **4**. Some of the following proofs are given in an abridged form; the reader, experienced at this stage, will complete them without difficulty. As to definitions by transfinite induction as used, for instance, for the series of alephs, cf. the remarks above in **3**.

The cardinal of an infinite well-ordered set is called an *aleph* [1]). The comparability of alephs is an immediate consequence of the comparability of ordinals (Theorem 3).

---

[1]) Aleph ($\aleph$), the first letter of the Hebrew alphabet, was introduced by Cantor for this purpose. So far we have used $\aleph_0$ for the cardinal of an enumerated (hence well-ordered) set, and therefore of any denumerable set. $\aleph$, however, was used for the cardinal of the continuum which is not well-ordered; regarding this use see **6** and **7**.

THEOREM 12. *The cardinals (alephs) of two well-ordered sets are either equal or one is less than the other.*

Proof. Let S and T be well-ordered sets with the ordinals σ and τ and the cardinals s and t. According to Theorem 3 we have either $\sigma = \tau$ or $\sigma < \tau$ or $\tau < \sigma$. In the first case S and T are similar, all the more equivalent, i.e. $s = t$. In the second case S is similar to a section of T, i.e. S is equivalent to a subset of T; hence by Theorem 4 of § 5, either $s = t$ or $s < t$. The third case is analogous and yields $t = s$ or $t < s$, which completes our proof.

Thus the "fourth" case of incomparability of cardinals (see § 5, **4** and **5**) is excluded for well-ordered sets. According to our proof, $\sigma = \tau$ implies $\overline{\sigma} = \overline{\tau}$, and $\sigma < \tau$ implies $\overline{\sigma} \leqslant \overline{\tau}$, while vice versa $\overline{\sigma} < \overline{\tau}$ implies $\sigma < \tau$ and $\overline{\sigma} = \overline{\tau}$ is compatible with each of the cases $\sigma = \tau$, $\sigma < \tau$, $\tau < \sigma$. Written in a scheme:

if	$\sigma = \tau$	$\sigma < \tau$	$\overline{\sigma} = \overline{\tau}$	$\overline{\sigma} < \overline{\tau}$
then	$\overline{\sigma} = \overline{\tau}$	$\overline{\sigma} \leqslant \overline{\tau}$	no conclusion	$\sigma < \tau$

We have, for instance, $\omega < \omega^2 < \omega^\omega$ while $\overline{\omega} = \overline{\omega^2} = \overline{\omega^\omega} = \aleph_0$.

The set of all ordinals which have a given aleph c as their cardinal, ordered by magnitude, is called *the number-class of* c and denoted by $Z(c)$. (Notations introduced by Cantor; number $=$ *Zahl* in German.) The *least* ordinal of $Z(c)$ is called *the initial number* of c (or of $Z(c)$). Every initial number is a limit-number; for otherwise it would possess an immediate predecessor which ought to have the same cardinal.

For finite cardinals the concept of number-class is trivial because there is only a single ordinal corresponding to a given finite cardinal (§ 8, **4**). After Cantor one calls the ordered set of all finite ordinals *the first number-class* and the ordered set of all denumerable ordinals $Z(\aleph_0)$ *the second number-class* [1]); the initial number of $Z(\aleph_0)$ is ω, in this context also written ω_0. $Z(\aleph_0)$ is a subset of the set $T(\aleph_0)$ of all denumerables types, and generally $Z(c)$ a subset of $T(c)$ (Theorem 2 of § 8). According to Theorem 5 of § 8 we have $\overline{\overline{Z(\aleph_0)}} \leqslant \aleph$.

---

[1]) The monograph Denjoy 46–54 chiefly deals with this number-class. Kurepa 53 represents its members (ordinals) as sets of rational numbers.

For an axiomatic characterization of the second number-class and problems connected herewith see Church 27; cf. already Veblen 05. Kleene 36, 38, 44, Church–Kleene 37, Church 38, Neumer 51 and 53–54, Spector 55 are some of the papers dealing with the intricate problems of constructibility in the second number-class.

An important property of the second number-class is stated by

THEOREM 13. *The sequent of a sequence D $(\overline{D} = \omega)$ of increasing ordinals of the first and the second number-classes belongs to the second number-class.*

Proof. This is an almost immediate consequence of Theorems 5 and 6. The sum $\sigma = \sum_n \delta_n$ of the members δ_n of D $(n = 1, 2, \ldots)$ is greater than each δ_n. On the other hand (see p. 145) $\overline{\sigma} \leqslant \aleph_0^2 = \aleph_0$ since the sum has $\aleph_0$ terms each of which has a cardinal $\leqslant \aleph_0$; but σ is transfinite, hence $\overline{\sigma} = \aleph_0$, which completes the proof.

Theorem 13 shows that all ordinals constructed above in 3 belong to $Z(\aleph_0)$; among them, for instance,

$$\omega^\omega = \lim_n \omega^n, \ \varepsilon_0 = \lim (\omega, \omega^\omega, \omega^{\omega^\omega}, \ldots).$$

If τ is any denumerable ordinal then the well-ordered set $W(\tau)$ (see Theorem 2) has the ordinal τ; hence $W(\tau)$ is denumerable. On the other hand, according to Theorem 7, the well-ordered set of *all* ordinals of the first two number-classes is $W(\omega_1)$ where ω_1 denotes the sequent of *all* denumerable ordinals; hence ω_1 is a non-denumerable ordinal. Therefore $\overline{\omega}_1$ is the aleph that immediately succeeds $\aleph_0$ by magnitude; it is denoted by $\aleph_1$, and ω_1 is its initial number. The cardinal (aleph) of the second number-class $Z(\aleph_0)$ is $\aleph_1$; for by Theorem 2, $\overline{W(\omega_1)} = \omega_1$, hence $\overline{\overline{W(\omega_1)}} = \overline{\omega}_1 = \aleph_1$, and clearly (cf. Theorem 5 of § 3) $W(\omega_1) \sim Z(\aleph_0)$. This is a particular case of a general statement (Theorem 16, below).

THEOREM 14. *Every set of alephs ordered according to magnitude is well-ordered. To every such set (all the more to every single aleph) there exist greater alephs, in particular a uniquely determined s e q u e n t aleph.*

This theorem on alephs conforms to Theorems 4 and 6 in 2 which state the same properties for ordinals. The term "sequent" has the same meaning as in 2.

Proof. The first statement is evident since the alephs may be replaced by the respective initial numbers, whereby we obtain a well-ordered set of ordinals. Let A be any set of alephs ordered by magnitude and B the set which contains all ordinals belonging to an aleph of A, as well as all smaller ordinals. B is a set of ordinals satisfying the condition of Theorem 7 in 2; if $\beta = \overline{B}$ we have $B = W(\beta)$, hence β is greater than all ordinal of B and $\bar{\beta}$ is an aleph exceeding all members of A. Clearly $\bar{\beta}$ is even the aleph-sequent [1]) of the members of A, for the initial number of every aleph less than $\bar{\beta}$ is contained in B.

Remarks. First, in a sense similar to the way in which ordinals were explicitly defined in 2, viz. as certain sets which ultimately refer to the null-set, *alephs can now be defined as initial numbers*, in view of the one-to-one correspondence between an aleph c and the initial number of $Z(c)$. According to the well-ordering theorem (see 6) this yields an explicit definition of cardinals in general. *Thus cardinals can be introduced independently*, while in § 4, 5 they were introduced only as "cardinals of sets" by the rather involved process of abstraction.

We have not used Cantor's theorem (2 of § 5) or Theorem 7 of § 6 for the proof of Theorem 14 because we are not yet able to demonstrate that the cardinals resulting from those theorems are indeed alephs.

Furthermore, Theorem 14 enables us to produce the *series of alephs* in the same sense as the series of ordinals was derived from Theorems 6 and 7 in 3. Beginning with the least aleph $\aleph_0$ we thus obtain the series

$$\aleph_0, \aleph_1, \ldots, \aleph_n, \cdots \aleph_\omega, \aleph_{\omega+1}, \cdots \aleph_{\omega \cdot 2}, \cdots$$

Each aleph is denoted by the letter $\aleph$ with an ordinal-index. $\aleph_\alpha < \aleph_\beta$ corresponds to $\alpha < \beta$, and $\aleph_\tau$ ($\tau \neq 0$) is the least aleph that exceeds all $\aleph_\sigma$ with $\sigma < \tau$. In other words, the index α of $\aleph_\alpha$ is the ordinal of the (well-ordered) set of all initial numbers preceding the initial number of $\aleph_\alpha$. (This may be taken as the definition of the indices α, whence we infer that $\alpha < \beta$ implies $\aleph_\alpha < \aleph_\beta$.) The initial number of $\aleph_\alpha$ is usually denoted by ω_α; we also write ω_0 for ω (p. 216).

Unfortunately, the analogy to the series of ordinals also produces the analogous antinomy. *There exists no set that contains all alephs* because otherwise there would be a greater aleph, by Theorem 14.

Theorem 13 can now be extended to the form: a well-ordered set of a type $< \omega_1$, the members of which are increasing ordinals $< \omega_1$, has a sequent which is also $< \omega_1$. This formulation can be generalized from ω_1 to any initial number ω_ν whose index ν is an isolated ordinal; see exercise 14) at the end of this section. Yet the statement does not generally remain true for limit-indices ν; for instance not for ω_ω. In fact $\lim\limits_n \omega_n$ ($n = 0, 1, 2, \ldots$) is not less than ω_ω but equals ω_ω. Any initial number for

---

[1]) This term has to be used because we cannot speak of "the sequent" of plain cardinals as long as the comparability of cardinals has not been proved (which will be done in 7).

which it holds true is called a *regular* (otherwise, *singular*) *initial number*. Besides the ω_ν with isolated ν, also ω_0 is regular, for every finite sequence of increasing finite ordinals has a finite sequent. An old and famous problem is whether there exist *regular initial numbers with a limit-index*, which are also called *inaccessible ordinals*; for these ordinals and the corresponding cardinals see *Foundations*, pp. 87f. (and 329ff.).

The *arithmetic of alephs* is far simpler than the arithmetic of plain cardinals. The reader is advised to consult the literature given at the begining of **4**; a few fundamental equalities only are proven here.

THEOREM 15. *If* σ *and* τ *are ordinals with* $\sigma \leqslant \tau$ *then*

(1)
$$\aleph_\sigma \cdot \aleph_0 = \aleph_\sigma \cdot \aleph_\sigma = \aleph_\sigma,$$

(2)
$$\aleph_\sigma + \aleph_\tau = \aleph_\sigma \cdot \aleph_\tau = \aleph_\tau,$$

(3)
$$\sum_{\xi \leqslant \sigma} \aleph_\xi = \aleph_\sigma;$$

if σ *is a limit number then we can replace* (3) *by the stronger*

(4)
$$\sum_{\xi < \sigma} \aleph_\xi = \aleph_\sigma;$$

(5)
$$\aleph_\sigma{}^{\aleph_\tau} = 2^{\aleph_\tau}.$$

Proof. While the first equality (1) is almost trivial the second is rather profound. (2) – (5) follow easily from (1).

According to the Corollary to Theorem 10 we may write the initial number of $\aleph_\sigma$ in the form $\omega_\sigma = \omega \cdot a$. By transition to the corresponding alephs we obtain

$$\aleph_\sigma = \aleph_0 \cdot \overline{a}, \ \aleph_\sigma \cdot \aleph_0 = \aleph_0^2 \cdot \overline{a} = \aleph_0 \cdot \overline{a} = \aleph_\sigma.$$

Hence also for every finite n we have $\aleph_\sigma \cdot n = \aleph_\sigma.$

To prove [1]) $\aleph_\sigma{}^2 = \aleph_\sigma$ we start from $\overline{W(\omega_\sigma)} = \omega_\sigma$, hence $\overline{\overline{W(\omega_\sigma)}} = \aleph_\sigma.$ Therefore the product $\aleph_\sigma \cdot \aleph_\sigma$, i.e. the cardinal of a corresponding Cartesian product, may be considered to be the cardinal of the set P of all ordered pairs (ξ, ζ) where both ξ and ζ range over $W(\omega_\sigma)$. We shall prove that P has a cardinal $\leqslant \aleph_\sigma$, hence the cardinal $\aleph_\sigma$.

For this purpose we use the natural sums (see the end of **4**)

$$\mathfrak{S}(\xi, \zeta) = \sum_n \omega^{\kappa_n} (x_n + z_n) \quad (x_n, z_n \text{ finite})$$

---

[1]) First proven by Hessenberg 06 (chapter XX) and 07. Cf. Lindenbaum–Tarski 26, pp. 308ff. and Zorn 44. A proof by transfinite induction is given in Hausdorff 14, pp. 127f.

corresponding to the members ξ, ζ of $W(\omega_\sigma)$, each sum arranged according to decreasing powers of ω and therefore containing a finite number of terms only with $x_n + z_n \neq 0$. The first term in $\mathfrak{S}(\xi, \zeta)$ is $\omega^{\kappa_1}(x_1 + z_1)$ where at least one of the finite ordinals x_1, z_1 is $\neq 0$; hence

$$\mathfrak{S}(\xi, \zeta) < \omega^{\kappa_1}(x_1 + z_1 + 1).$$

Since $\xi < \omega_\sigma$ and $\zeta < \omega_\sigma$ it easily follows that also $\mathfrak{S}(\xi, \zeta) < \omega_\sigma$.

Hence we obtain all $(\xi, \zeta) \in P$ by taking all ξ and ζ the natural sums of which assume values $\lambda < \omega_\sigma$. For a *given* λ there are *finitely many* solutions of the equation $\mathfrak{S}(\xi, \zeta) = \lambda$, as shown at the end of **4**. Since the set of all $\lambda < \omega_\sigma$ has the cardinal $\aleph_\sigma$, the set of all solutions has a cardinal which does not exceed $\aleph_\sigma \cdot \aleph_0 = \aleph_\sigma$; this completes the proof of $\aleph_\sigma^2 = \aleph_\sigma$. Therefore $\aleph_\sigma^n = \aleph_\sigma$ for every finite n.

(2) immediately follows from (1) in view of

$$\aleph_\sigma + \aleph_\tau \leqslant \aleph_\tau \cdot 2 = \aleph_\tau, \quad \aleph_\sigma \cdot \aleph_\tau \leqslant \aleph_\tau^2 = \aleph_\tau.$$

We may transform (2) into a inequality as follows. If $\lambda < \mu$ and $\sigma < \tau$, we distinguish between $\lambda \leqslant \sigma$ and $\sigma < \lambda$. In the first case we have by (2)

$$\aleph_\lambda + \aleph_\sigma = \aleph_\sigma, \quad \aleph_\lambda \cdot \aleph_\sigma = \aleph_\sigma,$$

in the second

$$\aleph_\lambda + \aleph_\sigma = \aleph_\lambda, \quad \aleph_\lambda \cdot \aleph_\sigma = \aleph_\lambda.$$

Hence in either case, on account of $\aleph_\lambda < \aleph_\mu$ and $\aleph_\sigma < \aleph_\tau$,

(2a) $$\aleph_\lambda + \aleph_\sigma < \aleph_\mu + \aleph_\tau, \quad \aleph_\lambda \cdot \aleph_\sigma < \aleph_\mu \cdot \aleph_\tau.$$

In (3) the terms of the sum form a well-ordered set of the type $\sigma + 1$, hence certainly of a cardinal $\leqslant \aleph_\sigma$; since the terms, too, do not exceed $\aleph_\sigma$, the sum is $\leqslant \aleph_\sigma^2 = \aleph_\sigma$. Yet it is also $\geqslant \aleph_\sigma$ because $\aleph_\sigma$ itself is one of the terms. For the same reason the sum in (4) is $\leqslant \aleph_\sigma$; that it *equals* $\aleph_\sigma$ follows from the fact that, σ being a limit-number, the sum exceeds *any* aleph that is less than $\aleph_\sigma$. In particular we have

(4a) $$\aleph_0 + \aleph_1 + \dots + \aleph_n + \dots = \aleph_\omega.$$

To prove (5), we lean on Theorem 2 of § 7 according to which

$$2^{\aleph_\tau} > \aleph_\tau \geqslant \aleph_\sigma.$$

Hence by (1), and by (3) of § 7, **4**

$$2^{\aleph_\tau} = 2^{\aleph_\tau \cdot \aleph_\tau} = (2^{\aleph_\tau})^{\aleph_\tau} \geqslant \aleph_\sigma^{\aleph_\tau}.$$

On the other hand, $2 < \aleph_\sigma$ implies $2^{\aleph_\tau} \leqslant \aleph_\sigma^{\aleph_\tau}$.[1]) Thus the proof of Theorem 15 is completed.

To be sure, (5) is not an equality between alephs since powers of alephs need not be alephs on account of the methods developed so far. This is in accordance with our having used here, save for the aleph-relation (1), only results of the arithmetic of cardinals (§§ 6 and 7).

One may raise the question whether there are alephs $> \aleph_0$ which are neither of the form $\aleph_{\sigma+1}$ nor of the form $c^{\aleph_\tau}$ with a finite or infinite base c. (Cf. § 7, 6.) The answer is in the affirmative; for instance, $\aleph_\omega$ is such an aleph. First, its index is a limit-number. Secondly, since $\aleph_n < \aleph_\omega$, the inequality of König (§ 6, 7) yields in view of (4a)

(4b)
$$\aleph_\omega = \aleph_0 + \aleph_1 + \aleph_2 + \ldots < \aleph_\omega^{\aleph_0}.$$

Now if $\aleph_\omega = c^{\aleph_\tau}$ were true then we would infer by (1)

$$\aleph_\omega^{\aleph_0} = c^{\aleph_\tau \cdot \aleph_0} = c^{\aleph_\tau} = \aleph_\omega$$

contrary to (4b), which proves our statement about $\aleph_\omega$. Hence, in particular, $\aleph_\omega$ *is not the cardinal* $\aleph = 2^{\aleph_0}$ *of the continuum.*

Finally we can now prove

THEOREM 16. *The number-class* $Z(\aleph_\sigma)$, *ordered according to the magnitude of its ordinals, has the cardinal (aleph)* $\aleph_{\sigma+1}$ *and the type (ordinal)* $\omega_{\sigma+1}$.

Proof. $Z(\aleph_\sigma)$ contains the ordinals a which satisfy $\omega_\sigma \leqslant a < \omega_{\sigma+1}$; hence we have, in the sense of ordered addition of ordered sets,

(6)
$$W(\omega_\sigma) + Z(\aleph_\sigma) = W(\omega_{\sigma+1}).$$

If $\overline{Z(\aleph_\sigma)}$ is denoted by ξ, (6) yields by Theorem 2

(7)
$$\omega_\sigma + \xi = \omega_{\sigma+1}, \text{ hence } \aleph_\sigma + \overline{\xi} = \aleph_{\sigma+1}.$$

This shows that $\overline{\xi} \leqslant \aleph_{\sigma+1}$. But $\overline{\xi} < \aleph_{\sigma+1}$ would mean $\overline{\xi} \leqslant \aleph_\sigma$ which, in view of (2) of Theorem 15, contradicts (7). Therefore we have $\overline{\xi} = \aleph_{\sigma+1}$, hence $\xi \geqslant \omega_{\sigma+1}$. Since $\xi > \omega_{\sigma+1}$ is excluded by (7), the proof is completed.

Theorem 16 comprises, as a particular case ($\sigma = 0$), the statement of p. 217 regarding the cardinal of the second number-class $Z(\aleph_0)$. Analogous specializations result for the third number-class $Z(\aleph_1)$, etc.

---

[1]) Cf. Kurepa 54.

6. The Well-Ordering Theorem. Notwithstanding the far-reaching results of the theory of ordered and well-ordered sets, we have not been able to solve the central problem of comparability formulated in § 5: is, of two given different *cardinals*, one less than the other? For *alephs* the question is answered in the affirmative by Theorem 12 above, and this is why the arithmetic of the (types and) cardinals of well-ordered sets is so simple. Because the ghost of incomparability regarding the cardinals of plain sets continued alarming them, Cantor and his successors refrained from endowing these cardinals with the title of *cardinal numbers* and preferred the paler term "power" (*Mächtigkeit*; power of the continuum, etc.) while reserving "cardinal number" for the alephs.

The gap separating the lucid and simple domain of well-ordered sets with their ordinals and cardinals from the vaguer one of other sets will be bridged if every set can be shown to be equivalent to a well-ordered set. This would mean (see below) the

WELL-ORDERING THEOREM. *For any (plain or ordered) set there exists a well-ordered set with the same members.* In short, *any set can be well-ordered.*

The superiority of the first formulation is due to the haziness of the term "can" in the second. What sets *exist* is a well-defined question, to be answered on account of a suitable system of axioms upon which set theory is based; yet "can be well-ordered" is open to subjective inter-pretations. On the other hand, by no means does the theorem maintain that a well-ordered set of the quality desired can be *constructed*, a differ-ence overlooked by most critics of the well-ordering theorem during many years after its first proof in 1904; see below and *Foundations*, pp. 54–59.

The well-ordering theorem may as well be expressed by saying that, given a set S, there exists a well-ordered set which *contains all members of S.* For then the set which contains *just* the members of S is a subset of a well-ordered set, hence also well-ordered. The existence of a well-ordered set *equivalent* to S is sufficient too, because any mapping of the latter onto S yields a well-ordering of S.

Cantor [1]) had called the well-ordering statement a "fundamental logical law of great consequence, noteworthy for its universal validity"; at the same time (1883) he promised to prove it, which promise has never

---

[1]) Cantor 79–84V, § 3. For the history of the theorem, including Jourdain's own (unsuccessful) attempts to prove it, cf. Jourdain 22.

been fulfilled. Also when at the Third International Congress of Mathematicians (1904, just before the publication of Zermelo's proof) an erroneous application of König's inequality (§ 6, 7) seemed to prove the existence of sets which *cannot* be well-ordered, Cantor refused to abandon his conviction.[1]) The first proofs (1904 and 1908) of the theorem by Zermelo constituted one of the most dramatic (and most disputed) events in the history of mathematics and logic.

What Cantor had in mind was an argument of the following type. Take out of S an arbitrary member s_1 as the first, of the remainder $S - \{s_1\}$ any member s_2 as the second, etc.; if S is infinite, then an arbitrary member s_ω of $S - \{s_1, s_2, \ldots, s_k, \ldots\}$ shall be placed after all s_k. Continue in this way according to indices gathered from the series of ordinals, until S is exhausted.

Three objections may be raised against this argument. First, against the use made of the questionable "series of ordinals", with the apparently groundless assumption that the ordinals are sufficient to *exhaust any given set*, however comprehensive it may be. Secondly, against the arbitrary character of the members taken out of S in the successive steps of the above procedure. Finally, against the infinity of choices of members s_ν without a law defining them simultaneously, which seems to ask for an infinite amount of time.

Of these objections, the first is serious and can be met only by a proof which avoids the series of ordinals and ensures that the given set will be indeed exhausted; such a proof will be given below. The second difficulty is nothing new for us; it arose several times, notably in the first proof of Theorem 4 of § 3, in the proofs of Theorems 1, 2, 3 of § 6, etc. The answer in all those cases was the *axiom of choice*, which also answers the present case as will be seen below. To be sure, historically this answer was produced just in connection with the well-ordering theorem, while in other cases the existence of a problem had been overlooked altogether. The third objection has a psychological rather than a logico-mathematical character. In principle, mathematical operations should be imagined not to require time; whenever we apply a procedure which is not arbitrary but defined by a given law, such as the determination of the successive digits in the decimal expansion of π, the result of infinitely many steps is anticipated without scruples. The main psychological difficulty here consists in that every successive step is dependent on the steps taken

---

[2])   See Schoenflies 22, pp. 100ff.

before; this "temporal" uneasiness is also removed by the axiom of choice, which transforms infinitely many *successive* arbitrary steps into *simultaneous* ones, while hereby increasing their multitude far beyond the actual need.

We shall now state the axiom of choice in the form suitable for the present purpose (cf. § 6, 5) [1]).

Principle of Choice. For every set S there exists a "choice-function" f — at least one; in fact many, except for trivial cases — **which assigns uniquely to each non-empty subset S_0 of S a member of S_0: $f(S_0) \in S_0$.**

$f(S_0)$ is called the chosen or *the distinguished member* of $S_0 \subseteq S$ (with respect to f).

This principle is not comprised in the "multiplicative" form introduced in § 6 as Axiom VII, since different subsets of S need not be disjoint. On the other hand, it is not as general as the form mentioned on p. 90 after Axiom VII.

If S is a finite set then the principle can be proven without introducing a new axiom; yet S can anyhow be well-ordered in this case by means of mathematical induction alone.

The set of all non-empty subsets of S has, for an infinite S with $\overline{\overline{S}} = \mathbf{s}$, the cardinal $2^{\mathbf{s}}$ (§ 7, 3). This multitude of choices is provided by our principle whereas actually only $\mathbf{s}$ choices are required, as is shown by the following proof. The excessive multitude is the price paid for simultaneous choices instead of successive ones.

We shall rather closely follow Zermelo's first proof [2]). The well-ordering of S obtained by the (following, or any other) proof essentially depends on the arbitrary choice-function used. There is, then, in general no "standard" well-ordering; hence the well-ordering theorem is useful only for such conclusions as hold true for *any* well-ordering of the given set.

Proof of the Well-Ordering Theorem. Let be given a set S and a choice-function f. In accordance with Zermelo we start with a special tool defined as follows.

---

[1]) B. Levi, E. Schmidt, and E. Zermelo were the first (1902–1904) to state the axiom; Schmidt and Zermelo for the very purpose treated here. For its history and for the derivation of this and more general forms from the multiplicative form (Russell, 1906), see *Foundations*, chapter II, §§ 4, 7, 8.

[2]) Zermelo 04. For his second proof of 1908 see subsection 7. Cf. Tarski 39, also Banaschewski 53. Bernays gave a comparative analysis of these and other proofs, including his own; cf. *Foundations*, p. 117, and Bernays–Fraenkel 58.

A subset Γ of S is called a *gamma-set* (of S, with respect to f) if

a) Γ is well-ordered,

b) for every section A of Γ, determined by $a \in \Gamma$, $f(S - A) = a$.

($S - A$ is the plain set-difference; it cannot be empty, even if $\Gamma = S$, since A is a section of Γ.)

The condition b) shall be illustrated by a few examples. The case $\Gamma = O$ in which both conditions are satisfied vacuously is insignificant. If $c_0 = f(S)$ is the distinguished member of S itself, (c_0) is a gamma-set; for the null-set O is the only section of (c_0), determined by c_0, and in fact $f(S - O) = c_0$. In the same way, denoting $f(S - \{c_0\})$ [1]) by c_1, we obtain the gamma-set (c_0, c_1); it is well-ordered and satisfies the two conditions $f(S - O) = c_0$ and $f(S - \{c_0\}) = c_1$, in accordance with (c_0) being the section of (c_0, c_1) determined by c_1. Thus we perceive that c_0 is the first and c_1 the second member of *any* gamma-set. In addition to all finite gamma-sets $(c_0, c_1, \ldots, c_{n-1})$ where, for each k, $c_k = f(S - \{c_0, c_1, \ldots, c_{k-1}\})$, we obtain the enumerated gamma-set $(c_0, c_1, \ldots, c_n, \ldots) = \Gamma_\omega$; if $\Gamma_\omega \subset S$, we denote $f(S - \Gamma_\omega)$ by c_ω and obtain $\Gamma_{\omega+1} = (c_0, c_1, \ldots c_\omega)$. Every infinite gamma-set, then, has the initial Γ_ω.

As shown by these examples, the condition b) means that any given gamma-set Γ which does not exhaust S, is enlarged to the "sequent" (next greater) gamma-set by including, after the members of Γ, the distinguished member of $S - \Gamma$, which determines the section Γ in the new gamma-set. If S were already well-ordered — which is our intention to achieve — we should consider $S - \Gamma$ to be a *remainder of S*, the distinguished member of which is just its first member.

We now enter the proof, splitting it up into four steps.

I. *Of two different gamma-sets, one is a section of the other.*

Proof. By the comparability of well-ordered sets (Theorem 8 of § 10) the gamma-sets Γ_1 and Γ_2 are either similar or one, say Γ_1, is similar to a section Γ_2' of the other Γ_2. We write $\Gamma_1 \simeq \Gamma_2'$, including the case $\Gamma_2' = \Gamma_2$. Transfinite induction will show that not only $\Gamma_1 \simeq \Gamma_2'$ but even $\Gamma_1 = \Gamma_2'$. The first member of both Γ_1 and Γ_2' is $c_0 = f(S)$, as we saw above. If $\Gamma_1 \neq \Gamma_2'$ then let c_1^* be the *first* member of Γ_1 which (by the mapping of Γ_1 onto Γ_2', see Theorem 13 of § 10) differs from its image c_2^* in Γ_2'.

---

[1])   The different notations (c_0) and $\{c_0\}$ correspond to our considering, in the first case, the (well-)ordered set, in the second the plain set. The same refers to the following instances.

Then the sections C_1 of Γ_1 determined by $c_1{}^*$ and C_2 of $\Gamma_2{}'$ determined by $c_2{}^*$ coincide; hence by condition b)

$$c_1{}^* = f(S - C_1) = f(S - C_2) = c_2{}^*$$

contrary to the assumption $\Gamma_1 \neq \Gamma_2{}'$. Therefore $\Gamma_1 = \Gamma_2{}'$, i.e. either $\Gamma_1 = \Gamma_2$ or Γ_1 is a section of Γ_2.

The identical beginning of any two gamma-sets thus proves to continue until one of them, at least, is exhausted. Hence *two gamma-sets with the common member c also share the sections determined by c*; moreover, if c_1 and c_2 are common to both then *in both sets either $c_1 \prec c_2$ or $c_2 \prec c_1$*.

II. *The totality of the members of all gamma-sets of S can be ordered in such a way that the order-relations existing in the single gamma-sets are retained, and this ordered set is even well-ordered.*

Proof. We start with the union of all gamma-sets; this union can be shown to exist on account of the axioms of power-set, of subsets, and of sum-set on the one hand, of the reduction of (well-) order to membership (§ 8, 2) on the other. An order shall be defined in the union as follows. If s_1 and s_2 are different members of the union belonging to Γ_1 and Γ_2 respectively then, if $\Gamma_1 \neq \Gamma_2$, one is a section of the other according to I, say Γ_1 a section of Γ_2. Hence Γ_2 contains both s_1 and s_2 and we define $s_1 \prec s_2$ in the union if this is their succession in Γ_2. This definition is arbitrary, but that does not matter because in every other gamma-set containing s_1 and s_2 we also have $s_1 \prec s_2$, according to the end of I. Moreover, the order defined is transitive since the same applies to every gamma-set. Thus we have uniquely defined an ordered set, to be denoted by $\sum$.

To show that $\sum$ is *well-ordered* let $\sum_0$ be any non-empty subset of $\sum$, s_0 an arbitrary member of $\sum_0$, and Γ a gamma-set that contains s_0. Then every member of $\sum_0$ which precedes s_0 is also a member of Γ and precedes s_0 in Γ, on account of the order defined in $\sum$ and of the end of I. Hence, if s_0 is not the first member of $\sum_0$ (in which case nothing remains to be proven), the section of $\sum_0$ determined by s_0 is a non-empty subset of Γ and therefore has a first member; this shows that $\sum$ is well-ordered.

III. $\sum$ *is a gamma-set.*

According to II, $\sum$ satisfies the condition a). As to b), let a be any member of $\sum$ and A the section of $\sum$ determined by a. According to the definition of $\sum$, a belongs to a gamma-set Γ, and since all members of $\sum$

which precede a belong to Γ (cf. the end of II), A is also the section of Γ determined by a. Γ satisfies the condition b), i.e. $a = f(S - A)$; but this expresses that $\sum$, too, satisfies the property b), for a was supposed to be an arbitrary member of $\sum$.

$\sum$, being a gamma-set and containing, by its definition in II, the members of all gamma-sets of S, is the maximal (most comprehensive) gamma-set of S (with respect to the choice-function f).

Evidently the proof of III (and of the last part of II) rests upon the possibility of identifying $\sum$, as far as desirable, with a suitable gamma-set, which transmits its properties to $\sum$.

IV. $\sum$ *contains all members of S.*

This property of $\sum$, which derives from its being the maximal gamma-set, shall be proven indirectly. If there existed members of S not belonging to $\sum$, $S - \sum$ were non-empty; we write $f(S - \sum) = z$, which involves that z is not a member of $\sum$. Then the ordered sum $\sum + (z)$ is not only well-ordered but also a gamma-set; the property b) was proven in III for its sections determined by the members of $\sum$, and is also satisfied for the section $\sum$ determined by z, for in this case b) demands $z = f(S - \sum)$ which was the very definition of z. Thus $\sum + (z)$ would be a gamma-set more comprehensive than $\sum$, contrary to III.

In view of the property a), $\sum$ is a well-ordered set which contains *all* members of S; incidentally, *just* these members since every gamma-set of S is a subset of S. Hereby the proof of the well-ordering theorem has been completed.

7. The Comparability of Plain Sets and Cardinals. The most important immediate application of the well-ordering theorem relates to the problem of comparability which has continued engaging us since § 5, so far without much success. Given two plain or ordered sets S and T, we now know that there exist well-ordered sets which respectively contain the same members as S and T. (In point of fact, we only use that they are *equivalent* to S and T.) Since by Theorem 12 these well-ordered sets are comparable regarding their cardinals, the same applies to S and T; in other words, at least one of the sets S and T is equivalent to a subset of the other. Hereby the fourth case with respect to the equivalence relations between sets (§ 5, **4**) is finally eliminated.

COMPARABILITY THEOREM. *Of any two sets, one at least is equivalent to a subset of the other. Hence two cardinals are either equal or one is less than the other.*

Accordingly, the distinction between "cardinal numbers", "powers" of sets, and "alephs" (pp. 68 and 215) becomes unnecessary. Still "aleph" is frequently used whenever the respective set shall be stressed to be well-ordered.

We have derived well-ordering from the axiom of choice, and comparability from well-ordering. A direct proof of comparability based upon the axiom of choice is given later in this subsection. However, these are not one-way tracks; the inverse direction can be taken as well. *The axiom of choice, the well-ordering theorem, and the comparability theorem are equipollent principles*; one of them having been admitted, the two others can be derived from it by means of Axioms I–VI (or part of them).

For the former two principles this is evident. For if the well-ordering theorem is granted and if S is a set of non-empty sets, then any well-ordering of the union $\cup S$ simultaneously well-orders all members of S; hence a function assigning to each $s \in S$ uniquely a member of s is produced by choosing the first member of each s in view of the well-ordering of $\cup S$.

Furthermore, a proof of the well-ordering theorem by means of comparability, without using the axiom of choice, has been given by Hartogs.[1])

The comparability theorem has various consequences for the arithmetic of cardinals. On the one hand, many problems which are difficult or unsolvable by limitation to the methods of §§ 5–7 become simple or even trivial in the light of the arithmetic of alephs (above, subsection 5). On the other hand, the *continuum problem* (§ 5, 2; § 7, 3) now becomes central and urgent; according to comparability, the cardinal $\aleph = 2^{\aleph_0}$ of the continuum must appear in the series of alephs (see 5) and the question arises, where? In the first place, since $2^{\aleph_0} > \aleph_0$, we shall ask whether $2^{\aleph_0} = \aleph_1$ or $> \aleph_1$.[2]) (Without the well-ordering theorem it would be

---

[1]) Hartogs 15; cf. *Foundations*, pp. 58f. For proofs of the well-ordering theorem by means of maximum principles, such as the principle of Zorn, see *Foundations*, pp. 68–70; these principles can be traced back to Hausdorff 14, pp. 140ff.

[2]) $\aleph \geqslant \aleph_1$ can, according to Sierpiński 46/47a (where an argument of Tarski is used), be proved — without the axiom of choice or the two other principles — by means of the following, seemingly evident assumption: the image of a set S obtained by a *unique* mapping cannot have a greater cardinal than S.

conceivable that $2^{\aleph_0}$ were *incomparable* with the alephs.) While this is the particular continuum problem of Cantor, the *generalized continuum problem*, according to § 7, 3, may be formulated [1]) as follows: is, for a given ordinal a, $2^{\aleph_a} = \aleph_{a+1}$ or $> \aleph_{a+1}$? A solution of the continuum problem would have a fundamental significance for the foundations of mathematics in general. The hypotheses $2^{\aleph_0} = \aleph_1$ and $2^{\aleph_a} = \aleph_{a+1}$ respectively are called Cantor's [2]) and the generalized *continuum hypothesis*.[3])

An important progress towards the solution of the problem was made by Gödel's proofs of 1938–40 which show that the generalized continuum hypothesis, as well as the axiom of choice, is *compatible* with suitable axiom systems of set theory; hence the hypothesis cannot be refuted.[4])

A solution of the continuum problem might consist in a proof of the *independence* of the (generalized) hypothesis, meaning that both $2^{\aleph_a} = \aleph_{a+1}$ and $2^{\aleph_a} > \aleph_{a+1}$ are compatible with the axioms of set theory. Except for Gödel's proof of 1938, no actual progress towards solving the problem has been reached during eighty years [5]), until in 1963 Paul J. Cohen, in most ingenious papers, succeeded in proving the independence both of the axiom of choice and of the continuum hypothesis. [6]) However, just these discoveries raise new difficulties in the foundations of mathematics in general. Long before, many interesting results had been proved which connect the continuum hypothesis with other unsolved mathematical problems [7]), in particular statements *equipollent* to the hypothesis in its particular or generalized form. Most of these results are due to Polish mathematicians, led by Sierpiński who in a monograph [8]) systematically exhibited

---

[1])   For other formulations, which are far from being equipollent, see *Foundations*.

[2])   An (implicit) extension of this original hypothesis, namely to $2^{\aleph_1} = \aleph_2$, is contained in Cantor's note 10) to his paper 1879–84V of 1883.

[3])   The conjecture $2^{\aleph_1} = 2^{\aleph_0}$ is called *Lusin's continuum hypothesis;* see Lusin 35.

[4])   See Gödel 40. Cf. the exposition in *Foundations*, ch. II.

[5])   Cf., e.g., Bernstein 38 and the critical remarks of Neumer 53. Also the meta-mathematical attempt of Hilbert 25 was essentially unsuccessful. Baer 29 (§ 5) points out that the continuum hypothesis cannot be deduced from the formal laws of cardinal arithmetic.

[6])   See P. J. Cohen 63–64 (and 63); Gödel 47. Cf. ch. II of the 2nd ed. of *Foundations*.

[7])   Surprisingly also problems of algebra; see, for instance, Baer 30.

[8])   Sierpiński 34/56; in the edition of 1956 more than a dozen subsequent papers of Sierpiński's on the same subject are added. For results of other authors up to 1954 cf. the survey in H. Bachmann 55, particularly §§ 35–37. Of later papers we mention Bruns–Schmidt 55, Popruženko 55, Kapuano 56, de Vries 57, Bagemihl 59; also Tsuchikura 49.

the results obtained up to 1934. The problems in the arithmetic of cardinals which still remain open after comparability is ensured, can for the most part be easily solved by means of the continuum hypothesis; the same applies to some other open problems of abstract set theory [1]) and even of the theory of sets of points.

The proof of the comparability theorem given above, in spite of its being rigorous, suffers from a serious drawback. While it is a fundamental theorem of the arithmetic of *cardinals*, easy to formulate and to comprehend, it is proven not within the theory of cardinals and plain sets but by means of the concept of order and ordered sets, namely on the basis of the comparability of well-ordered sets and of the well-ordering theorem.

True, there are mathematical theorems, also in basic branches such as theory of number or projective geometry, which cannot be proven within the bounds of their proper domain. The incompletability theorem of Gödel (cf. *Foundations*, pp. 303ff.) states this to be a somewhat general situation. However, the comparability theorem is not of this kind; in principle this may be inferred from the fact that (well-)ordering can be reduced to the membership relation (§ 8, 2). Therefore the detour via theory of order made above is not agreeable from the logical or psychological viewpoint.

In fact we shall now give a proof of the comparability theorem which uses the axiom of choice but not the concept of order, let alone well-ordering and the comparability of well-ordered sets. (Those readers who have well grasped the gist of reducing order to membership will perceive that the proof almost grazes the order concept.) The proof has two side advantages: it contains the chief arguments of Zermelo's *second* proof of the well-ordering theorem, which has an abstract logical character and uses nothing from the theory of well-ordered sets and ordinals; instead the proof leans on the fundamental concepts of the *theory of chains* originating from Dedekind [2]).

In a shorter way the comparability theorem can be derived, without the axiom of choice, from a maximum principle such as Zorn's (see p. 228) [3]); implicitly a maximum statement lies at the bottom of the following proof (cf. the part "Ad 2)"). However, in

---

    [1]) Cf., in particular, Tarski 30a.
    [2]) Dedekind 1888; cf. (also for the connection with well-ordering) Hessenberg 09. For Zermelo's second proof see Zermelo 08 and Hausdorff 14, pp. 136–138.
    [3]) See Zorn 44; cf. the penetrating analysis in J. Schmidt 57.

the present elementary exposition of abstract set theory the introduction of a maximum principle seems out of place. Therefore the proof, first published [1]) long before maximum principles had been used, is given in its original shape.

Direct Proof of Comparability. To prove that the plain (non-empty) sets S and T are comparable we show that at least one of them is equivalent to a subset of the other.

Any mapping φ of a subset $S' \subseteq S$ onto a subset $T' \subseteq T$ shall be called a *partial mapping* between S and T; we write $T' = \varphi(S')$. Between every two non-empty sets S, T there exist partial mappings, for instance those which relate a single member of T to a single member of S.

If $T' = \varphi(S')$ and $T'' = \psi(S'')$ are different partial mappings between S and T, then ψ is said to be an *extension* of φ if $S' \subset S''$ and if φ and ψ yield the same images in T for their common domain S'; hence also $T' \subset T''$. That ψ is an extension of φ shall be expressed by

$$\psi \supset \varphi, \text{ or by } \varphi \subset \psi.$$

If, in particular, $\psi \supset \varphi$ and $S'' - S'$ is a *unit-set*, then we call ψ a *simple extension* of φ. Any partial mapping for which an extension exists is called *extensible*.

A set M of partial mappings between S and T is called *monotone* if, of any two different members of M, one is an extension of the other. Hence, if M is monotone and $\varphi_1 \in M$, $\varphi_2 \in M$, then one and only one of the following statements holds true:

$$\varphi_1 \supset \varphi_2, \quad \varphi_2 \supset \varphi_1, \quad \varphi_1 = \varphi_2.$$

Since the relation $\subset$ is transitive we have a natural order from less to more comprehensive partial mappings in a monotone set [2]). (Cf. the use of monotone sets of subsets of A for introducing an order in A, as explained in *Foundations*, pp. 128ff.)

A member (mapping) φ of a set Φ of partial mappings is said to be *comparable in Φ* if, for every other $\psi \in \Phi$, either $\varphi \supset \psi$ or $\psi \supset \varphi$. Hence Φ is monotone if and only if *every* member of Φ is comparable in Φ.

Finally, if Φ is a monotone set of partial mappings between S and T,

---

[1])   In Fraenkel 28, pp. 206–208.
[2])   The monotone sets of partial mappings are particular cases of a more general type of sets, namely of the sets Ψ of partial mappings which satisfy the following condition: any member of S which is disposed of in several partial mappings has the *same image in T* on account of each mapping of Ψ.

the *resultant of* Φ shall be the partial mapping that relates, to each $s \in S$ disposed of in at least one member of Φ, the respective image in T, i.e. the $t \in T$ which is related to $s \in S$ in all members of Φ referring to s.

After these preparations we start the proof. If $T' = \varphi(S')$ is a partial mapping for which $S' \subset S$ and $T' \subset T$, then φ clearly has simple extensions; they are obtained by relating an arbitrary member of $T - T'$ to an arbitrary member of $S - S'$. Hence it will be sufficient to prove that *among the partial mappings between S and T there is at least one which does not admit of a simple extension.* For if $T' = \varphi(S')$ is such a mapping, we have either $S' = S$ or $T' = T$, i.e. φ maps at least one of the given sets onto a subset of the other.

To prove this statement we start, analogically as in the proof of the well-ordering theorem in **6**, with *an arbitrary choice of "distinguished" partial mappings* by choosing, for any *extensible* partial mapping φ between S and T, a uniquely determined "distinguished" simple extension φ^+ of φ. This choice remains fixed throughout the proof. We call φ^+ *the sequent of* φ.

A set Φ of partial mappings is called a *chain* if Φ satisfies the following three conditions:

1) Φ contains a *fixed* partial mapping φ_0. (The simplest way is taking φ_0 as the empty mapping of $O \subset S$ onto $O \subset T$.)

2) If $\varphi \in \Phi$ is extensible then $\varphi^+ \in \Phi$.

3) If Φ_0 is a monotone subset of Φ then the resultant of Φ_0 is a member of Φ.

Similarly as in the expression of the axiom of infinity by two conditions a) and b) (see the end of § 2), our definition of chain does not exclude that Φ contains also other mappings, in addition to those *required* by 1)–3). Such "superfluous" mappings will presently be eliminated.

From the definition of chain it follows that the intersection of different chains is also a chain. Hence, φ_0 and φ^+ having been fixed, a uniquely determined *least* chain exists, namely the *intersection C of all chains* (referring to the sets S and T). We are going to prove that *C is a monotone set*; for this purpose it suffices to show that the set of all members of C which are comparable in C is a chain. Regarding the conditions 1)–3), we obtain:

Ad 1) *Every $\varphi \in C$ is $= \varphi_0$ or $\supset \varphi_0$* (in short $\supseteq \varphi_0$). This is self-evident if the empty mapping is taken for φ_0 (see 1) above), for every non-empty partial mapping is an extension of the empty one. It is also true if any other mapping is chosen for φ_0. For if there existed members of C which are not extensions of φ_0 then they could be dropped from C without altering the fact that C is a chain, and this would yield a chain which is a proper subset of C, contrary to the definition of C. Hence φ_0 *is comparable in* C.

Ad 2) If $\varphi \in C$ is an *extensible* mapping and comparable in C then *also* φ^+ *is comparable in* C. (That $\varphi^+ \in C$ follows from the chain-property 2).)

To prove this we show that the subset $\overline{C} \subseteq C$ of those $\psi \in C$ which for the given φ satisfy either $\varphi \supseteq \psi$ or $\psi \supseteq \varphi^+$, *is a chain*; from this we conclude $\overline{C} = C$ since C is the least chain. That $\overline{C}$ satisfies the conditons 1) and 3) is evident. As to 2), we distinguish between the cases $\varphi \supset \psi$ and $\psi \supseteq \varphi$. In the first case (in which ψ certainly is extensible) we have $\varphi \supseteq \psi^+$, for otherwise, by the comparability of φ in C, we should have $\psi^+ \supset \varphi$ which is incompatible with $\varphi \supset \psi$. Secondly, $\psi \supseteq \varphi$ implies $\psi^+ \supset \varphi$, provided ψ is extensible.

Ad 3) Let C_0 be a monotone subset of C each of whose members is comparable in C. Then *the resultant χ of C_0*, which is a member of C according to the chain-property 3), *is comparable in* C.

To prove this we distinguish between those $\varphi \in C$ which are extensions of *each* member of C_0, and the others, i.e. those $\varphi \in C$ which either belong to C_0 or have extensions belonging to C_0. The φ's of the first kind, save possibly for χ itself, are extensions of χ, whereas for the φ's of the second kind we have $\chi \supseteq \varphi$.

According to these three results, the members of C which are comparable in C form a chain which, since C is the least chain, must equal C. Hence *each* member of C is comparable in C, i.e. the intersection C is a monotone set as we proposed to prove. By the chain-property 3) the resultant $\overline{\varphi}$ of C is a member of C. But *this mapping $\overline{\varphi}$ is not extensible*, for otherwise its sequent $\overline{\varphi}^+$ would also belong to C, contrary to the definition of $\overline{\varphi}$ as the resultant of C.

$\overline{\varphi}$, not being extensible, relates to each member of S or of T an image in the other set; hence at least one of these sets is equivalent to a subset of the other, which completes the proof of the comparability theorem.

Let us finally remark that this proof, like the proof of the well-ordering theorem given in 6, only requires our axioms (I–VI, in addition to the axiom of choice). In particular, the intersection C of all chains exists on account of I–VI.

Exercises (most of them rather difficult)

1) Prove that the type of any ordered set can be changed by adding a

single member. (Hint: consider the maximal well-ordered initial of the set.[1]))

2) Prove that an order-type τ is finite if and only if τ satisfies the following condition: however the position of a single member in a set of the type τ is changed, there always re-emerges the type τ.

3) A set $\sum$ of ordinals shall be called *closed* if, for every subset $\sum_0 \subseteq \sum$ which has no maximum, the least ordinal which is greater than every ordinal of $\sum_0$ belongs to $\sum$. Prove that the set of all left-hand divisors of any given ordinal is closed.[2]) (For the set of all right-hand divisors the property is trivial because this set is finite.)

4) For any infinite set $\sum$ of ordinals (or any infinite well-ordered set) there exists a set T whose members are *triads* of $\sum$ [3]) such that *every pair* of members of $\sum$ is a subset of a single triad. Prove this theorem by contemplating nine different cases.[4])

5) Complete the proof of the formal law (2) on p. 206.

6) Prove the equalities (3) on p. 207 by means of Theorem 8.

7) Prove, on account of Definition III in 3, the following theorem which is analogous to a well-known theorem on real functions: the power $p(a) = \sigma^a$ is the *only* continuous (p. 205/6) function of the ordinal a with $p(1) = \sigma$ that satisfies the functional equation

$$p(a_1) \cdot p(a_2) = p(a_1 + a_2).$$

On the other hand, σ^a is not a continuous function of its basis σ; for instance, if k is finite and > 1, $\lim n^k = \omega \neq \omega^k$ for $\lim n = \omega$.

8) Let $\sigma > 1$ and $a_1 < a_2$; prove the inequalities

$$a_1{}^\sigma \leqslant a_2{}^\sigma, \quad \sigma^{a_1} < \sigma^{a_2}.$$

9) Generalize the equality $\overline{\overline{T(\aleph_0)}} = 2^{\aleph_0}$ (see Theorem 5 in § 8, 6) to any aleph, i.e. prove $\overline{\overline{T(\aleph_a)}} = 2^{\aleph_a}$. (By assuming the generalized continuum hypothesis one hence obtains $\overline{\overline{T(\aleph_a)}} = \aleph_{a+1}$; that is to say, the set of all *types* of the cardinal $\aleph_a$ is equivalent to its subset which contains all *ordinals* of the cardinal $\aleph_a$.)

---

[1]) See Chajoth 30.
[2]) See Sierpiński 29.
[3]) That is to say, subsets of Σ with three members each.
[4]) See Sierpiński 46. This theorem is a generalization to infinity of a finite combinatorial problem treated by J. Steiner in 1853.

10) From the first equality of Theorem 15 we at once obtain the cancellation law for alephs

$$m \aleph_\sigma \leqslant m \aleph_\tau \text{ implies } \aleph_\sigma \leqslant \aleph_\tau, \text{ in particular } m \aleph_\sigma = m \aleph_\tau \text{ implies } \aleph_\sigma = \aleph_\tau,$$

where m is a finite cardinal $\neq 0$. *On account of the well-ordering theorem* one may here replace $\aleph_\sigma$ and $\aleph_\tau$ respectively by any cardinals s and t.

But it is remarkable that the cancellation law for cardinals

$$m \mathsf{s} \leqslant m \mathsf{t} \text{ implies } \mathsf{s} \leqslant \mathsf{t}$$

can, with considerable ingenuity, be proved *without the axiom of choice*, as shown by Tarski.[1])

11) Prove $\aleph_a{}^2 = \aleph_a$ by means of transfinite induction, instead of using natural sums as in 5.

12) Generalize the inequality $2^{\aleph_0} \neq \aleph_\omega$, replacing ω by other limit-numbers.[2])

13) The equality holding for isolated σ

$$\aleph_\sigma{}^{\aleph_\tau} = \aleph_\sigma \cdot \aleph_{\sigma-1}{}^{\aleph_\tau},$$

which essentially reduces a power of $\aleph_\sigma$ to a power of $\aleph_{\sigma-1}$, is called *Hausdorff's recursion formula*.[3]) For $\sigma \leqslant \tau$ it easily follows from (5) in Theorem 15. Show its truth for $\sigma > \tau$ by means of the following theorem the proof of which is not difficult: if T is a well-ordered set of ordinals τ_ν such that $\overline{T} \leqslant \aleph_{a-1}$ and $\overline{\tau}_\nu \leqslant \aleph_{a-1}$ for every ν, then there is an ordinal $\zeta < \omega_a$ such that $\tau_\nu < \zeta$ for every ν. (Hint: use the formula which holds for every isolated σ: $\aleph_\sigma{}^{\aleph_\tau} \leqslant \sum_\kappa \overline{\xi_\kappa}{}^{\aleph_\tau}$ where ξ_κ ranges over $W(\omega_\sigma)$; this formula may be proven by considering the left-hand power as the cardinal of an insertion-set.)

14) Generalize Theorem 13 by proving that a well-ordered set of a type $< \omega_{\sigma+1}$, the members of which are increasing ordinals $< \omega_{\sigma+1}$, has a sequent which is also $< \omega_{\sigma+1}$.

15) Ascertain, in view of the proof of the well-ordering theorem given in 6, the ordinal of the set N of all integers > 1 according to the following choice-functions (for non-empty subsets $N' \subseteq N$):

a) $f(N')$ is the integer which has the least prime divisor or, if several

---

[1])   Tarski 49a; cf. 49, Part I.

[2])   Cf., in particular, Bagemihl 48.

[3])   At first published in Hausdorff 04. For generalizations and completions cf. Tarski 25a.

have this divisor, which has it in the lowest power; if this applies to several integers, then $f(N')$ shall be the least of them.

b) $f(N')$ is the integer which, according to its decomposition into prime divisors, contains the least number of (different or equal) divisors; if there are several of this kind, $f(N')$ shall be the one with the least prime divisor, and among several of this kind, the least of them.

By well-ordering N according to such choice-functions it becomes evident that a tiny part only of the choices provided for by the function f is actually utilized.

Of course, the axiom of choice is not required in these cases, for the rules are constructive.

16) Prove, by means of a suitable choice-function, the theorem: If $A = (S_1, S_2, S_3, \ldots)$ is an increasing sequence of sets, i.e. $S_k \subset S_{k+1}$ for every k, and if T is a set such that every $t \, \epsilon \, T$ is contained in at least one S_k and that every infinite subset of T has an infinite intersection with at least one S_k, then there exists an m such that $T \subseteq S_m$.

This theorem has important applications in the theory of sets of points, in particular regarding the *covering theorems* of Borel and others.[1])

§ 12. THE ORIGIN AND THE SIGNIFICANCE OF SET THEORY

We have surveyed the edifice of abstract set theory, the basis and outlines of which were created by Cantor in a bold intuition. In regard of the foundation of the theory we took a middle course between Cantor's naive attitude based on a definition which is untenable because leading to contradiction, and a modern axiomatic basis (cf. *Foundations*). The main axioms of one among the current axiom systems were introduced, but at chosen junctures only were fundamental concepts and theorems explicitly derived by means of the axioms.

Certain features of the theories of plain sets with their cardinals on the one hand and of (well-) ordered sets with their types and ordinals on the other, have chiefly originated from a *philosophic* ground; this especially applies to the legitimacy of transfinite magnitudes or numbers. The philosophical attitude played a considerable part in the later phase of Cantor's work from 1885 on. Several decades earlier one of the greatest logicians, the Bohemian clergyman Bernard Bolzano who was far ahead of his contemporaries in the foundations of logic and mathematics, had

---

[1]) See Veress 32.

taken this direction but remained short of final success; only long after his death were his (limited) achievements duly appreciated.[1])

Cantor, however, had originally and foremost been driven by purely *mathematical* motives to develop what became set theory. In various parts of *analysis*, especially in the theory of trigonometric series and of the integration of discontinuous functions, certain problems arose about 1870 which necessitated the discrimination of specific infinite aggregates of real numbers or points out of the continuum; for instance, the aggregate of the discontinuity points of a function. At that time, several mathematicians such as P. du Bois-Reymond, H. Hankel, A. Harnack, H. J. S. Smith, V. Volterra worked in this direction [2]) but, for want of an adequate methodical tool for defining general enough aggregates, reached limited results only.

At the suggestion of E. Heine, Cantor had in 1869 [3]) started researches on trigonometric series and their singular points and succeeded in proving the uniqueness of the expansion into a trigonometric series. By this work he was led to the concept of limit-point and to his theory of irrational numbers (cf. § 9, 1). In his attempts at generalizations he slowly and at first reluctantly convinced himself that a tool of a fundamentally new type was required for such problems, namely a general notion and classification of infinite sets; once convinced, he engaged in the task with ever growing verve. Gradually the analytical applications became secondary and set theory was developed for its own sake.

The set-theoretical solution of analytical problems was not only central in the early *development* of the new discipline but also in its *applications* since the end of the 19th centrury. The ties between the theory

---

[1])   After isolated remarks in Bolzano 1810 and 1837 (e.g. I, § 87) pointing to actual infinity, a comprehensive attempt was made in Bolzano 1851 where the term *Menge* (set) appears for the first time. Some of the shortcomings of this posthumously published book, which was known to Cantor (see Cantor 79–84V, p. 561), may be attributed to its editor who on his own account inserted several would-be corrections (cf. Jašek 22).

Bolzano's main achievement in philosophy is his comprehensive work 1837; cf., for instance, Scholz 31 (pp. 44ff.) and 37, Bar–Hillel 52, and the literature cited there.

Bolzano's achievements in the theory of real numbers and functions were duly appreciated only in the present century, especially with the publication of his manuscripts (from 1930 on); he was the first to define a continuous and nowhere derivable real function.

[2])   Hankel 1870, Smith 1875, du Bois–Reymond 1882, should be mentioned particularly. Cf. Jourdain 05–14 and Hardy 24.

[3])   See Cantor–Stäckel 1897; cf. Cantor 1870, p. 130 footnote. The proof of the uniqueness theorem is contained in Cantor 1870a.

of sets, particularly of sets of points, and the theory of (real, and also complex) functions have become so close that nowadays most textbooks of function theory begin with a chapter dealing with sets. Since 1919 there exists a first-rate international journal, the *Fundamenta Mathematicae* appearing in Warsaw, which is dedicated to set theory and its applications to analysis, logic, etc. Perhaps the most splendid among the applications is the modern development of various notions of measure and integral, starting with Lebesgue [1]) (half a century after Riemann). These achievements for their part led to an impetuous development of the theory of probability and other branches of applied mathematics, including even astronomy and physics [2]).

The analytical problems which led to set theory are closely connected with *geometry*. In § 9 we touched upon some of the problems of sets of points treated early by Cantor, mostly by the methods of ordered sets; such examples illuminate the enormously increased subtlety and efficiency of these methods in comparison with the classical ones. The most spectacular among the early achievements was the full description of the linear continuum in terms of order alone. Somewhat later set-theoretical topology began its triumphal progress; one of its results, the modern theory of dimension, was mentioned in § 6, 8. Yet beyond order theory and topology, set-theoretical geometry is of a suprising diversity, and certainly no methodical progress has so much enlarged the object of geometrical research since the invention of analytic geometry and calculus [3]). Incidentally, at the birth of set theory a stimulating part was played by questions of synthetic geometry, where a line is conceived as the set of the "incident" points or a point as the set of the "incident" lines or planes, etc; on this ground Cantor's term *Mächtigkeit* (power, cardinal; see p. 68) has originated.

Another domain participating in the creation of set theory and then

---

[1]) Lebesgue 02. Cf. the historical survey Lebesgue 27.

[2]) For early applications outside (pure) mathematics we mention Bernstein 12, van Vleck 15, Carathéodory 19, Bouligand 31, Vitali 31. The more recent applications to probability theory are legion; a good survey of the initial stage of these applications is contained in Kolmogoroff 33. Also the ergodic theorem, first attacked with set-theoretical methods in 1913, and its solution by G. D. Birkhoff and J. von Neumann may be mentioned.

In a different sense, applications of set theory to physics had been predicted by Cantor in 1882, see Cantor 79–84III, pp. 120f. Cf. Rosenthal–Borel 23, p. 905, footnote 160; Schoenflies 28, p. 22 (also p. 20).

For applications to chemistry cf. Habermann 36.

[3]) Cf. the programmatic expositions in Hahn 29 and Menger 33.

fostered by it is the theory of *integers*, i.e. of finite numbers and sets [1]); cf. § 10, **6**. The pioneer in this respect was Dedekind, a personal friend of Cantor's; in Cantor's later work the influence of Dedekind's "logical" attitude can easily be traced. Dedekind particularly excelled in utilizing the concept of one-to-one correspondence [2]) which since has attained an ever increasing significance and applicability. Remarkable are also the applications of set theory to *algebra*, especially to abstract algebra, where transfinite induction or equipollent procedures have become an indispensable instrument.[3])

Finally set theory, as the most general field of mathematics and on account of its close connection with logic, has to fulfil the task of methodically investigating and basing the primary concepts of mathematics in general, such as number, function, mapping, order, etc. (§§ 2, 4, 7, 8, 10) and of hence deducing the fundamental branches of mathematics. As the most comprehensive contemporary exposition of mathematics puts it, *on sait aujourd'hui qu'il est possible... de faire dériver presque toute la mathématique actuelle d'une source unique, la Théorie des Ensembles* (= theory of sets)[4]). It had been Cantor's explicit design to create by set theory "a genuine fusion between arithmetic and geometry"; set theory is fit for this purpose because its methods almost equally apply to continuous and to discrete subjects, hence seem apt to span the gap between both domains.

The achievements of set theory as a tool both for special mathematical disciplines and for the foundation of mathematics in its entirety are all the more remarkable since it is a quite young branch of a science which is two and half thousand years old; its roots started less than a century ago. True, there were and still are antagonists among mathematicians and philosophers; the bold character of set theory and its sometimes daring methods curbed its early development for two decades, and still to-day they seem suspect or even untenable to some constructivistic-minded scholars. Yet the foremost mathematician of the last generation, David Hilbert, retorted

---

[1]) Finite (and sometimes denumerable) sets are mostly involved in the applications of set theory to the theory of games, including chess, and of graphs. Early researches in this field are Zermelo 13, Kalmár 29, Euwe 29, D. König 36.

[2]) See, in particular, Dedekind 1888; also the posthumous work, including correspondence with Cantor, published in the third volume of Dedekind 30–32 and in Cantor–Dedekind 37.

[3]) The applications to algebra were first introduced in the comprehensive paper Steinitz 10 which largely is the pioneer work of abstract algebra. Cf. the exposition in van der Waerden 50.

[4]) Bourbaki 51-56 (booklet of 1954, p. 4).

upon those attacks by calling set theory "one of the most vigorous and fruitful branches of mathematics", "a paradise created by Cantor from which nobody shall ever expel us", "the most admirable blossom of the mathematical mind and altogether one of the outstanding achievements of man's purely intellectual activity"[1]).

A. N. Whitehead in his essay on *Mathematics as an element in the history of thought* [2]) calls mathematics the most original production of the human mind. His way of establishing this claim ought to award the corresponding distinction, among the various branches of mathematics, to set theory as to the branch which least of all is connected with external experience and most genuinely originates from free intellectual creation. Thus the conquest of actual infinity may be considered an expansion of our scientific horizon no less revolutionary than the Copernican system or than the theory of relativity, or even of quantum theory and nuclear physics.

[1])   Hilbert 18, p. 411; 25, pp. 170 and 167.
[2])   Whitehead 26, chapter II.

BIBLIOGRAPHY

Only those works are listed that are referred to in the book.

For some publications, especially those with whose languages the author is not familiar, he relied on the (almost always highly authoritative) reviews in the *Journal of Symbolic Logic*.

Regarding the date of the publication, differences of one year may occur, since in general the year of the appearance of the *volume* is stated, yet in particular cases the year indicated on the fascicle or the reprint.

Reviews and Abstracts are only included in exceptional cases.

An Index of those authors who (also) appear outside the alphabetical order is added at the end of this Bibliography, on pp. 268/9.

Works published after 1959, and some published earlier, are found in the Supplementary Bibliography on pp. 270 ff.

ABBREVATIONS USED IN THE BIBLIOGRAPHY

(Self-evident abbreviations such as Acad., ed., Encycl., Inst., Intern., Math., Philos., Ph(ys)., Psychol., Soc., Univ., etc. are not mentioned. "The" is often omitted.)

A.M.S. = American Mathematical Society
Abh. (Hamburg) = Abhandlungen (aus dem mathematischen Seminar der Hamburgischen Universität)
Acad. U.S.A. = Proceedings of the National Academy of Sciences (U.S.A.)
Act. Sc. Ind. = Actualités Scientifiques et Industrielles
Acta Szeged = Acta litterarum ac scientiarum Universitatis Hungaricae Francisco-Josephinae, Sectio scientiarum mathematicarum
Afd. = Afdeeling
Alg. = Algemeen
Am. = American
Ann. = Annales
appl. = appliquées etc.
Archiv Logik Gr. = Archiv f. math. Logik u. Grundlagenforschung
Ber. (Leipzig) = Berichte (über die Verh. der Sächsischen Akad. der Wiss. zu Leipzig, Math.-Ph. Klasse)
Bull. = Bulletin
C.R. = Comptes Rendus
C.R. Paris = Comptes Rendus Hebdomadaires des Séances de l'Acad. des Sc. (Paris)
C.R. Varsovie = Comptes Rendus des Séances de la Soc. des Sc. et des Lettres de Varsovie, Classe III
Časopis = Časopis pro Peštováni Matematiky a Fysiky
Cl. = Classe
Colloq. = Colloquium, Colloque, etc.
Comm. = Commentarii
Congr. = Congress(o), Congrès, etc.
Congr. Amsterdam 1954 = Proc. of the Intern. Congress of Mathematicians, Amsterdam 1954
Congr. Bologna 1928 = Atti del Congresso Intern. dei Matematici, Bologna 1928
Congr. Cambridge Mass. 1950 = Proc. of the Intern. Congress of Mathematicians, Cambridge (Massachusetts) 1950
D.M.V. = Deutsche Mathematiker-Vereinigung
Ens. = Enseignement
f. = for, für, etc.
Fac. = Faculty, etc.
F.M. = Fundamenta Mathematicae
Forschungen zur Log(ist)ik etc. = Forschungen zur Log(ist)ik und zur Grundlegung der exakten Wissenschaften
Ges. = Gesellschaft
Grundl. = Grundlagen
Helv. = Helvetici
I.M. = Indagationes Mathematicae
J. = Journal
J.f.M. = Journal für die reine und angewandte Mathematik (Crelle)

J.S.L. = Journal of Symbolic Logic
Jahrb. = Jahrbuch
Jahresb. = Jahresbericht
Kon. = Koninklijke etc.
Kongr. Heidelberg 1904 = Verh. des Dritten Intern. Math.-Kongresses in Heidelberg 1904
Kongr. Zürich 1932 = Verh. des Intern. Mathematiker-Kongresses, Zürich 1932
Les Entretiens de Zurich = Les Entretiens de Zurich sur les Fondements et la Méthode des Sciences Math. 1938
M.S. = Math. Society
Monatsh. = Monatshefte
N.S. = New Series, Neue Folge, Nieuwe Reeks, etc.
Nachr. (Göttingen) = Nachrichten (der Gesellschaft der Wissenschaften zu Göttingen, Math.-Ph. Klasse)
Nat. = National, etc.; Natural, etc.
Naturvid. = Naturvidenskab
p. = pures etc.
Polon. = Polonaise
Proc. = Proceedings
Proc. Amsterdam, = Kon. Nederlandse Akademie van Wetenschappen te Amsterdam, Proc. of the Section of Sciences
Publ. = Publications
R. = Royal(e)
R.M.M. = Revue de Métaphysique et de Morale
Rendic. = Rendiconti
Rendic. Lincei = Rendic della R. Accad. Nazionale dei Lincei (Roma), Cl. di Sc. Fis. etc.
Rev. = Revue, Review, etc.
Riv. = Rivista
s.a. = sine anno
Sc. = Science(s), etc.
Scand. = Scandinavica
Scr. = Scripta
Sem. = Seminar, etc.
Semesterberichte Münster = Semesterberichte zur Pflege des Zusammenhangs von Universität und Schule (Math. Seminar, Münster i. W.)
Sitz. (Berlin) = Sitzungsberichte (der Preussischen Akademie der Wissenschaften, Phys.-Math. Klasse)
Sitz. Heidelberg = Sitz. der Heidelberger Akad. der Wiss., Math.-Naturwiss. Kl.
Sitz. Wien = Akad. der Wiss. in Wien, Math.-Naturw. Kl., Sitz.
Tr. = Transactions
u. = und
v. = van, voor
Verh. = Verhandlungen, Verhandelingen
Wiss. = Wissenschaft(en)
Z. = Zeitschrift
Z. Logik Gr. = Z. f. math. Logik u. Grundl. der Math.
(2) = second series (and similarly for other numerals)

BIBLIOGRAPHY

ACKERMANN, W.⁻
1951. Konstruktiver Aufbau eines Abschnitts der zweiten Cantorschen Zahlen-
klasse. *Math. Z.* **53**, 403–413.

ALEXANDROFF, P.
1932. Dimensionstheorie. Ein Beitrag zur Geometrie der abgeschlossenen Mengen.
Math. Annalen **106**, 161–238.

ALEXANDROFF, P. S.
1956. *Einführung in die Mengenlehre und die Theorie der reellen Funktionen.*
(Appeared in Russian 1948.) Berlin. 279 pp.

ALTWEGG, M.
1950. Zur Axiomatik der teilweise geordneten Mengen. *Comm. Math. Helv.* **24**,
149–155. (Cf. K. MORINAGA and N. NISHIGORI: *J. Sc. Hiroshima Univ.*, A **16**,
177–221, 399–408, 1952; M. SHOLANDER: *Proc. A.M.S.* **3**, 369–381, 1952.)

ARONSZAJN, N.
1953. Characterization of types of order satisfying $a_0 + a_1 = a_1 + a_0$. *F.M.* **39**, 65–96.

ARTIN, E. and SCHREIER, O.
1927. Algebraische Konstruktion reeller Körper. *Abh. Hamburg* **5**, 85–99.

AUBERT, K. E.
1949. Relations généralisées et indépendance logique des notions de réflexivité,
symétrie et transitivité. *C.R. Paris* **229**, 284–286, 538–540.
1952. On the foundation of the theory of relations and the logical independence
of generalized concepts of reflexiveness, symmetry, and transitivity. *Archiv f.
Math. og Naturvid.* (Oslo) **52**, No. 2. 48 pp.

BACHMANN, F.
1934. Untersuchungen zur Grundlegung der Arithmetik mit besonderer Bezie-
hung auf Dedekind, Frege und Russell. *Forschungen zur Logistik* etc., No. 1.
Leipzig. 78 pp.

BACHMANN, H.
1950. Die Normalfunktionen und das Problem der ausgezeichneten Folgen von
Ordnungszahlen. *Vierteljahrsschrift der Naturforsch. Ges. Zürich* **95**, 115–147.
(Cf. *Comm. Math. Helv.* **28**, 9–16, 1954.)
1955. *Transfinite Zahlen.* (*Ergebnisse der Math.* etc., N.S., Heft **1**.) Berlin, Göttingen und Heidelberg. 204 pp.

BAER, R.
1927. Über nicht-archimedisch geordnete Körper. *Sitz. Heidelberg*, 1927, **8**. Abh.,
pp. 3–13.
1929. Zur Axiomatik der Kardinalzahlarithmetik. *Mat. Z.* **29**, 381–396.
1930. Eine Anwendung der Kontinuumhypothese in der Algebra. *J. f. M.* **162**,
132–133. (Cf. the *Anhang* to the new edition of Steinitz 1910.)
1932. Hegel und die Mathematik. *Verh. des 2. Hegelkongresses, Berlin 1931*,
pp. 104–120.

BAGEMIHL, F.
1948. Some theorems on powers of cardinal numbers. *Ann. of Math.* (2) **49**,
341–346. (Cf. *Quart. J. of Math.*, Oxford Ser. **19**, 200–203, 1948.)

1959. Some propositions equivalent to the continuum hypothesis. *Bull. A.M.S.* **65**, 84–88.

BAIRE, R.
1899. Sur les fonctions des variables réelles. *Annali di Mat. p. ed appl.* (3) **3**, 1–123. (Appeared also as a Thesis, Paris.)
1905. *Leçons sur les fonctions discontinues.* Paris.
See also under SCHOENFLIES.

BANACH, S.
1924. Un théorème sur les transformations biunivoques. *F.M.* **6**, 236–239. (Cf. *ibid.* **19**, 10–16, 1932.)

BANASCHEWSKI, B.
1953. Über die Konstruktion wohlgeordneter Mengen. *Math. Nachrichten* **10**, 239–245.

BAR-HILLEL, Y.
1952. Bolzano's propositional logic. *Archiv Logik Gr.* **1**, 65–98.
See also under FRAENKEL.

BAYS, S.
1946. Les concepts mathématiques sont-ils inventés ou découverts? *Actes de la Soc. Helvét. des Sc. Nat.* **125**, 9–26.

BELL, E. T.
1920. On proofs by mathematical induction. *Am. Math. Monthly* **27**, 413–415.

BENDIXSON, I.
1883. Quelques théorèmes de la théorie des ensembles de points. *Acta Math.* **2**, 415–429.
1883a. Nagra studier öfver oändliga punktmängder. *Oefvers. af K. Svenska Vet.-Akad. Förhandl.* **40**, No. 2, pp. 31–35.
1884. Sur la puissance des ensembles parfaits de points. *Bihang till K. Svenska Vet.-Akad. Handlingar* **9**, No. 6.
1884a. Un théorème auxiliaire de la théorie des ensembles. *Ibid.*, No. 7.

BENNETT, A. A.
1922. Remarks (to mathematical induction). *Am. Math. Monthly* **29**, 163–164. (Cf. R. S. HOAR, *ibid.*, 162; Y. R. CHAO, *Bull. A.M.S.* **26**, 17–18, 1920; G. E. RAYNOR, *Am. Math. Monthly* **33**, 376–377, 1926.)

BENTLEY, A. F.
1932. *Linguistic analysis of mathematics.* Bloomington Ind., 1932 and London, 1934. 315 pp.

BERKELEY, E. G.
1937. Boolean algebra and applications to insurance. *The Record of the Am. Inst. of Actuaries* **26** (part II, No. 54), 373–414.

BERNAYS, P.
1937–54. A system of axiomatic set theory. I–VII. *J.S.L.* I: **2**, 65–77, 1937; II: **6**, 1–17, 1941; III: **7**, 65–89, 1942; IV: *ibid.*, 133–145; V: **8**, 89–106, 1943; VI: **13**, 65–79, 1948; VII: **19**, 81–96, 1954.
See also under HILBERT.

BERNAYS, P. and FRAENKEL, A. A.
1958. Axiomatic set theory. Amsterdam. 226 pp.

BERNSTEIN, F.
1905. Untersuchungen aus der Mengenlehre. *Math. Annalen* **61**, 117–155. (Appeared already 1901 as a Thesis, Göttingen.) Cf. *ibid.* **60**, 463–464, 1905.
1912. Über eine Anwendung der Mengenlehre auf ein aus der Theorie der säkularen Störungen herrührendes Problem. *Ibid.* **71**, 417–439. (Cf. P. BOHL, E. BOREL, F. BERNSTEIN: *ibid.* **72**, 295–296, 578–584, 585–587, 1912.)

1938. The continuumproblem. *Acad. U.S.A.* **24**, 101–104.

BETH, E. W.

1959. *The foundations of mathematics.* Amsterdam. 741 pp.

BIRKHOFF, GARRETT

1937. An extended arithmetic. *Duke Math. J.* **3**, 311–316.

1942. Generalized arithmetic. *Ibid.* **9**, 283–302.

1948. *Lattice theory.* Revised ed. New York. 283 pp.

BIRKHOFF, GARRETT and MACLANE, S.

1953. Algebra of classes. In *A survey of modern algebra* (revised ed., New York, 1953), pp. 335–355.

BLUMBERG, H.

1936. Remarks on the inductive principle and related existence theorems. *Bull. A.M.S.* **42**, 852–856.

BOCHEŃSKI, I. M.

1934. Logistique et logique classique. *Bull. Thomiste* **11**, 240–248.

1938. De consequentiis scholasticorum earumque origine. *Angelicum* (Roma) **15**, 1–18. (Cf. *ibid.* **12**, 397–399, 1935, and **13**, 109–123, 1936.)

1956. *Formale Logik.* Freiburg und München. 639 pp.

BODEWIG, E.

1932. Die Stellung des hl. Thomas von Aquino zur Mathematik. *Archiv f. Geschichte der Philos.* **41**, 401–434. (Cf. the essays of LANGENBERG and ISEN-KRAHE quoted at the beginning of this paper.)

BOEHM, K.

1929. Anmerkungen zu einer Arbeit des Herrn N. Oglobin. *Jahresb. D.M.V.* **38**, 182–187.

DU BOIS-REYMOND, P.

1882. *Die allgemeine Functionentheorie.* I. Teil. (No. continuation has appeared.) Tübingen. 292 pp. (Cf. *Math. Annalen* **16**, 127–128, 1880.)

BOLZANO, B.

1810. *Philosophie der Mathematik oder Beiträge zu einer begründeteren Darstellung der Mathematik.* (Appeared originally in 1810.) New ed. with introduction and notes by H. FELS. (*Sammlung philos. Lesestoffe*, vol. **9**.) Paderborn s.a. (1926).

1837. *Wissenschaftslehre. Versuch einer ausführlichen Darstellung der Logik.* (4 vols. Sulzbach, 1837. – Vols. I and II reprinted Leipzig, 1914–15, ed. by A. HÖFLER.) New edition in 4 vols. by W. SCHULTZ. Leipzig, 1929–1931.

1851. *Paradoxien des Unendlichen.* (Originally ed. posthumously by F. PŘI-HONSKY, 1851.) New edition by A. HÖFLER, with notes by H. HAHN. (*Philos. Bibliothek*, vol. **99**.) Leipzig, 1920. English ed. 1950. 189 pp.

BOREL, É.

1898. *Leçons sur la théorie des fonctions.* Paris. 2nd. ed., 1914, 260 pp. (3rd [4th] ed., 1928 [1950])

1919. Sur les ensembles effectivement énumérables et sur les définitions effectives. *Rendic. Lincei* (5) **28** II, 163–165.

See also under ROSENTHAL.

BOULIGAND, G.

1931. Les courants de pensée Cantorienne et l'hydrodynamique. *Revue Générale des Sc. p. et appl.* **42**, 103–110.

BOURBAKI, N.

1951–56. *Éléments de mathématique.* Première Partie, Livre I. Théorie des ensembles. Fascicule de résultats (1939); 2nd ed., *Act. Sc. Ind.* **1141** (1951), 50 pp. Chap. I–II, *Act. Sc. Ind.* **1212** (1954), 136 pp. Chap. III, *Act. Sc. Ind.* **1243** (1956), 118 pp.

BRIDGMAN, P. W.
  1934. A physicist's second reaction to *Mengenlehre*. *Ser. Math.* **2**, 101–117, 224–234.
BRODERICK, T. S. and SCHRÖDINGER, E.
  1940. Boolean algebra and probability theory. *Proc. R. Irish Acad.*, A **46**, 103–112.
BROUWER, L. E. J.
  1911. Beweis der Invarianz der Dimensionenzahl. *Math. Annalen* **70**, 161–165. (Cf. **71**, 305–313, 1912 and **72**, 55–56, 1912.) Cf. *Proc. Amsterdam* **26**, p. 799, note 19, 1923.
  1913. Über den natürlichen Dimensionsbegriff. *J. f. Math.* **142**, 146–152. (Cf. **153**, p. 253, 1923.) Reprinted in *Proc. Amsterdam* **26**, 1923.
BRUNS, G. and SCHMIDT, J.
  1955. Eine filtertheoretische Formulierung der Kontinuumshypothese. *Z. Logik Gr.* **1**, 91–92. (Cf. *Math. Nachr.* **13**, 169–186, 1955.)
  1958. Eine Verschärfung des Bernsteinschen Äquivalenzsatzes. *Math. Annalen* **135**, 257–262.

CANTOR, G.
  1870. Über einen die trigonometrischen Reihen betreffenden Lehrsatz. *J. f. Math.* **72**, 130–138.
  1870a. Beweis, dass eine für jeden reellen Werth von *x* durch eine trigonometrische Reihe gegebene Funktion $f(x)$ sich nur auf eine einzige Weise in dieser Form darstellen lässt. *Ibid.*, 139–142. (Cf. *ibid.* **73**, 294–296, 1871.)
  1872. Über die Ausdehnung eines Satzes aus der Theorie der trigonometrischen Reihen. *Math. Annalen* **5**, 123–132.
  1874. Über eine Eigenschaft des Inbegriffs aller reellen algebraischen Zahlen. *J. f. Math.* **77**, 258–262. (Cf. B. MINNIGERODE: *Math. Annalen* **4**, 497–498, 1871.)
  1878. Ein Beitrag zur Mannigfaltigkeitslehre. *Ibid.* **84**, 242–258.
  1879–84. Über unendliche, lineare Punktmannichfaltigkeiten. *Math. Annalen:* I. **15**, 1–7, 1879. II. **17**, 355–358, 1880. III. **20**, 113–121, 1882. IV. **21**, 51–58, 1883. V. *Ibid.*, 545–591. (Appeared also as a book: Grundlagen einer allgemeinen Mannichfaltigkeitslehre. Ein mathematisch-philosophischer Versuch in der Lehre des Unendlichen. Leipzig, 1883. 47 pp.) VI. **23**, 453–488. 1884. (I–V appeared in French, partly in form of extracts, in *Acta Mathematica* **2**, 1883.)
  1886. Über die verschiedenen Standpunkte in Bezug auf das actuale Unendliche. *Z. f. Philos. u. philos. Kritik*, N.S. **88**, 224–233. (Appeared with some changes also in *Bihang till K. Svenska Vet.-Akad. Handlingar* **11**, No. 19, 1887.)
  1887–88. Mitteilungen zur Lehre vom Transfiniten. I. *Ibid.* **91**, 81–125, 252–270, 1887. II. *Ibid.* **92**, 240–265, 1888.
  1892. Über eine elementare Frage der Mannigfaltigkeitslehre. *Jahresb. D.M.V.* **1**, 75–78. (In Italian in *Riv. di Mat.* **2**, 165–167, 1892.)
  1895. Beiträge zur Begründung der transfiniten Mengenlehre. I. *Math. Annalen* **46**, 481–512.
  1897. *Idem.* II. *Ibid.* **49**, 207–246.
    These two papers appeared also in English, ed. by P. E. B. JOURDAIN, Chicago, 1915. French ed., *Mémoires de la Soc. des Sc. Phys. et Nat. de Bordeaux* (5) **3**, 343–437, 1899; also separately: Paris, 1899. Italian ed. of I in *Riv. di Mat.* **5**, 129–162, 1895.)
  1895a. Sui numeri transfiniti. Estratto d'una lettera di G. CANTOR a G. VIVANTI. *Riv. di Mat.* **5**, 104–108. (Cf. *ibid.*, 108–109; O. STOLZ, *ibid.*, 166–167.)

1932. *Gesammelte Abhandlungen mathematischen und philosophischen Inhalts.* Ed. by E. ZERMELO. Berlin. 486 pp.

CANTOR, G. and DEDEKIND, R.

1937. (*Briefwechsel,* ed. by E. NOETHER and J. CAVAILLÈS.) *Act. Sc. Ind.* **518.** Paris. 61 pp.

CANTOR-STÄCKEL

1897. (This quotation is used for a lecture delivered by G. CANTOR in Braunschweig, on September 24, 1897, which has not been published but was taken down by P. STÄCKEL; the present author was allowed to use it.)

CARATHÉODORY, C.

1919. Über den Wiederkehrsatz von Poincaré, *Sitz. Berlin,* 1919, 580–584.

CARMICHAEL, P. A.

1943. The null class nullified. *Philos. Review* **52,** 61–68.

CARNAP, R.

1927. Eigentliche und uneigentliche Begriffe. *Symposion* I, 355–374.

1934. Die Antinomien und die Unvollständigkeit der Mathematik. *Monatsh. Math. Ph.* **41,** 263–284.

1937. *The logical syntax of language.* New York and London. 352 pp. (Revised translation of *Logische Syntax der Sprache,* Wien, 1934. Contains a translation of 1934.)

1958. *Introduction to symbolic logic and its applications.* New York. 241 pp. (Revised translation of *Symbolische Logik,* Wien, 1954; 2nd ed. 1960.)

CARRUTH, P. W.

1942. Arithmetic of ordinals with applications to the theory of ordered Abelian groups. *Bull. A.M.S.* **48,** 262–271. (Cf. *Proc. A.M.S.* **2,** 896–900, 1951 and **3,** 983–987, 1952; W. NEUMER: *Archiv der Math.* **5,** 244–248, 1954.)

CASSIRER, E.

1910. *Substanzbegriff und Funktionsbegriff.* Berlin. English edition: Chicago, 1923.

1929. *Philosophie der symbolischen Formen.* III. Teil: Phänomenologie der Erkenntnis. Berlin.

CAVAILLÈS, J.

1932. Sur la deuxième définition des ensembles finis donnée par Dedekind. *F.M.* **19,** 143–148.

1938. *Remarques sur la formation de la théorie abstraite des ensembles. Étude historique et critique.* (Thèse.) Paris. 156 pp.

CHAJOTH, Z.

1930. Beitrag zur Theorie der geordneten Mengen. *F.M.* **16,** 132–133. (Cf. A. DENJOY: *C.R. Paris* **229,** 570–573, 1949.)

CHANG, C., see under TARSKI 1956.

CHURCH, A.

1927. Alternatives to Zermelo's assumption. *Tr. A.M.S.* **29,** 178–208.

1938. The constructive second number class. *Bull. A.M.S.* **44,** 224–232.

1952. (Review) *J.S.L.* **17,** 199–200.

CHURCH, A. and KLEENE, S. C.

1937. Formal definition in the theory of ordinal numbers. *F.M.* **28,** 11–21. (Cf. W. MARKWALD: *Math. Annalen* **127,** 135–149, 1954.)

CIPOLLA, M.

1937. Nulla e zero. *Esercitazioni Mat.* (2) **10,** 1–10.

COURANT, R. and ROBBINS, H.

1943. *What is mathematics?* 2nd ed. London and New York. 521 pp.

COUTURAT, L.

1896. *De l'infini mathématique.* (Thèse.) Paris.

CUESTA, D. N.
1942. (Generalized real numbers; Spanish) *Revista Mat. Hisp.-Am.* (4) **2**, 5–12. (Cf. *ibid.* **3**, 38–40, 1943; **7**, 3–9, 1947.)
1943. (Decimal theory of the order types) *Ibid.* **3**, 186–205, 242–268. (Cf. *ibid.* **4**, 16–23, 45–47, 1944; **6**, 59–65, 1946; **8**, 57–71, 1948.)
1945. (Continuous permutations with real numbers) *Ibid.* **5**, 191–203. (Cf. *ibid.* **9**, 131–140, 1949.)
1954. (Ordinal arrangement) *Ibid.* **14**, 237–268. (Cf. *Rev. Acad. Ci. Madrid* **48**, 103–145, 1954.)
1959. *Matematica del orden.* Madrid. 513 pp.

DANTZIG, T.
1930. *Number. The language of science.* London. (French ed., Paris, 1931.)
DAVIS, ANNE C. and SIERPIŃSKI, W.
1952. Sur les types d'ordre distincts dont les carrés sont égaux. *C.R. Paris* **235**, 850–852. (Cf. *ibid.*, 924–926; *Bull. A.M.S.* **58**, 382, 1952.)
DAY, M. M.
1945. Arithmetic of ordered systems. *Tr. A.M.S.* **58**, 1–43.
DEDEKIND, R.
1872. *Stetigkeit und irrationale Zahlen.* Braunschweig. (5th ed. 1927). 24 pp. —Reprinted in 1930—32 III.
1888. *Was sind und was sollen die Zahlen?* Braunschweig. (6th ed. 1930.) 58 pp. —Reprinted in 1930–32 III.—English ed. by W. W. BEMAN in: *Essays on the theory of numbers* by R. DEDEKIND, Chicago and London, 1901; Italian ed. by O. ZARISKI, Bologna, 1926.
1930–32. *Gesammelte mathematische Werke.* Ed. by R. FRICKE, E. NOETHER, O. ORE. 3 vols. Braunschweig.
See also under CANTOR.
DEHN, M., see under PASCH.
DENJOY, A.
1941. Sur les nombres transfinis. *C.R. Paris* **213**, 430–433. (Cf. *ibid.* **212**, 885–888, 1941; **221**, 429–432, 679–682, 1945; **229**, 637–640, 1949.)
1946. Les ensembles rangés. *Ibid.* **222**, 981–983. (Cf. *ibid.* **224**, 612–615, 1081–1083, 1129–1132, 1947; *Ann. de la Soc. Polon. de Math.* **21**, 187–195, 1948.)
1946–54. *L'Énumération transfinie.* Livres I–IV. Paris. 971 pp.
1953. Le problème de Souslin. *C.R. Paris* **236**, 435–439, 558–559, 641. (Cf. *ibid.*, 981–983; G. KUREPA: *ibid.*, 564–565, 655–657.)
DEVIDÉ, V.
1956. Eine Charakterisierung des Ordnungstypus $*\omega + \omega$ der Menge der ganzen Zahlen mittels der Nachfolge-Funktion. *Periodicum Math.-Ph. et Astron.* (Zagreb) **11**, 11–15. (Cf. *Z. Logik Gr.* **2**, 228–232, 1956.)
DEWEY, J., see under PEIRCE 1892/1923.
DUBISLAV, W.
1931. *Über die Definition.* 3rd ed. Leipzig. 160 pp. (Cf. *Erkenntnis* **3**, 201–203, 1933.)
DUBREIL, P. and DUBREIL-JACOTIN, MARIE-LOUISE
1939. Théorie algébrique des relations d'équivalence. *J. de Math. p. et appl.* (9) **18**, 63–95. (Cf. *C. R. Paris* **205**, 704–706, 1349–1351, 1937.)
DUREN, W. L. JR.
1957. Mathematical induction in sets. *Am. Math. Monthly* **64** (No. 8, II), 19–22.
DUSHNIK, B. and MILLER, E. W.
1940. Concerning similarity transformations of linearly ordered sets. *Bull. A.M.S.* **46**, 322–326.

ERDÖS, P.
  1950. Some remarks on set theory. *Proc. A.M.S.* **1**, 127–141. (Cf. ERDÖS and
    G. FODOR: *Acta Szeged* **17**, 250–260, 1956 and the literature cited there.)
ERDÖS, P. and RADO, R.
  1953. A problem on ordered sets. *J. London M.S.* **28**, 426–438.
  1956. A partition calculus in set theory. *Bull. A.M.S.* **62**, 427–489. (Cf. E.
    SPECKER. *Comm. Math. Helv.* **31**, 302–314, 1957.)
ÉSÉNIN-VOL'PIN, A. S.
  1954. Nédokazuémost' gipotézy Suslina béz pomošči aksiomy vybora v sistémé
    aksiom Bérnajsa-Mostovskogo (The unprovability of Suslin's hypothesis
    without the aid of the axiom of choice in the system of axioms of Bernays-
    Mostowski). *Doklady Akad. Nauk SSSR* **96**, 9–12.
EUWE, M.
  1929. Mengentheoretische Betrachtungen über das Schachspiel. *Proc. Amsterdam*
    32, 633–642.
EYRAUD, H.
  1940. Schémas bifurqués et représentations transfinies. *Ann. Univ. Lyon*, A(3) **3**,
    25–32.

FABER, G.
  1905. Über die Abzählbarkeit der rationalen Zahlen. *Math. Annalen* **60**, 196–203.
FELSCHER, W. and SCHMIDT, J.
  1958. Natürliche Zahlen, Ordnung, Nachfolge. *Archiv Logik Gr.* **4**, 81–94.
FORADORI, E.
  1933. Stetigkeit und Kontinuität als Teilbarkeitseigenschaften. *Monatsh. Math.
    Ph.* **40**, 161–180. (Cf. *ibid.* **41**, 133–173, 1934.)
FRAENKEL, A. (A.)
  1928. *Einleitung in die Mengenlehre.* 3rd ed. Berlin. 424 pp. Repr. New York, 1946.
  1930. Georg Cantor. *Jahresb. D.M.V.* **39**, 189–266.
  1935. Zum Diagonalverfahren Cantors. *F.M.* **25**, 45–50.
  See also under BERNAYS.
FRAENKEL, A. A. and BAR-HILLEL, Y.
  1958. *Foundations of set theory.* Amsterdam. 415 pp. Second revised ed., with
    A. LÉVY as co-author, Amsterdam, 1966.
FRAISSÉ, R.
  1948. Sur la comparaison des types d'ordre. *C.R. Paris* **226**, 1330–1331. (Cf. *ibid.*,
    987–988.)
  1953. Sur certaines relations qui généralisent l'ordre des nombres rationnels.
    Ibid. **237**, 540–542. (Cf. *ibid.*, 508–510; *Annales Scient. de l'École Normale Sup.*
    (3) **71**, 363–388.)
  1955. *Sur quelques classifications des systèmes de relations.* Thèse, Fac. des Sc.,
    Univ. de Paris. 154 pp. (Also *Public. Scientif. Univ. Alger* **A1**, 35–182, 1954/5.)
  1958. Un modèle définissant une théorie aberrante des ensembles où sont niés
    les axiomes du choix et d'extensionalité. *Publ. Scient. Univ. Alger* **A5**, 17–98.
FRANKLIN, P.
  1925. Analytic transformations of everywhere dense point sets. *Tr. A.M.S.* **27**,
    91–100. (Cf. H. MINKOWSKI: *Kongr. Heidelberg 1904*, 171–172, 1905.)
FREGE, G.
  1884. *Die Grundlagen der Arithmetik. Eine logisch-mathematische Untersuchung
    über den Begriff der Zahl.* Breslau. 119 pp. (Reprinted: Breslau 1934; English-
    German ed. by J. L. AUSTIN, 1950; Ital. ed. by L. GEYMONAT, 1948.)

FREUDENTHAL, H.
1953. Zur Geschichte der vollständigen Induktion. *Archives Intern. d'Histoire des Sc.* No. **22**, 17–37.

GILLMAN, L.
1958. A continuous exact set. *Proc. A.M.S.* **9**, 412–418.

GINSBURG, S.
1953. Some remarks on order types and decompositions of sets. *Tr. A.M.S.* **74**, 514–535. (Cf. *ibid.* **76**, 590–598; **77**, 122–150; **79**, 341–361; 1954/5.)
1954. Fixed points of products and ordered sums of simply ordered sets. *Proc. A.M.S.* **5**, 554–565.
1955. Uniqueness in the left division of order types. *Ibid.* **6**, 120–123.

GLEYZAL, A.
1940–41. Order types and structure of orders. I and II. *Tr. A.M.S.* **48**, 451–466; **49**, 111–116. (Cf. *Acad. U.S.A.* **23**, 291–292, 1937.)

GÖDEL, K.
1940. *The consistency of the axiom of choice and of the generalized continuum-hypothesis with the axioms of set theory.* (*Annals of Math. Studies*, No. **3**.) Lithoprinted. Princeton. 66 pp. Revised ed., 1951, 74 pp.
1947. What is Cantor's continuum problem? *Am. Math. Monthly* **54**, 515–525.

GODFREY, E. W.
1938. Enumeration of the rational points between 0 and 1. *Nat. Math. Magazine* (Louisiana) **12**, 163–166.

GOODSTEIN, R. L.
1948. Proof by *reductio ad absurdum*. *Math. Gazette* **32**, 198–204.

GRAVES, L. M.
1946/56. *The theory of functions of real variables.* New York and London, 1946. 300 pp. 2nd ed., 1956. 375 pp.

GRELLING, K.
1910. *Die Axiome der Arithmetik mit besonderer Berücksichtigung der Beziehungen zur Mengenlehre* (Thesis). Göttingen. 26 pp.

GRÜNBAUM, A.
1955. Modern science and refutation of the paradoxes of Zeno. *Scientific Monthly* **81**, 234–239.

GUTBERLET, C.
1886. Das Problem des Unendlichen. *Z. f. Philos. u. philos. Kritik*, N.S. **88**, 179–223.
1919. (Review of A. FRAENKEL, Einleitung in die Mengenlehre, 1919) *Philos. Jahrbuch der Görresgesellschaft* **32**, 364–370.

HAALMEIJER, B. P. and SCHOGT, J. H.
1926. *Inleiding tot de leer der verzamelingen.* Groningen. 159 pp.

HAAR, A. and KÖNIG, D.
1911. Über einfach geordnete Mengen. *J. f. Math.* **139**, 16–28.

HABERMANN, E.
1936. Mengentheoretische Betrachtungsweise in der Chemie. *Act. Sc. Ind.* **392**, 46–53.

HAENZEL, G.
1934. Eine geometrische Konstruktion der transfiniten Zahlen Cantors. *J. f. Math.* **170**, 123–128.

HAHN, H.
1907. Über die nicht-archimedischen Grössensysteme. *Sitz. Wien* **116IIA**, 601–655.

1913. Über die Abbildung der Strecke auf ein Quadrat. *Annali di Mat.* (3) **21**, 33–55. (Cf. *Congr. Bologna 1928*, II, 217–220, 1930.)

1929. Mengentheoretische Geometrie. *Die Naturwissenschaften* **17**, 916–919.

HANANI, H.

1955. Enumeration of rational numbers. (Hebrew with English summary) *Riveon Lematematika* (Jerusalem) **9**, 23–24.

HANKEL, H.

1870. *Untersuchungen über die unendlich oft oscillirenden und unstetigen Funktionen.* (Reprinted in *Math. Annalen* **20**, 63–112, 1882.)

HARDY, G. H.

1924. *Orders of infinity. The "Infinitärcalcül" of Paul du Bois-Reymond.* (*Cambridge Tracts in Math.* etc., No. **12**.) 2nd ed. Cambridge.

HARTOGS, F.

1915. Über das Problem der Wohlordnung. *Math. Annalen* **76**, 438–443.

HASSE, H. and SCHOLZ, H.

1928. Die Grundlagenkrisis der griechischen Mathematik. *Kantstudien* **33**, 4–34.

HAUSDORFF, F.

1904. Der Potenzbegriff in der Mengenlehre. *Jahresb. D.M.V.* **13**, 569–571.

1906–07. Untersuchungen über Ordnungstypen. I and II. *Ber. Leipzig* **58**, 106–169; **59**, 84–159. (Cf. *Jahresb. D.M.V.* **16**, 541–546, 1907.)

1908. Grundzüge einer Theorie der geordneten Mengen. *Math. Annalen* **65**, 435–505. (Cf. *Ber. Leipzig* **53**, 460–475, 1901.)

1914. *Grundzüge der Mengenlehre.* Leipzig. 476 pp. Reprinted New York, 1949.

1927. *Mengenlehre* (2nd revised ed. of 1914). Berlin und Leipzig. 285 pp. 3rd ed., 1935; reprinted New York, 1944. English ed., New York, 1957.

HERMES, H.

1955. *Einführung in die Verbandstheorie.* Berlin, Göttingen und Heidelberg. 164 pp.

1956. Über die gegenwärtige Lage der mathematischen Logik und Grundlagenforschung. *Jahresb. D.M.V.* **59** (1), 49–69.

HESSENBERG, G.

1906. Grundbegriffe der Mengenlehre. (*Abh. der Friesschen Schule*, N.S. [**1**], Heft 4.) Göttingen. 220 pp.

1907. Potenzen transfiniter Ordnungszahlen. *Jahresb. D.M.V.* **16**, 130–137.

1908. Willkürliche Schöpfungen des Verstandes? *Ibid.* **17**, 145–162. (Cf. P. FRANK: *ibid.*, 227–230, 232–234; HESSENBERG: *ibid.*, 230–231.)

1909. Kettentheorie und Wohlordnung. *J. f. Math.* **135**, 81–133.

HILBERT, D.

1891. Über die stetige Abbildung einer Linie auf ein Flächenstück. *Math. Annalen* **38**, 459–460.

1899/1930. *Grundlagen der Geometrie.* (Appeared first in 1899.) 7th. ed. (essentially revised), Leipzig & Berlin, 1930, 125 + 201 pp.; 8th ed., 1956. (English ed. by E. J. TOWNSEND. Chicago & London, 1902.) Cf. H. FREUDENTHAL: *N. Archief v. Wiskunde* (4) **5**, 105–142, 1957.

1918. Axiomatisches Denken. *Math. Annalen* **78**, 405–419. (In French: *L'Ens. Math.* **20**, 122–136, 1918; in Dutch: *Wiskundig Tijdschrift* **16**, 208–222, 1920.)

1925. Über das Unendliche. *Ibid.* **95**, 161–190. (In French: *Acta Math.* **48**, 91–122, 1926.)

HILBERT, D. and BERNAYS, P.

1934. *Grundlagen der Mathematik.* Vol. I. Berlin. 471 pp. Reprinted, Ann Arbor Mich., 1944.

HÖLDER, O.

1930. Ein Versuch im Gebiet der höheren Mächtigkeiten. *Ber. Leipzig* **82**, 83–96.

HUDEKOFF, N.
1930. Über eine Verallgemeinerung des Begriffes der geordneten Menge. *Mat. Sbornik* **37**, 169–212. (Cf. R. FRAÏSSÉ: *C.R. Paris* **228**, 1682–1684, 1949; **230**, 1022–1024, 1950.)

HUNTINGTON, E. V.
1905–06. The continuum as a type of order: an exposition of the modern theory. *Annals of Math.* (2) **6**, 151–184; **7**, 15–43. Appeared also as a book: The continuum and other types of serial order. 2nd ed., Cambridge Mass., 1917; reprinted 1921. In Esperanto: Paris, 1907; 125 pp.

HUREWICZ, W. and WALLMAN, H.
1941. *Dimension theory.* (*Princeton Math. Series* 4.) Princeton N.J. 165 pp.

HURWITZ, A.
1883. Beweis des Satzes etc. *J. f. Math.* **95**, 201–206.

ISENKRAHE, K.
1920. *Die Lehre des hl. Thomas vom Unendlichen... und ihr Verhältnis zur neuzeitlichen Mathematik.* Bonn. 230 pp.

ITÔ, M.
1933–35. Einige Anwendungen der Theorie des Entscheidungsproblems zur Axiomatik. *Tôhoku Math. J.* **37**, 222–235; **40**, 241–251.

JACOBSTHAL, E.
1907. Vertauschbarkeit transfiniter Ordnungszahlen. *Math. Annalen* **64**, 475–488. (Cf. *ibid.* **65**, 160, 1908.)
1909. Über den Aufbau der transfiniten Arithmetik. *Ibid.* **66**, 145–194. (Cf. *ibid.* 67, 144, 1909; A. HOBORSKI: *F.M.* **2**, 193–198, 1921.)
1909a. Zur Arithmetik der transfiniten Zahlen. *Ibid.* **67**, 130–144.

JAŠEK, M.
1922. Über den wissenschaftlichen Nachlass Bernard Bolzanos. *Jahresb. D.M.V.* **31**, 109–110 ital. (Cf. *Časopis* **51**, 69–76, 1922; *Věstník*, 1921/22, No. 1; V. JARNÍK: *Časopis* **51**, 248–264, 1922.)

JOHNSTON, L. S.
1948. Denumerability of the rational number system. *Am. Math. Monthly* **55**, 65–70. (Cf. I. NIVEN: *ibid.*, p. 358.)

JÓNSSON, B., see under TARSKI (1949 and 1956).

JOURDAIN, P. E. B.
1905. On the general theory of functions. *J. f. Math.* **128**, 169–210. (Cf. *Messenger of Math.* (2) **33**, 78, 1903.)
1905–14. The development of the theory of transfinite number. *Archiv der Math. u. Ph.* (3) **10**, 254–281, 1905; **14**, 289–311, 1909; **16**, 21–43, 1910; **22**, 1–21, 1914.
1908. On infinite sums and products of cardinal numbers. *Quarterly J. of Math.* **39**, 375–384.
1922. A proof that any aggregate can be well-ordered. *Acta Math.* **43**, 239–261. (Cf. already *Math. Annalen* **60**, 465–470, 1905; *Mind*, N.S. **27**, 386–388, and **28**, 382–384, 1918/19.)

KALMÁR, L.
1929. Zur Theorie der abstrakten Spiele. *Acta Szeged* **4**, 65–84.
1940. On the possibility of definition by recursion. *Ibid.* **9**, 227–232.

KALUZA, T.
1917. Eine Abbildung der transfiniten Kardinaltheorie auf das Endliche. *Schriften der Ph.-Ökon. Ges. zu Königsberg i. Pr.* **57**, 1–49.

KALUZA, T., JR.
1950. Zur Rolle der Epsilonzahlen bei der Polynomdarstellung von Ordinalzahlen. *Math. Annalen* **122,** 321–322.

KAMIYA, H.
1927. On the representation of a square on a linear interval. *Tôhoku Math. J.* **28,** 147–151.

KAMKE, E.
1928 (1950). *Mengenlehre.* (*Samml. Göschen* **999.**) Berlin & Leipzig, 1928. 160 pp. 2nd ed., 1947. English ed., New York, 1950. 144 pp.
1939. Allgemeine Mengenlehre. *Enzykl. der math. Wiss.*, Band I, 1. Teil, Heft 2, Art. A5. Leipzig. 56 pp.

KAPUANO, I.
1956. Deux propositions nouvelles équivalentes à l'hypothèse du continu. *C.R. Paris* **242,** 2614–2617.

KASNER, E.
1945. The recent theory of the horn angle. *Scr. Math.* **11.** 263–267.

KEYSER, C. J.
1916. *The human worth of rigorous thinking.* Essays and addresses. New York. (2nd ed., 1925.)
1918. The rôle of the concept of infinity in the work of Lucretius. *Bull. A.M.S.* **24,** 321–327. (Cf. *Scr. Math.* **4,** 221–240, 1936; also the essay of P. SCHRECKER "On the infinite number of infinite orders": *Studies and Essays... in Homage to G. Sarton etc.* [New York, 1947], pp. 359–373.)
1941. Charles Sanders Peirce as a pioneer. *Galois Lectures* (*Scr. Math. Library* **5**), 87–112. (Cf. *Scr. Math.* **3,** 11–37, 1935; also the review by A. CHURCH: *J.S.L.* **6,** 161–162, 1941.)

KHINTCHINE, A.
1923. Das Stetigkeitsaxiom des Linearkontinuums als Inductionsprinzip betrachtet. *F.M.* **4,** 164–166.

KLEENE, S. C.
1936. General recursive functions of natural numbers. *Math. Annalen* **112,** 727–742.
1938. On notation for ordinal numbers. *J.S.L.* **3,** 150–153.
1944. On the forms of the predicates in the theorie of constructive ordinals. *Am. J. of Math.* **66,** 41–58. (Cf. *ibid.* **77,** 405, 428, 1955.)
See also under CHURCH.

KLEIN, FELIX
1926. *Vorlesungen über die Entwicklung der Mathematik im 19. Jahrhundert.* Teil I. Berlin. 386 pp.

KOLMOGOROFF, A.
1933. *Grundbegriffe der Wahrscheinlichkeitsrechnung.* (*Ergebnisse der Math. etc.*, vol. II 3.) Berlin. 62 pp.

KÖNIG, D.
1926. Sur les correspondances multivoques des ensembles. *F.M.* **8,** 114–134. (Cf. already *Math. Annalen* **77,** 453–465, 1916; D. KÖNIG and S. VALKÓ: *ibid.* **95,** 135–138, 1925; D. KÖNIG: *R.M.M.* **30,** 443–449, 1923; also N. G. DE BRUIN: *N. Archief v. Wiskunde* (2) **22,** 48–52, 1943.)
1936. *Theorie der endlichen und unendlichen Graphen.* New York. 258 pp. (Cf. R. RADO: *Sitz. Berliner Math. Gesellschaft* **32,** 60–75, 589–596, 1933; *Proc. London M.S.* (2) **48,** 122–160, 1943.)
See also under HAAR.

KÖNIG, J.
1905. Zum Kontinuumproblem. *Math. Annalen* 60, 177–180, 462. (Cf. *ibid.* 61, 156–160, 1905; 63, 217–221, 1907; *Kongr. Heidelberg 1904*, 144–147, 1905; N. LUSIN and W. SIERPIŃSKI: *C.R. Paris* 175, 1922.)
1906. Sur la théorie des ensembles. *C.R. Paris* 143, 110–112.
1914. *Neue Grundlagen der Logik, Arithmetik und Mengenlehre* (ed. by D. KÖNIG). Leipzig. 259 pp.

KOOPMAN, B. O.
1940. The axioms and algebra of intuitive probability, *Annals of Math.* (2) 41, 269–292. (Cf. *Bull. A.M.S.* 46, 763–774, 1940.)

KORSELT, A.
1911. Über einen Beweis des Äquivalenzsatzes. *Math. Annalen* 70, 294–296.

KREISEL, G.
1950. Note on arithmetic models for consistent formulae of the predicate calculus. *F.M.* 37, 265–285.

KURATOWSKI, C.
1921. Solution d'un problème concernant les images continues d'ensembles de points. *F.M.* 2, 158–160.
1921a. Sur la notion d'ordre dans la théorie des ensembles. *Ibid.*, 161–171.
1922. Une méthode d'élimination des nombres transfinis des raisonnements mathématiques. *Ibid.* 3, 76–108.
1922a. Théorie des continus irréductibles entre deux points. I. *Ibid.*, 200–231
1925. Une propriété des correspondances biunivoques. *Ibid.* 6, 240–243.
1937. Sur la géométrisation des types d'ordre dénombrable. *Ibid.* 28, 167–185. (Cf. *ibid.*, 186–196; S. HARTMAN: *ibid.* 29, 209–214, 1937; KURATOWSKI and J. VON NEUMANN: *Annals of Math.* (2) 38, 521–525, 1937.)

KURATOWSKI, C. and MOSTOWSKI, A.
1952. *Teoria mnogości* (Theory of sets). *Monografie Mat.* XXVII. Warszawa & Wrocław. 311 pp.

KURATOWSKI, C. and TARSKI, A.
1931. Les opérations logiques et les ensembles projectifs. *F.M.* 17, 240–248. (Cf. *ibid.* 27, 269–276, 1936.)

KUREPA, G.
1934. Sur le continu linéaire. *C.R. Paris* 198, 703–705. (Cf. *ibid.*, 882–885.)
1935. *Ensembles ordonnés et ramifiés.* (*Publications Math. de l'Univ. de Belgrade* 4, 1–138.) — Appeared also as a Thesis, University of Paris. (Cf. *ibid.* 6/7, 129–160, 1938; *C.R. Paris* 202, 185–187, 1936; *Studia Math.* 9, 23–42, 1940; *Acta Math.* 75, 139–150, 1943.)
1937. Transformations monotones des ensembles partiellement ordonnés. *C.R. Paris* 205, 1033–1035. (Cf. *ibid.*, 1196–1198.)
1948. Sur les ensembles ordonnés dénombrables. *Societas Sc. Nat. Croatica, Period. Math.-Ph. et Astr.* 3, 145–151.
1948a. L'hypothèse du continu et le problème de Suslin. *Acad. Serbe des Sc., Publ. Inst. Math.* 2, 26–36.
1950. Ensembles partiellement ordonnés et ensembles partiellement bien ordonnés. *Ibid.* 3, 119–125.
1950a. La condition de Souslin et une propriété caractéristique des nombres réels. *C.R. Paris* 231, 1113–1114. (Cf. *Acad. Serbe Sc., Publ. Inst. Math.* 4, 97–108, 1952.)
1953. Real and ordinal numbers as sets of rational numbers. *Period. Math.-Ph. et Astr.* (Zagreb) 8, 270–279.
1953a. Sur les correspondances multivoques. *C.R. Paris* 237, 1133–1135.

1954. Über die Faktoriellen endlicher und unendlicher Zahlen. *Bull. Intern. Acad. Yougoslave, Cl. Sc. Math.* etc., N.S. **12**, 51–64. (T. **296**, 105–122.)

1954a. Some induction principles. *Congr. Amsterdam 1954*, II, 130.

KUROSCH, A.

1939. Zur Theorie der teilweise geordneten Systeme von endlichen Mengen. (Russian, with German summary.) *Mat. Sbornik*, N.S. **5**, 343–346. (Cf. *ibid.* [First Ser.] **42**, 613–616, 1935.)

LANDAU, E.

1930. *Grundlagen der Analysis*. Leipzig. 134 pp. (English ed., New York, 1951.)

LANGFORD, C. H.

1927. Some theorems on deducibility. *Annals of Math.* (2) **28**, 16–40, 459–471.

1939. A theorem on deducibility for second-order functions. *J.S.L.* **4**, 77–79. See also under LEWIS.

LEBESGUE, H.

1902. *Intégrale, longueur, aire*. Thèse Paris. 129 pp. (Also in *Annali di Mat.* (3) **7**, 231–359, 1902.)

1904. *Leçons sur l'intégration et la recherche des fonctions primitives*. Paris. (2nd ed., 1928.)

1927. Sur le développement de la notion d'intégrale. *R.M.M.* **34**, 149–167. (In Spanish in *Revista Mat. Hispano-Am.* (2) **2**, 65–74, 97–106, 1927.)

LEVI-CIVITA, T.

1893. Sugli infiniti ed infinitesimi attuali quali elementi analitici. *Atti del R. Istituto Veneto di Sc.* etc. (7) **4**, 1765–1815.

LÉVY, AZRIEL

1958. *Contributions to the metamathematics of set theory*. (Hebrew with English summary.) Thesis, Hebrew University. Jerusalem.

1958a. A note on definitions of finiteness. *Bull. of the Research Council of Israel*, F No. 2, 83–84. (Cf. *F.M.* **46**, 1–13, 1958.)

LEWIS, C. I. and LANGFORD, C. H.

1932. *Symbolic logic*. New York & London. 506 pp. (2nd ed., New York, 1959. 518 pp.)

LICHTENSTEIN, L

1932. La philosophie des mathématiques selon M. Émile Meyerson. *Revue Philosophique* **113**, 169–206.

LINDENBAUM, A.

1927. Sur l'arithmétique des types ordinaux. *Ann. Soc. Polon. de Math.* **5**, 103–104.

1934. Sur la théorie de l'ordre multiple. (Polish, with French summary.) *Wiadom. Mat.* **37**, 1–35.

LINDENBAUM, A. and TARSKI, A.

1926. Communication sur les recherches de la théorie des ensembles. *C.R. Varsovie* **19**, 299–330. (Cf. W. SIERPIŃSKI: *F.M.* **29**, 2–4, 1937; **34**, 6–8, 72–74, 113–118, 119–126, 148–154, 1947; **35**, 1–12, 1948; *C.R. Varsovie* **40**, 1–3, 1947.)

LITTLEWOOD, J. E.

1926. *The elements of the theory of real functions*. 2nd ed. Cambridge. 60 pp.

LORENZEN, P.

1939. Die Definition durch vollständige Induktion. *Monatsh. Math. Ph.* **47**, 356–358. (Cf. P. BERNAYS: *J.S.L.* **6**, p. 11, footnote 23, 1941; A. CHURCH: *ibid.* **11**, p. 126, 1946.)

LÖWENHEIM, L.

1946. On making indirect proofs direct. (Translated from the German by W. V. O. QUINE.) *Scr. Math.* **12**, 125–139.

LÜROTH, J.
  1907. Über Abbildung von Mannigfaltigkeiten. *Math. Annalen* 63, 222–238.
LUSIN, N.
  1933. Sur les ensembles toujours de première catégorie. *F.M.* 21, 114–126.
  1935. Sur les ensembles analytiques nuls. *Ibid.* 25, 109–131. (Cf. W. SIERPIŃSKI: *ibid.*, 132–135.)

MACLANE, S., see under BIRKHOFF
MACNEILLE, H. M.
  1937. Partially ordered sets. *Tr. A.M.S.* 42, 416–460. (Cf. *Acad. U.S.A.* 24, 188–193, 1938.)
MAHLO, P.
  1911. Über lineare transfinite Mengen. *Ber. Leipzig* 63, 187–225. (Cf. *ibid.*, 319–347.)
  1917. Über Teilmengen des Kontinuums von dessen Mächtigkeit. *Jahresb. D.M.V.* 25, 163–208. (Cf. *Ber. Leipzig* 65, 283–315, 1913.)
MAXIMOFF, J.
  1940. On a continuum of power $2^{\aleph_1}$. *Annals of Math.* (2) 41, 321–327. (Cf. D. N. CUESTA: *Revista Mat. Hisp.-Am.* (4) 7, 128–131, 1947.)
MENDELSON, E.
  1958. On a class of universal ordered sets. *Proc. A.M.S.* 9, 712–713. (Cf. W. SIERPIŃSKI: *F.M.* 36, 56–67, 1949; L. GILLMAN: *ibid.* 43, 77–82, 1956.)
MENGER, K.
  1928. *Dimensionstheorie.* Leipzig & Berlin. 319 pp. (Cf. *Monatsh. Math. Ph.* 36, 411–432, 1929; 37, 175–182, 1930.)
  1933. Neuere Methoden und Probleme der Geometrie. *Kongr. Zürich 1932*, I, 310–323.
MEYERSON, É.
  1931. *Du cheminement de la pensée.* 3 vols. (See, in particular, vol. II, Livre III.) Paris.
MILLER, E. W., see under DUSHNIK.
MITTAG-LEFFLER, G.
  1884. Sur la représentation analytique des fonctions monogènes uniformes d'une variable indépendante. *Acta Math.* 4, 1–79.
  1928. Zusätzliche Bemerkungen (zu Schoenflies 1928). *Ibid.* 50, 25–26.
MONTAGUE, R.
  1955. Well-founded relations; generalizations of principles of induction and recursion. (Abstract) *Bull. A.M.S.* 61, 442.
MORRIS, C. W.
  1929. Has Russell passed the Tortoise? *J. of Philos.* 26, 449–459.
MOSTOWSKI, A., see under KURATOWSKI.
MOSTOWSKI, A. and TARSKI, A.
  1939. Boolesche Ringe mit geordneter Basis. *F.M.* 32, 69–86.

NAGEL, E.
  1939. The formation of modern conceptions of formal logic in the development of geometry. *Osiris* 7, 142–224.
NATORP, P.
  1923. *Die logischen Grundlagen der exakten Wissenschaften.* 3rd ed. Leipzig & Berlin. 416 pp.
VON NEUMANN, J.
  1923. Zur Einführung der transfiniten Zahlen. *Acta Szeged* 1, 199–208.

1925. Eine Axiomatisierung der Mengenlehre. *J. f. Math.* **154**, 219–240. Corrections, *ibid.* **155**, 128, 1926.

1928. Über die Definition durch transfinite Induktion und verwandte Fragen der allgemeinen Mengenlehre. *Math. Annalen* **99**, 373–391. (Cf. A. FRAENKEL: *ibid.*, 392–393.)

1928a. Die Axiomatisierung der Mengenlehre. *Math. Z.* **27**, 669–752.

VON NEUMANN, J. and STONE, M. H.

1935. The determination of representative elements in the residual classes of a Boolean algebra. *F.M.* **25**, 353–378. (Cf. J. VON NEUMANN: *J. f. Math.* **165**, 109–115, 1931.)

NEUMER, W.

1951. Über den Aufbau der Ordnungszahlen. *Math. Z.* **53**, 59–69. (Cf. *ibid.*, 419–449; **54**, 388, 1951; **55**, 399–400, 1952.)

1953. Bemerkungen zur allgemeinen Hypothese $2^{\aleph_a} = \aleph_{a+1}$ im Anschluss an einige Beweisversuche von H. Eyraud. *Math. Nachrichten* **9**, 321–342. (Cf. D. N. CUESTA: *Rev. Mat. Hisp.-Am.* (4) **9**, 83–96, 168, 1949.)

1953–54. Zur Konstruktion von Ordnungszahlen. *Math. Z.* **58**, 391–413; **59**, 434–454; **60**, 1–16; **61**, 47–69. (Cf. *ibid.* **64**, 435–456, 1956.)

NICOD, J. G. P.

1922. Mathematical logic and the foundations of mathematics. *Encyclop. Britannica*, 12th ed., **31**, 874–876.

OBREANU, F.

1947. La puissance de certaines classes de fonctions. *Duke Math. J.* **14**, 377–380. (Cf. *ibid.* **15**, 593, 1948.)

OGLOBIN, N.

1929. Eine Anwendung der Fareyschen Reihen. *Jahresb. D.M.V.* **38**, 49–53.

OHKUMA, T.

1954. Sur quelques ensembles ordonnés linéairement. *Proc. Japan Acad.* **30**, 805–808.

OLMSTED, J. M. H.

1945. Transfinite rationals. *Bull. A.M.S.* **51**, 776–780.

ORE, O.

1942. Theory of equivalence relations. *Duke Math. J.* **9**, 573–627.

OTCHAN, G.

1942. Quelques questions de l'équivalence des familles d'ensembles. *Bull. Acad. Sc. de l'URSS*, Sér. Math. **6**, 171–188.

PADOA, A.

1930. Proposizioni assiomatiche. *Congr. Bologna 1928*, III, 381–387.

PASCH, M.

1882. *Vorlesungen über neuere Geometrie.* Leipzig. — New ed. with a supplement of M. DEHN: *Die Grundlegung der Geometrie in historischer Entwicklung.* Berlin, 1926. 275 pp.

PEANO, G.

1890. Sur une courbe qui remplit toute une aire plane. *Math. Annalen* **36**, 157–160.

1895. *Formulaire de Mathématiques.* (In collaboration with other scholars.) Originally published Torino, 1895. 144 pp. 5th ed.: Formulario Matematico. Torino, 1905–08. 463 pp.

1906. Super theorema de Cantor-Bernstein. *Rendic. Palermo* **21**, 360–366. Reprinted in *Revista de Math.* **8**, 136–143, 1906. (Cf. *ibid.* **8**, 143–157, 1906; A. PADOA: *Period. di Mat.* (3) **4**, 23–28, 1906.)

1924. De aequalitate. *Acad. pro Interlingua, Circulare*, 1924, No. **5**, 8–11. Reprinted in *Proc. of the Intern. Congr. of Math.*, *Toronto 1924*, II, 988–989, 1928.

PEIRCE, C. S.
1892/1923. *Chance, love, and logic.* Philosophical Essays, ed. by M. R. COHEN, with a supplementary essay by J. DEWEY. New York & London, 1923. (The essay "The law of mind" contained in this volume appeared originally in *The Monist* 1892.)
1933. *Collected papers.* Ed. by C. HARTSHORNE and P. WEISS. Vol. III. Cambridge Mass. 433 pp.

PERRON, O.
1921/47. *Irrationalzahlen.* Berlin & Leipzig, 1921, 186 pp. 3rd ed., 1947.
1926. Die vollständige Induktion im Kontinuum. *Jahresb. D.M.V.* **35**, 194–203.

PICCARD, SOPHIE
1935. Sur les fonctions définies dans les ensembles finis quelconques. *F.M.* **24**, 298–301. (Cf. W. SIERPIŃSKI: *ibid.*, 209–212.)

POINCARÉ, H.
1883. Mémoire sur les groupes Kleinéens. *Acta Math.* **3**, 49–92.
1908. *Science et méthode.* Paris. 311 pp. English ed., 1952.
1909. Réflexions sur les deux notes précédentes. *Acta Math.* **32**, 195–200.
1910. Über transfinite Zahlen. *Sechs Vorträge über ausgewählte Gegenstände aus der reinen Mathematik und mathematischen Physik* (Leipzig & Berlin). pp. 43–48.

POPRUŻENKO, J.
1955. Sur certains ensembles indénombrables singuliers de nombres irrationels. *F.M.* **42**, 319–338. (Cf. *ibid.* **41**, 29–37, 1954; **43**, 148–155, 1956.)

QUINE, W. V. O.
1937. On Cantor's theorem. *J.S.L.* **2**, 120–124.
1941. Element and number. *Ibid.* **6**, 135–149.
1960. *Word and object.* Cambridge Mass., New York & London. 294 pp.

RABIN, M.
1959. Arithmetical extensions with prescribed cardinality. *Proc. Amsterdam* A62 (= *I.M.* **21**). 439–446.

RADO, R.
1954. The minimal sum of a series of ordinal numbers. *J. London M.S.* **29**, 218–232.
See also under ERDÖS.

REICHBACH, M.
1955. Une simple démonstration du théorème de Cantor-Bernstein. *Colloq. Math.* (Wrocław) **3**, 163.

RIESZ, F.
1905. Über mehrfache Ordnungstypen. I. *Math. Annalen* **61**, 406–421.

ROBBINS, H., see under COURANT.

ROBINSON, ABRAHAM
1941. On a certain variation of the distributive law for a commutative algebraic field. *Proc. of the R. Soc. of Edinburgh*, A 61, Part I, 93–101. (Cf. A. R. RICHARDSON: *Proc. London M.S.* (2) **47**, 38–59, 1940.)

ROSENFELD, L.
1925. Sur le concept de structure et le théorème de Cantor-Bernstein. *C.R. Assoc. Française pour l'Avancement des Sc.* **48** (Liège 1924), 144–145.

ROSENTHAL-BOREL.

1923. *Neuere Untersuchungen über Funktionen reeller Veränderlichen.* Nach den unter der Leitung von É. BOREL redigierten französischen Referaten bearbeitet von A. ROSENTHAL. *Encykl. der math. Wiss.*, II C 9, pp. 851–1187. Leipzig.

ROSSER, J. B.

1953. *Logic for mathematicians.* New York, 540 pp.

RUSSELL, B.

1903. *The principles of mathematics.* I. London. 2nd ed. with a new introduction. London 1937 & New York 1938. 534 pp. Reprinted 1950. Italian ed., 1951.

1906. On some difficulties in the theory of transfinite numbers and order types. *Proc. London M.S.* (2) **4**, 29–53.

1914/26. *Our knowledge of the external world.* (appeared originally in 1914.) 2nd ed.: London, 1926, 251 pp.; New York, 1929, 268 pp. German ed.: Leipzig, 1926. French ed. "Méthode scientifique en philosophie": Paris, 1929.

1919. *Introduction to mathematical philosophy.* London & New York. 206 pp. 2nd ed., 1920. 6th impression, 1948. German ed., 1923; French ed., 1928; Spanish ed., 1945.

See also under WHITEHEAD.

RUST, W. M. JR.

1934. An operational statement of Cantor's Diagonalverfahren. *Scr. Math.* **2**, 334–336.

SCHEEFFER, L.

1884. Allgemeine Untersuchungen über Rectification der Curven. *Acta Math.* **5**, 49–82. (Cf. *ibid.* **4**, 387. 1884.)

1884a. Zur Theorie der stetigen Funktionen einer reellen Veränderlichen. *Ibid.*, 183–194, 279–296.

SCHLICK, M.

1925. *Allgemeine Erkenntnislehre.* 2nd ed. Berlin. 375 pp.

SCHMIDT, F. K.

1933. Mehrfach perfekte Körper. *Math. Annalen* **108**, 1–25. (Cf. *ibid.* **106**, 457–472. 1932.)

SCHMIDT, JÜRGEN

1953. Über die Minimalbedingung. *Archiv der Math.* **4**, 172–181.

1955. Eine verallgemeinerte Wohlordnung und die Endlichkeitsbedingungen der Ordnungstheorie. *Ibid.* **6**, 374–381.

1955a. Lexikographische Operationen. *Z. Logik Gr.* **1**, 127–170.

1957. Einfacher, ordinalzahlfreier Beweis für die Wohlordnung der Mächtigkeiten. *Math. Z.* **67**, 299–302.

1957a. Die transfiniten Operationen der Ordnungstheorie. *Math. Annalen* **133**, 439–449.

See also under BRUNS and FELSCHER.

SCHNEIDER, T.

1959. Introduction aux nombres transcendants. Paris. 151 pp. (The German original appeared 1957.)

SCHOENFLIES, A.

1900–07. *Die Entwickelung der Lehre von den Punktmannigfaltigkeiten.* I. Teil. (*Jahresb. D.M.V.* **8**, part 2.) Leipzig, 1900. 251 pp. II. Teil (2. *Ergänzungsband zu den Jahresb. D.M.V.*). Leipzig, 1907. 331 pp.

1913. *Entwickelung der Mengenlehre und ihrer Anwendungen. 1. Hälfte.* Leipzig & Berlin. 388 pp.

1922. Zur Erinnerung an Georg Cantor. *Jahresb. D.M.V.* **31**, 97–106.

1928. Die Krisis in Cantors mathematischem Schaffen. *Acta Math.* **50**, 1–23.

SCHOENFLIES–BAIRE
1909. *Théorie des ensembles.* Exposé d'après l'article Allemand de A. SCHOENFLIES par R. BAIRE. *Encycl. des Sc. Math.*, I 1, 489–531. Paris & Leipzig.

SCHOLZ, H.
1931. *Geschichte der Logik.* Berlin. 78 pp.
1937. Die Wissenschaftslehre Bolzanos. Eine Jahrhundert-Betrachtung. *Abh. der Friesschen Schule*, N. S. 6, 399–472. (Cf. *Semesterber. Münster*, 9. Sem., 1–54. 1936/37.)
See also under HASSE.

SCHOLZ, H. and SCHWEITZER, H.
1935. *Die sogenannten Definitionen durch Abstraktion.* (Lithographed) Leipzig. 106 pp.

SCHREIER, O., see under ARTIN.

SCHRÖDINGER, E., see under BRODERICK.

SCHÜTTE, K.
1954. Kennzeichnung von Ordnungszahlen durch rekursiv erklärte Funktionen. *Math. Annalen* **127**, 15–32. (Cf. *ibid.* **122**, 47–65, 369–389. 1951.)

SCHWARZ, G.
1954. Some theorems on Hudekoff's axioms of orientation. (Hebrew with English summary) *Riveon Lemematika* (Jerusalem) 7, 13–22.

SCHWARZ, H.
1888. *Ein Beitrag zur Theorie der Ordnungstypen.* Thesis Halle a.S. (Cf. G. VIVANTI: *Annali di Mat.* (2) **17**, 1–35, 1889.)

SCHWEITZER, H., see under SCHOLZ.

SHANNON, C. E.
1938. A symbolic analysis of relay and switching circuits. *Tr. of the Am. Inst. of Electrical Engineers* 57, 713–723.

SHEPHERDSON, J. C.
1951. Well-ordered subseries of general series. *Proc. London M.S.* (3) **1**, 291–307.

SHIRAISHI, S.
1954. The structure of the continuity of psychological experiences and the physical world. *The Sc. of Thought* (Tokyo), No. **1**, 12–24.

SIECZKA, F.
1924. Sur l'unicité de la décomposition de nombres ordinaux en facteurs irréductibles. *F.M.* **5**, 172–176.

SIERPIŃSKI, W.
1921. Les exemples effectifs et l'axiome du choix. *F.M.* **2**, 112–118.
1922. Sur la notion d'isomorphisme des ensembles. *Ibid.* 3, 50–51.
1927. Sobre la correspondencia entre los pontos de un segmento y los de un cuadrado. *Revista Mat. Hispano–Am.* (2) **2**, 193–197.
1928. *Leçons sur les nombres transfinis.* Paris. 240 pp. Reprinted 1950.
1928a. Sur une décomposition d'ensembles. *Monatsh. Math. Ph.* **35**, 239–242. (Cf. *Ann. de la Soc. Polon. de Math.* 7, 265–266, 1929; *F.M.* **28**, 115–119, 1937; *Mathematica* [Cluj] 14, 15–17, 1938; A. TARSKI: *F.M.* **12**, 188–205 and **14**, 205–215, 1928/29; P. ERDÖS and A. TARSKI: *Annals of Math.* (2) **44**, 315–329, 1943.)
1929. A property of ordinal numbers. *Bull. of the Calcutta M.S.* **20**, 21–22.
1932. Sur les ensembles de la même puissance qui ne sont pas effectivement de la même puissance. *F.M.* **18**, 189–192.
1932a. Sur les familles croissantes de sous-ensembles d'un ensemble dénombrable. *L'Ens. Math.* 30, 240–242.

1934/56. *Hypothèse du continu*. Warszawa & Lwów, 1934. 192 pp. 2nd ed. (with 16 research papers 1934–1956), New York, 1956. 274 pp.

1936. Remarque sur la courbe péanienne. *Wiadom. Mat.* **42**, 1–3.

1946. Sur un problème de triades. *C.R. Varsovie* **33–38** (1940–1945), 13–16.

1946a. Sur les types d'ordre de puissance du continu. *Revista de Ci.* (Lima) **48**, 305–307.

1946/47. Les correspondances multivoques et l'axiome du choix. *F.M.* **34**, 39–44.

1946/47a. Sur une proposition qui entraîne l'existence des ensembles non-mesurables. *Ibid.*, 157–162.

1948. Sur la division des types ordinaux. *Ibid.* **35**, 1–12. (Cf. *C. R. du premier Congr. des Math. Hongrois 1950*, 397–399. 1952; also Lindenbaum-Tarski 1926.)

1950. Le dernier théorème de Fermat pour les nombres ordinaux. *Ibid.* **37**, 201–205.

1950a. Sur un type ordinal dénombrable qui a une infinité indénombrable de diviseurs gauches. *Ibid.*, 206–208.

1950b. Sur les types d'ordre des ensembles linéaires. *Ibid.*, 253–264. (Cf. K. PADMAVALLY: *ibid.* **42**, 312–318, 1955.)

1951. *Algèbre des ensembles*. Warszawa & Wrocław. 205 pp.

1952. Sur les fonctions continues d'une variable ordinale. *F.M.* **38**, 204–208.

1956. Sur une propriété des nombres ordinaux. *Ibid.* **43**, 139–140. (Cf. *Acta Szeged* **12B**, 49–50, 1950.)

1958. *Cardinal and ordinal numbers*. Warszawa. 487 pp.

See also under DAVIS.

SIKORSKI, R.
1948. On a generalization of theorems of Banach and Cantor-Bernstein. *Colloq. Math.* (Wrocław) **1**, 141–144.

1950. On an ordered algebraic field. *C.R. Varsovie* **41**, 69–96.

SKOLEM, T.
1919. Untersuchungen über die Axiome des Klassenkalkuls und über Produktations- und Summationsprobleme, welche gewisse Klassen von Aussagen betreffen. *Skrifter utgit av Videnskapsselskapet i Kristiania*, I. Mat.-Nat. Kl. 1919, No. 3, 1–37. (Cf. *Avh. utgit av Det Norske Vid.-Ak. i Oslo*, I. 1935, No. **8**, 1–10, 1936.)

1920. Logisch-kombinatorische Untersuchungen über die Erfüllbarkeit oder Beweisbarkeit mathematischer Sätze nebst einem Theoreme über dichte Mengen. *Ibid.*, 1920, No. **4**, 1–36. (Cf. F. BAGEMIHL: *Math. Scand.* **1**, 256–260, 1953.)

1957. An ordered set of arithmetic functions representing the least ε-number. *Norske Vid. Selsk. Forh.* (Trondheim) **29**, 54–59.

SŁUPECKI, J.
1954. Sur la multiplication des types ordinaux. *Colloq. Math.* (Wrocław) **3**, 41–45.

SMART, H. R.
1945. Frege's logic. *Philos. Review* **54**, 489–505. (Cf. A. CHURCH: *J.S.L.* **10**, 101–103, 1945.)

SMITH, H. J. S.
1875. On the integration of discontinuous functions. *Proc. London M.S.* **6**, 140–153. (Also in the *Collected Math. Papers* of H. J. S. SMITH, vol. II, Oxford, 1894.) Cf. W. H. YOUNG: *ibid.* **34**, 286, 1902; A. SCHOENFLIES: *Nachr. Göttingen*, 1896, 255–266.

SOUSLIN (SUSLIN), M.
1920. Problème. *F.M.* **1**, 223.

SPECKER, E.
1954. Die Antinomien der Mengenlehre. *Dialectica* **8**, 234–244.

SPECTOR, C.
  1955. Recursive well-orderings. *J.S.L.* **20**, 151–163.
STÄCKEL, P., see under CANTOR.
STEBBING, L. SUSAN
  1930. *A modern introduction to logic.* London, 1930 & New York, 1931. 505 pp.
STECKEL, S.
  1928. Remarque sur une classe d'ensembles ordonnés. *F.M.* **11**, 285–286.
STEINITZ, E.
  1910. Algebraische Theorie der Körper. *J. f. Math.* **137**, 167–309. New ed. by
    R. BAER and H. HASSE, Berlin & Leipzig, 1930. 155 pp + 27 pp. notes.
STÖHR, A.
  1942. Über zweifach geordnete Mengen und Zerlegungen in Rechtecke. *J. f. Math.*
    184, 138–157.
STONE, M. H.
  1934. Boolean algebras and their application to topology. *Acad. U.S.A.* **20**,
    197–202.
  1935. Postulates for Boolean algebras and generalized Boolean algebras. *Am. J.
    of Math.* **57**, 703–732. (Cf. M. H. A. NEWMAN; *J. London M. S.* **16**, 256–272;
    17, 34–47; **19**, 28–31; 1941–44.)
  1937. Applications of the theory of Boolean rings to general topology. *Tr. A.M.S.*
    41, 375–481.
  1945. On characteristic functions of families of sets. *F.M.* **33**, 27–33. (Cf. *Duke
    Math. J.* **7**, 453–457, 1940; E. SZPILRAJN: *F.M.* **31**, 207–233, 1938.)
SUDAN, G.
  1931. Zur Jacobsthalschen transfiniten Arithmetik. *Math. Annalen* **105**, 40–51.
    (Cf. *F.M.* **18**, 293–297, 1932.)
  1946. Sur les nombres delta. *Acad. Roum., Bull. de la Sect. Scient.* **26**, 212–223.
    (Cf. *ibid.* **27**, 108–117, 258–264, 1947.)
SUSLIN, M., see under SOUSLIN.
SZPILRAJN, E.
  1930. Sur l'expansion de l'ordre partiel. *F.M.* **16**, 386–389.
SZYMAŃSKI, P.
  1944. Sur une correspondance effective entre l'ensemble des fonctions continues
    et un ensemble de nombres réels. *Bull. Sc. de l'École Polytechn. de Timişoara* **11**,
    185–195.

TARSKI, A.
  1924. Sur quelques théorèmes qui équivalent à l'axiome du choix. *F.M.* **5**,
    147–154.
  1925. Sur les ensembles finis. *Ibid.* **6**, 45–95. (Cf. C. KURATOWSKI: *ibid.* **1**, 131–132,
    1920.)
  1925a. Quelques théorèmes sur les alephs. *Ibid.* **7**, 1–14. (Cf. F. BAGEMIHL: *Am.
    J. of Math.* **70**, 207–211 and 460, 1948.)
  1925b. Sur les principes de l'arithmétique des nombres ordinaux (transfinis).
    (Abstract) *Ann. Soc. Polon. de Math.* **3**, 148–149.
  1928. Sur quelques propriétés caractéristiques des images d'ensembles. —Quelques
    théorèmes généraux sur les images d'ensembles. (Abstracts) *Ibid.* **6**, 127–128,
    132–133. (Cf. B. KNASTER: *Ibid.*, 133–134.)
  1929. Geschichtliche Entwicklung und gegenwärtiger Zustand der Gleichmäch-
    tigkeitstheorie und der Kardinalzahlarithmetik. *Ibid.* **7**, 48–54.
  1930. Über Äquivalenz der Mengen inbezug auf eine beliebige Klasse von
    Abbildungen. *Congr. Bologna 1928*, II, 243–252.

1930a. Sur les classes d'ensembles closes par rapport à certaines opérations élémentaires. *F.M.* **16**, 181–304. (Cf. *ibid.* **27**, 277–288, 1936.)

1935. Zur Grundlegung der Booleschen Algebra. I. *Ibid.* **24**, 177–198.

1935–36. Grundzüge des Systemenkalküls. *Ibid.* **25**, 503–526; **26**, 283–301.

1938. Einige Bemerkungen zur Axiomatik der Booleschen Algebra. *C.R. Varsovie* **31**, 33–35.

1938a. Ein Überdeckungssatz für endliche Mengen nebst einigen Bemerkungen über die Definitionen der Endlichkeit. *F.M.* **30**, 156–163. (Cf. *ibid.*, 132–155.)

1938b. Der Aussagenkalkül und die Topologie. *Ibid.* **31**, 103–134.

1939. On well-ordered subsets of any set. *Ibid.* **32**, 176–183.

1948. Axiomatic and algebraic aspects of two theorems on sums of cardinals. *Ibid.* **35**, 79–104.

1949. *Cardinal algebras.* With an appendix (60 pp.): Cardinal products of isomorphism types, by B. JÓNSSON and A. TARSKI. New York. 326 pp.

1949a. Cancellation laws in the arithmetic of cardinals. *F.M.* **36**, 77–92. (Cf. W. SIERPIŃSKI: *ibid.* **3**, 1–6, 1922; **34**, 148–154, 1946.)

1956. *Ordinal algebras.* With appendices by C. CHANG and B. JÓNSSON. Amsterdam. 133 pp.

See also under KURATOWSKI, LINDENBAUM, MOSTOWSKI.

TERNUS, J., S.J.

1926. Zur Philosophie der Mathematik. *Philos. Jahrb. der Görresgesellschaft* **39**, 217–231.

1929. Ein Brief Georg Cantors an P. Joseph Hontheim S.J. *Scholastik* **4**, 561–571.

THOMAS, I.

1958. A 12th century paradox of the infinite. *J.S.L.* **23**, 133–134.

TSUCHIKURA, T.

1949. Quelques propositions équivalentes à l'hypothèse du continu. *Tôhoku Math. J.* (2) **1**, 69–76.

TUKEY, J. W.

1940. *Convergence and uniformity in topology.* (*Annals of Math. Studies* **2**.) 95 pp.

ULAM, S.

1929. Remark on the generalized Bernstein's theorem. *F.M.* **13**, 281–283.

DE LA VALLÉE POUSSIN, C.

1916. *Intégrales de Lebesgue, fonctions d'ensembles, classes de Baire.* Paris. 2nd ed. 1934. 193 pp. (Cf. *Tr. A.M.S.* **16**, 435–501, 1915.)

VANDIVER, H. S.

1936. On the ordering of real algebraic numbers by constructive methods. *Annals of Math.* (2) **37**, 7–16.

VAUGHT, R. L.

1954. Applications of the Löwenheim-Skolem-Tarski theorem to problems of completeness and decidability. *Proc. Amsterdam* A**57** (= *I.M.* **16**), 467–472. (Cf. *Bull. A.M.S.* **59**, 396–397, 1953.)

VEBLEN, O.

1905. Definitions in terms of order alone in the linear continuum and in well-ordered sets. *Tr. A.M.S.* **6**, 165–175.

1908. Continuous increasing functions of finite and transfinite ordinals. *Ibid.* **9**, 280–292.

VERESS, P.

1932. Über eine Beweismethode in der Theorie der abstrakten Räume. *Acta Szeged* **6**, 34–45.

VERONESE, G.
  1891. *Fondamenti di geometria*. Padova. German ed., prepared from a new
    version of the book, translated by A. SCHEPP: Grundzüge der Geometrie von
    mehreren Dimensionen etc. Leipzig, 1894. 710 pp.
VITALI, G.
  1931. Un risultato di F. Hausdorff e la compressibilità della materia. *Rendic.
    Lincei* (6) **13**, 903–905.
VAN VLECK, E. B.
  1915. The rôle of the point-set theory in geometry and dynamics. *Bull. A.M.S.* **21**,
    321–341.
DE VRIES, H.
  1957. Compactification of a set which is mapped onto itself. *Bull. Acad. Polon. Sc.*,
    III **5**, 943–945.

VAN DER WAERDEN, B. L.
  1950. *Moderne Algebra*. Vol. I, 3rd ed., Berlin. (English ed., New York, 1949.)
WALLMAN, H., see under HUREWICZ.
WANG, H.
  1953. Between number theory and set theory. *Math. Annalen* **126**, 385–409.
  1957. The axiomatization of arithmetic. *J.S.L.* **22**, 145–158.
WEBBER, W. J.
  1931. The ordinal characterization of linear sets. *Tr. R. Soc. of Canada*, III
    (Math. Sc.), (3) **25**, 65–74. (Cf. F. ZUBIETA RUSSI and R. VÁSQUEZ GARCÍA:
    Bolet. Soc. Mat. Mexicana **1**, No. 2, 15–17, 1944.)
WEISS, P.
  1938. *Reality*. Princeton N.J. 314 pp.
WERNICK, G.
  1930. Die Unabhängigkeit des zweiten distributiven Gesetzes von den übrigen
    Axiomen der Logistik. *J. f. Math.* **161**, 123–134.
WEYL, H.
  1925. Die heutige Erkenntnislage in der Mathematik. *Symposion* **1**, 1–32. (Ap-
    peared also as a pamphlet: *Sonderdrucke des Symposion*, No. **3**, Erlangen, 1926.)
  1926/49. *Philosophie der Mathematik und Naturwissenschaft*. Part I. (*Handbuch
    der Philos.* IIA.) München & Berlin 1926. 64 pp. Reprinted 1950. Hebrew ed.:
    Jerusalem 1945. —*Philosophy of mathematics and natural science*. (Revised and
    augmented English ed. of Parts I and II.) Princeton, 1949. 311 pp.
  1931. *Die Stufen des Unendlichen*. Jena. 19 pp.
  1932. *The open world*. Three lectures on the metaphysical implications of science.
    New Haven and London. (The essay *Infinity* on pp. 57–84.)
WHITEHEAD, A. N.
  1926. *Science and the modern world*. Cambridge. (4th ed., 1929.) French ed.,
    Paris, 1930. Italian ed., 1945.
WHITEHEAD, A. N. and RUSSELL, B.
  1910–13. *Principia Mathematica*. 3 vols. Cambridge, 1910, 1912, 1913. 666 + 772
    + 491 pp. —2nd ed.: 1925, 1927, 1927. 674 + 742 + 491 pp., besides an
    Introduction to the 2nd ed. and Appendices A, B, C in vol. I: 34 + 15 + 9 + 8
    pp.
WHITNEY, H.
  1933. Characteristic functions and the algebra of logic. *Annals of Math.* (2) **34**,
    405–414.
WHITTAKER, J. M.
  1927. A note on the correlation of classes. *Proc. Edinburgh M.S.* (2) **1**, 47–48.

WIENER, N.
> 1920. A new theory of measurement. A study in the logic of mathematics. *Proc. London M.S.* (2) **19**, 181–205.

WOLFSON, H. A.
> 1929. *Crescas' critique of Aristotle.* Cambridge Mass.

WRINCH, DOROTHY M.
> 1920. On the exponentiation of well-ordered series. *Proc. Cambridge Philos. Soc.* **19**, 219–233.
> 1929. On the structure of serial relations. *Philos. Magazine* (7) **8**, 698–702.
> 1929a. On the multiplication of serial relations. *Ibid.*, 1025–1033.

YOUNG, W. H.
> 1926. The progress of mathematical analysis in the twentieth century. *Proc. London M.S.* (2) **24**, 421–434.

YOUNG, W. H. and YOUNG, GRACE C.
> 1906. *The theory of sets of points.* Cambridge. 316 pp.

ZAKON, E.
> 1953. Left side distributive law of the multiplication of transfinite numbers. (Hebrew with English summary) *Riveon Lematematika* (Jerusalem) **6**, 28–32.
> 1954. The relation of similarity between transfinite numbers. (Hebrew with English summary) *Ibid.* **7**, 44–49. (Cf. S. ISAAK: *ibid.* **11**, 47–49, 1957.)
> 1955. On fractions of ordinal numbers. *Israel Institute of Technology, Scient. Public.* **6**, 94–103.

ZERMELO, E.
> 1904. Beweis, dass jede Menge wohlgeordnet werden kann. *Math. Annalen* **59**, 514–516. (Cf. A. SCHOENFLIES, E. BOREL, P. E. B. JOURDAIN: *Ibid.* **60**, 181–186, 194–195, 465–470, 1905.)
> 1908. Neuer Beweis für die Wohlordnung. *Ibid.* **65**, 107–128.
> 1908a. Untersuchungen über die Grundlagen der Mengenlehre. I. *Ibid.*, 261–281. (Has not been continued.)
> 1909. Sur les ensembles finis et le principe de l'induction complète. *Acta Math.* **32**, 185–193. (Cf. *Congr. Roma 1908*, II, 8–11, 1909.)
> 1913. Über eine Anwendung der Mengenlehre auf die Theorie des Schachspiels. *Proc. 5th Intern. Congr. of Math., Cambridge 1912*, II, 501–504.

ZORN, M.
> 1944. Idempotency of infinite cardinals. *Univ. of California Publ. in Math.*, N.S. **2**, No. 1, pp. 9–12. 1944.

SUPPLEMENTARY INDEX OF AUTHORS
MENTIONED IN THE BIBLIOGRAPHY

R. Baer, mentioned under: Steinitz
F. Bagemihl: Skolem 20, Tarski 25a
W. Beman: Dedekind 1888
P. Bernays: Lorenzen
P. Bohl: Bernstein 12
É. Borel: Bernstein 12, Zermelo 04
N. G. de Bruin: D. König 26

J. Cavaillès: Cantor-Dedekind
Y. R. Chao: Bennett
A. Church: Keyser 41, Lorenzen, Smart
M. R. Cohen: Peirce 1892/1923
D. N. Cuesta: Maximoff, Neumer 53

A. Denjoy: Chajoth

P. Erdös: Sierpiński 28a

H. Fels: Bolzano 1810
G. Fodor: Erdös 50
A. Fraenkel: von Neumann 28
R. Fraïssé: Hudekoff
P. Frank: Hessenberg 08
H. Freudenthal: Hilbert 1899/1930
R. Fricke: Dedekind 30–32

L. Gillman: Mendelson

H. Hahn: Bolzano 1851
S. Hartman: Kuratowski 37
C. Hartshorne: Peirce 33
H. Hasse: Steinitz
R. S. Hoar: Bennett
A. Hoborski: Jacobsthal 09
A. Höfler: Bolzano 1837, 1851

S. Isaak: Zakon 55
K. Isenkrahe: Bodewig

V. Jarník: Jašek
P. E. B. Jourdain: Cantor 1897, Zermelo 04

B. Knaster: Tarski 28

C. Kuratowski: Tarski 25
G. Kurepa: Denjoy 53

Langenberg: Bodewig
N. Lusin: J. König 05

W. Markwald: Church-Kleene
H. Minkowski: Franklin
B. Minnegerode: Cantor 1874
K. Morinaga: Altwegg

J. von Neumann: Kuratowski 37
W. Neumer: Carruth
M. H. A. Newman: Stone 35
N. Nishigori: Altwegg
I. Niven: Johnston
E. Noether: Cantor-Dedekind, Dedekind 30–32

O. Ore: Dedekind 30–32

K. Padmavally: Sierpiński 50b
A. Padoa: Peano 06
F. Přihonsky: Bolzano 1851

W. V. O. Quine: Löwenheim

R. Rado: D. König 36
G. E. Raynor: Bennett
A. R. Richardson: A. Robinson

A. Schepp: Veronese
A. Schoenflies: Smith, Zermelo 04
P. Schrecker: Keyser 18
M. Sholander: Altwegg
W. Sierpiński: J. König 05, Lindenbaum-Tarski, Lusin 35, Mendelson, Piccard, Tarski 49a
E. Specker: Erdös-Rado 56
O. Stolz: Cantor 1895a
E. Szpilrajn: Stone 45

A. Tarski: Sierpiński 28a
E. J. Townsend: Hilbert 1899/1930

R. Vásquez García: Webber
S. Valkó: D. König 26
G. Vivanti: H. Schwarz

P. Weiss: Peirce 33

W. H. Young: Smith

O. Zariski: Dedekind 1888
E. Zermelo: Cantor 32
F. Zubieta Russi: Webber

SUPPLEMENTARY BIBLIOGRAPHY

CANTOR, G.
   1932. Reprinted, Hildesheim, 1962.

COHEN, PAUL J.
   1963-1964. The independence of the continuum hypothesis. I & II. *Acad. U.S.A.*
      50 (1963), 1143-1148 and **51** (1964), 105-110.
   1963. A minimal model for set theory. *Bull. A. M. S.* **69**, 537-540.

COHN, JONAS
   1896. *Geschichte des Unendlichkeitsproblems im abendländischen Denken bis Kant.*
      Leipzig. 270 pp. — Reprinted, 1960.

CUESTA, D. N.
   1945. *Add*: Cf. L. GILLMAN, *Proc. A. M. S.* **9**, 412-418. 1958.

HALMOS, P. R.
   1960. *Naive set theory.* Princeton. 104 pp.

HAUSDORFF, F.
   1927. English ed. (*Set theory*), 2nd ed., 1962. 352 pp.

HILBERT, D.
   1899/1930. 9th ed., revised by P. BERNAYS. 1962.

KEENE, G. B.
   1961. *Abstract sets and finite ordinals.* Oxford. 106 pp.

KLAUA, D.
   1964. *Allgemeine Mengenlehre.* Berlin. 581 pp.

LAUGWITZ, D.
   1961. Anwendungen unendlich kleiner Zahlen. I & II. *J. f. Math.* **207**, 53-60, and
      208, 22-34.

LUXEMBURG, W. A. J.
   1962. Two applications of the method of construction by ultrapowers to analysis.
      Bull. A.M.S. **68**, 416-419.

NEUMER, W.
   1953-54. *Add.* Cf. *Z. Logik Gr.* **3**, 108-150, 1957; **6**, 1-65, 1960.

QUINE, W. V. O.
   1963. *Set theory and its logic.* Cambridge, Mass. 359 pp.

ROBINSON, ABRAHAM
1939. On the independence of the axioms of definiteness (*Axiome der Bestimmt-heit*). *J.S.L.* **4**, 69–72.
1961. Non-standard analysis. *Proc. Amsterdam* A **64** = *I.M.* **23**, 432–440.
1963. *Introduction to model theory and to the metamathematics of algebra.* Amsterdam. 284 pp.

SCHOLZ, H.
1931. *Add:* English ed. (*Concise history of logic*), New York, 1961. 140 pp.

SIKORSKI, R.
1964. *Boolean algebras.* 2nd ed. Berlin etc. 237 pp.

SKOLEM, T.
1962. *Abstract set theory.* Notre Dame, Ind. 70 pp.

STEIN, S. K.
1960. Full classes and ordinals. *J. S. L.* **25**, 217–219.

SUPPES, P.
1960. *Axiomatic set theory.* Princeton. 265 pp.

THOMSON, J. F.
1962. On some paradoxes. *Analytical Philosophy* (ed. by R. J. BUTLER), New York, pp. 104–119.

VAN DER WAERDEN, B. L.
1950. *Add:* 6th. ed. (*Algebra*), 1964.

WHITESITT, J. E.
1961. *Boolean algebra and its applications.* Reading, Mass. 182 pp.

LIST OF THE LITERATURE
REFERRED TO BY AN ASTERISK *

in A. A. FRAENKEL and Y. BAR-HILLEL, *Foundations of Set Theory* (1958)

compiled for the readers of that book who do not have at their disposal
the *first* edition (1953) of *Abstract Set Theory.*

(Directions of the form "*Artin-Schreier 1 = Artin-Schreier 1927"
refer to the Bibliography *of the present book.*)

For abbreviations see above pp. 243/4, and *Foundations,* pp. 351–353.

W. *Ackermann 11, Bemerkungen zu den logisch-mathematischen Grundlagen-
problemen. *Act. Sc. Ind.* 837, 76–82. 1939.

K. *Ajdukiewicz 3, Die syntaktische Konnexität. *Studia Philos.* 1, 1–27. 1935.

F. *Albergamo 1, La tesi finitista contro l'infinito attuale e potenziale. *Atti della Soc.
Italiana per il Progresso delle Sc.*, Riun. XXIV, V, 374–386. 1936. (Cf. R. Pavese:
ibid., p. 373.)

Alice *Ambrose 1, A controversy in the logic of mathematics. *Philos. Review* 42,
594–611. 1933.

— 2, Finitism in mathematics. *Mind*, N.S. 44, 186–203, 317–340. 1935.

— 3, The nature of the question "are there three consecutive 7's in the expansion
of π?". *Papers of the Michigan Acad. of Sc., Arts and Letters* 22, 505–513. 1936.
(Cf. *Mind*, N.S. 46, 379–385. 1937.)

G. *Andreoli 1, Le antinomie: loro formazione in matematica, in logica formale, nel
raggionamento. *Atti della Soc. Italiana per il Progresso delle Sc.*, Riun. XXIV, V,
368–373. 1936. (Cf. F. Albanese: *ibid.*, p. 386.)

*Artin-Schreier 1 = Artin-Schreier 1927.

A. E. *Avey 3, The law of contradiction: its logical status. *J. of Philos.* 26, 519–526.
1929.

R. *Baer 1 = Baer 1927.

R. *Baldus 1, Formalismus und Intuitionismus in der Mathematik. Karlsruhe i. B.,
1924. 45 pp.

S. *Banach 2, Über additive Massfunktionen in abstrakten Mengen. *F.M.* 15, 97–101.
1930.

Y. *Bar-Hillel 1 (The present state of the antinomies problem. The semantic antinomies.
[Hebrew]) *Tarbits* (Jerusalem) 12, 275–286. 1941.

J. A. *Barrau 1, De onbemindheid der wiskunde. *Jaarboek der Rijksuniv. Groningen*
1925/26, 9–25. 1926.

F. *Barry 1, The scientific habit of thought. New York, 1927.

M. *Barzin and A. Errera 2, Sur le principe du tiers exclu. *Archives de la Soc. Belge
de Philos.* 1, No. 2, 1–26. 1929.

— 3, Sur la logique de M. Heyting. *L'Ens. Math.* 30, 248–250. 1932. (Cf. *ibid.*, vol.
31, 122–124, 273–274. 1933.)

— 4, La logique de M. Brouwer. État de la question. *Bull. Math. de la Soc. Roumaine
de Sc.* 35, 51–52. 1933.

*Basileioy (*ΒΑΣΙΛΕΙΟΥ,Φ.*) 1, Περὶ τῆς συγχρόνου ἀξιωματικῆς μεθόδον Δελτίον τῆς Ἑλληνικῆς Μαθηματικῆς Ἑταιρείας. 17, 119–136. 1937. (Cf. *ibid.* 25, 23–39. 1951.)

C. A. *Baylis 3, Are some propositions neither true nor false? *Philos. of Sc.* 3, 156–166. 1936.

A. *Becker 1, Die Aristotelische Theorie der Möglichkeitsschlüsse etc. Thesis Münster i.W. 1932. Berlin, 1933. 98 pp.

O. *Becker 1, Beiträge zur phänomenologischen Begründung der Geometrie und ihrer physikalischen Anwendungen. *Jahrb. f. Philos. und phänomenol. Forschung* 6, 385–560. 1923.

— 2, Mathematische Existenz. Untersuchungen zur Logik und Ontologie mathematischer Phänomene. *Ibid.* 8, 439–809. 1927. (Reprinted as a book; Halle a.S., 1927.)

— 4, Über den sogenannten "Anthropologismus" in der Philosophie der Mathematik. *Philos. Anzeiger* 3, 369–387. 1929.

H. *Behmann 1, Beiträge zur Algebra der Logik, insbesondere zum Entscheidungsproblem. *Math. Annalen* 86, 163–229. 1922. (Cf. *ibid.* 88, p. 168. 1923.)

— 5, I principii della logica simbolica. *Period. di Mat.* (4) 7, 213–230. 1927.

— 7, Sind die mathematischen Urteile analytisch oder synthetisch? *Erkenntnis* 4, 1–27. 1934.

— 8, The paradoxes of logic. *Mind*, N.S. 46, 218–221. 1937.

G. *Behrens 1, Die Prinzipien der mathematischen Logik bei Schröder, Russell und König. Thesis Kiel. Hamburg, 1918. 64 pp.

H. J. *Belinfante 2, Über eine besondere Klasse von non-oszillierenden Reihen. *Proc. Amsterdam* 33, 1170–1179. 1930.

— 3, Absolute Konvergenz in der intuitionistischen Mathematik. *Ibid.*, 1180–1184.

— 4, Die Hardy-Littlewoodsche Umkehrung des Abelschen Stetigkeitssatzes in der intuitionistischen Mathematik. *Ibid.* 34, 401–412. 1931.

— 6, Das Riemannsche Umordnungsprinzip in der intuitionistischen Theorie der unendlichen Reihen. *Compositio Math.* 6, 118–123. 1938.

— 7, Der Lévysche Umordnungssatz und seine intuitionistische Übertragung. *Ibid.*, 124–135.

*Bentley 2 = Bentley 1932.

G. *Bergmann 1, Zur Axiomatik der Elementargeometrie. *Monatsh. Math. Ph.* 36, 269–284. 1929. (Cf. *Anzeiger Akad. Wien* 65, 292–295. 1928.)

P. *Bernays 10, Methoden des Nachweises von Widerspruchsfreiheit und ihre Grenzen. *Kongr. Zürich 1932*, II, 342–343. 1932.

— 11, Hilberts Untersuchungen über die Grundlagen der Arithmetik. *David Hilbert, Gesammelte Abhandlungen*, III (Berlin, 1935), 196–216.

B. A. *Bernstein 6, Irredundant sets of postulates for the logic of propositions. *Bull. A.M.S.* 35, 545–548. 1929.

F. *Bernstein 2, Über die Reihe der transfiniten Ordnungszahlen. *Math. Annalen* 60, 187–193. 1905.

— 4, Zur Theorie der trigonometrischen Reihen. *Ber. Leipzig* 60, 325–338. 1908.

— 6, Die Mengenlehre Georg Cantors und der Finitismus. *Jahresb. D.M.V.* 28, 63–78. 1919.

E. W. *Beth 4, Une démonstration de la non-contradiction de la logique des types au point de vue fini. *N. Archief v. Wiskunde* 19, 59–62. 1936.

— 5, Rede en aanschouwing in de wiskunde. Thesis Utrecht 1935. Groningen–Batavia, s.a. (1936). 120 pp. (Cf. *Act. Sc. Ind.* 535, 161–165. 1937.)

— 6, De significa van de pasigrafische systemen. Bijdrage tot de psychologie van het wiskundig denkproces. *Euclides* 13, 145–158. 1937.

— 9, Wijsbegeerte der wiskunde. *Ibid.* 17, 141–158. 1941.

— **11,** Inleiding tot de wijsbegeerte der wiskunde. 2nd ed. Nijmegen & Utrecht, 1942. 270 pp. (New ed., 1948, 387 pp.) Cf.: Symbolische Logik und Grundlegung der exakten Wissenschaften. (*Bibliograph. Einführungen* etc., No. 3.) Bern, 1948. 28 pp.

— **12,** De wijsbegeerte der wiskunde van Parmenides tot Bolzano. Antwerpen & Nijmegen, 1944. 204 pp. (Cf. *Synthese* **5,** 248–260, 1947; P. Rucker: *Philos. Jahrb. der Görresgesellschaft* **53,** 1940.)

C. *Betsch **1,** Fiktionen in der Mathematik. Stuttgart, 1926. 372 pp. (Cf. *Unterrichtsblätter f. Math. und Naturwiss.* **38,** 79–83. 1932.)

M. *Black **3,** The claims of intuitionism. *The Philosopher* **18,** 89–97. 1936.

— **4,** Truth-functions: a criticism. *Analysis* **4,** 15–16. 1936.

J. *Blaquier **1,** El axioma de Zermelo. *Anales Ac. Nac. de Ci. etc. de Buenos Aires* **8,** 1942. 23 pp.

B. P. *Bogoslovsky **1,** The technique of controversy. Harcourt, 1928.

B. *Bolzano **2** = Bolzano 1837.

— **3** = Bolzano 1851.

É. *Borel **4** = Borel 1919.

— **5,** Méthodes et problèmes de la théorie des fonctions. Paris, 1922. 148 pp. (Cf. *Bull. de la Soc. Math. de France* **47,** 1919.)

— **6,** À propos de la récente discussion entre M. R. Wavre et M. P. Lévy. *R.M.M.* **34,** 271–276. 1927. — Reprinted in Borel 1914, 3rd ed. (Cf. *C.R. Paris* **224,** 765–767, 1537–1538, 1579–1599, 1947; **230,** 1989–1990, 1950.)

G. *Bouligand **6,** Sur quelques points relatifs à l'intervention des collections infinies en analyse mathématique. *Act. Sc. Ind.* **535,** 174–180. 1937.

— **7,** Les crises de l'unité dans la mathématique. *Revue Gén. des Sc. p. et appl.* **52,** 215–221. 1945. (Cf. *ibid.* **53,** 183–186, 1946; *R.M.M.* **52,** 308–321, 1947.)

P. *Boutroux **3,** L'idéal scientifique des mathématiciens dans l'antiquité et dans les temps modernes. Paris, 1920. (German ed. 1927. 253 pp.)

P. W. *Bridgman **1,** The logic of modern physics. New York, 1927. 242 pp. (German ed. 1932.)

— **2** = Bridgman 1934.

C. D. *Broad **2,** Scientific thought. London, 1923.

W. *Bröcker **1,** Antinomien und Paradoxien in der Logik. *Blätter f. Deutsche Philos.* **12,** 365–368. 1939.

T. *Brodén **1,** Über uneigentliche Redeweisen in der Mengenlehre und über einen Aufsatz des Herrn Hj. Eklund. *Nyt Tidsskrift f. Mat.* **29,** afd. B, 36–43. 1918. (Cf. *ibid* **27,** 28–35, 1916; **28,** 21–32, 1917.)

— **4,** Einige Worte über aktuelle mathematische Prinzipfragen. *Den Sjette Skandinaviske Mat.-Kongr. i København 1925,* pp. 229–239. 1926.

— **5,** Om den Russellska Antinomien. Lund, 1926. 21 pp.

L. E. J. *Brouwer **3,** Die möglichen Mächtigkeiten. *Congr. Roma 1908,* III, 569–571. 1909.

— **8,** (Review of Schoenflies 1913) *Jahresb. D.M.V.* **23,** 78–83 ital. 1914.

— **9,** Addenda en corrigenda over de grondslagen der wiskunde. *K. Akad. v. Wetens. te Amsterdam, Versl.* etc. *Natuurk. Afd.* **25,** 1418–1423. 1917. (Reprinted in *N. Archief v. Wiskunde* (2) **12,** 439–445. 1918.)

— **11,** Wiskunde, waarheid, werkelijkheid. Groningen, 1919. (Reprint of Brouwer 1908 and 1912, as cited in *Foundations.*)

— **13,** Besitzt jede reelle Zahl eine Dezimalbruchentwicklung? *Math. Annalen* **83,** 201–210. 1921. (Also in *Proc. Amsterdam* **23,** 955–964. 1922.)

— **18,** Intuitionistische Zerlegung mathematischer Grundbegriffe. *Jahresb. D.M.V.* **33,** 251–256. 1924. (Cf. *ibid.* **36,** 127–129. 1927.) In Dutch: *K. Akad. v. Wetens. te Amsterdam, Versl.* etc. *Natuurk. Afd.* **32,** 877–880. 1923.

— **24,** Zum freien Werden von Mengen und Funktionen. *Proc. Amsterdam* **45,** 322–323. 1942. (Cf. *ibid.,* 443; **50,** 307, 1947.)

— **25,** Beweis, dass der Begriff der Menge höherer Ordnung nicht als Grundbegriff der intuitionistischen Mathematik in Betracht kommt. *Ibid.,* 791–793.

W. *Burkamp **2,** Die Krisis des Satzes vom ausgeschlossenen Dritten. *Beiträge zur Philos. des deutschen Idealismus* **4,** No. 2, 59–81. 1927.

— **3,** Diskussion über Grundfragen der Mathematik und Logik. *Erkenntnis* **1,** 308–309. 1931.

— **4,** Logik. Berlin, 1932. 175 pp.

— **5,** Wirklichkeit und Sinn. Berlin, 1938. 2 vols. 327 & 538 pp. (Cf. P. G. J. Vredenduin: *Alg. Nederlandsch Tijdschrift v. Wijsbegeerte en Psychol.* **37,** 41–51. 1943.)

J. J. *Burkhardt **1,** Zur Neubegründung der Mengenlehre. *Jahresb. D.M.V.* **48,** 146–165. 1938.

— **2,** Zur Neubegründung der Mengenlehre. (Folge.) *Ibid.* **49,** 146–155. 1939.

C. *Burstin **1,** Ein Beitrag zur Theorie der Ordnung der linearen Systeme. *Tôhoku Math. J.* **31,** 296–299. 1929.

R. *Carnap **3** = Carnap 1927.

— **18,** Testability and meaning. *Philos. of Sc.* **3,** 419–471; **4,** 1–40, 1936/37.

R. *Carnap and F. Bachmann **1,** Über Extremalaxiome. *Erkenntnis* **6,** 166–188. 1936.

H. *Cartan **1,** Sur le fondement logique des mathématiques. *Revue Scientif.* **81,** 3–11. 1943.

U. *Cassina **2,** Paradoxo mathematico. *Schola et vita* **6,** 22; **7,** 40–41. 1931/32.

E. *Cassirer **4** = Cassirer 1929.

J. *Cavaillès **1** = Cavaillès 1932.

— **2,** Réflexions sur le fondement des mathématiques. *Act. Sc. Ind.* **535,** 136–139. 1937.

— **3** = Cavaillès 1938.

K. *Chandrasekharan **1,** Intuitionistic theory of linear order. *The Math. Student* (India) **10,** 149–162. 1942. (Cf. *ibid* **9,** 143–154, 1941; **13,** 49–51, 1945.)

P. *Chaslin **1,** Essai sur le mecanisme psychologique des opérations de la mathématique pure. Paris, 1926. (Cf. *Scientia* **29,** 111–120. 1921.)

[J. *Chevalier] **1,** Continu et discontinu (par Chevalier and others). *Cahiers de la Nouvelle Journée,* No. 15. Paris, 1929. (Cf. *Aristotelian Soc.,* suppl. vol. **4,** 170–196, 1924; *Annales Univ. Grenoble* (2) **2,** 13–39, 1925; G. Voisine, *Revue de Philos.* **33,** 531–541, 1926.)

A. *Church **4,** A set of postulates for the foundation of logic. *Annals of Math.* (2) **33,** 346–366; **34,** 839–864. 1932/33.

— **6,** A proof of freedom from contradiction. *Acad. U.S.A.* **21,** 275–281. 1935.

— **9,** Mathematical logic. (Mimeographed) Princeton N.J., 1936. 113 pp.

— **12,** Schröder's anticipation of the simple theory of types. Preprinted from *J. of Unified Sc.* **9,** 1939. 4 pp.

L. *Chwistek **1,** Über die Antinomien der Prinzipien der Mathematik. *Math. Ztschr.* **14,** 236–243. 1922.

— **3,** Sur les fondements de la logique moderne. *Atti del V Congr. Intern. di Filos.,* Napoli 1924, pp. 24–28. 1925.

— **5,** Neue Grundlagen der Logik und Mathematik. *Math. Z.* **30,** 704–724; **34,** 527–534. 1929/32.

R. G. *Collingwood **1,** An essay on philosophical method. Oxford, 1933.

G. *Combébiac **1,** Sur les éléments de la théorie des ensembles ordonnés. *L'Ens. Math.* **8,** 201–203. 1906.

J. G. *van der Corput 1, On the fundamental theorem of algebra. III. *Proc. Amsterdam* 49, 985–994. 1946. (Cf. *ibid.*, 722–732, 878–886.) Also in *I.M.* 8, 605–614. 1946. (Cf. *ibid.*, 430–440, 549–557.)

H. B. *Curry 2, Grundlagen der kombinatorischen Logik. I and II. *Am. J. of Math.* 52, 509–536, 789–834. 1930. (Cf. *ibid.* 54, 551–558. 1932.) Appeared also as a thesis, Göttingen, 1930.

D. *van Dantzig 1, Over de elementen van het wiskundig denken. Groningen, 1932. 15 pp. (Also in *Euclides* 9, 102–116. 1933.)
— 4, Wiskunde, logica en ervaringswetenschappen. *Studium Generale: Syllabus...* *Technische Hoogeschool te Delft*, 1946, pp. 71–104. (Cf. *Synthese* 5, 441–455, 1947.)

C. C. *Dassen 1, Réflexions sur quelques antinomies et sur la logique empiriste. *Anales de la Soc. Cient. Argentina* 115, 135–166, 199–232, 275–296. 1933. (Also in *Anales de la Acad. Nac. de Ci. Exactas, Fis. y Nat. de Buenos Aires* 3, 39–70, 73–128, 1933; and as a book: Buenos Aires, 1933.)
— 2, Sobre una objection a la logica Brouweriana. *Anales de la Acad. Nac. de Ci. Exactas, Fis. y Nat. de Buenos Aires* 4, 7–20. 1939.

H. T. *Davis 1, A survey of the problem of mathematical truth. Introduction (30 pp.) to: *Counting and Measuring*, by H. v. Helmholtz. New York, 1930.

R. *Dedekind 3 = Dedekind 1930–32.

M. *Dehn 1, Raum und Zeit bei Aristoteles vom mathematischen Standpunkt aus. *Scientia* 60, 12–21, 69–74. 1936.

A. *Denjoy 1, Sur les extensions de continu. *C.R. Paris* 203, 1220–1222. 1936.
— 2, La part de l'empirisme dans la logique mathématique. *Act. Sc. Ind.* 535, 111–120. 1937.

J. *Dewey 2, The applicability of logic to existence. *J. of Philos.* 27, 174–179. 1930.

W. *Dieck 1, Die Paradoxien der Mengenlehre. *Annalen der Philos. und philos. Kritik* 5, 43–56. 1926. (Cf. T. Schjelderup-Ebbe: *ibid.*, 325–328.)
— 2, Der Widerspruch im Richtigen. Sterkrade, 1926. 153 pp.

P. *Dienes 2, Logic of algebra. *Act. Sc. Ind.* 614, Paris, 1938. 77 pp.

J. G. *Dijkman 1, Einige Sätze über mehrfach negativ-konvergente Reihen in der intuitionistischen Mathematik. *Proc. Amsterdam* 49, 829–833. 1946. (Cf. 51, 681–692, 1948.) Also in *I.M.* 8, 532–536 (10, 232–243).

H. *Dingler 1, Über die Bedeutung der Burali-Fortischen Antinomie für die Wohlordnungssätze der Mengenlehre. München, 1911.
— 2, Über die logischen Paradoxien der Mengenlehre und eine paradoxienfreie Mengendefinition. *Jahresb. D.M.V.* 22, 307–315. 1913. (Also in *Z. f. positivistische Philos.* 1, 143–150, 1913.)—Cf. *ibid.* 28, 138–158. 1919.
— 5, Der Zusammenbruch der Wissenschaft und der Primat der Philosophie. 2nd ed. München, 1931.
— 7, Philosophie der Logik und Arithmetik. München, 1931. 198 pp.

A. *Dresden 1, Brouwer's contributions to the foundations of mathematics. *Bull. A.M.S.* 30, 31–40. 1924.
— 2, Mathematics and natural science. *The Monist* 37, 120–130. 1927.
— 3, Some philosophical aspects of mathematics. *Bull. A.M.S.* 34, 438–452. 1928.
— 4, Mathematical certainty. *Scientia* 45, 369–376. 1929.

J. *Droste 1, De eenheid der wiskunde. Leiden, 1930. 29 pp.

W. *Dubislav 1, Über das Verhältnis der Logik zur Mathematik. *Ann. der Philos. und philos. Kritik* 5, 193–208. 1926.
— 2 = Dubislav 1931.
— 3, Über die sogenannten analytischen und synthetischen Urteile. Berlin–Schöneberg, 1926.

— 12, Die Philosophie der Mathematik in der Gegenwart. Berlin, 1932. 88 pp.

C. J. *Ducasse 1, Symbols, signs, and signals. *J.S.L.* 4, 41–52. 1939.

A. *Dumitriu 1, Paradoxele logice. Bucharest, 1944. 200 pp.

K. *Dürr 3, Die Bedeutung der Negation. *Erkenntnis* 5, 205–227. 1935.

L. *Egyed 1, Über das Auswahlaxiom und mit ihm zusammenhängende Fragen. (Hungarian, with German abstract) *Mat. Fiz. Lap.* 45, 133–150. 1938.

H. *Eklund 1, Über Mengen, die Elemente ihrer selbst sind. *Nyt Tidsskrift f. Mat.*, Avd. B 29, 8–28. 1918.

F. *Enriques 2, Sur quelques questions soulevées par l'infini mathématique. *R.M.M.* 24, 149–164. 1917.

P. *Erdös and A. Tarski 1, On families of mutually exclusive sets. *Annals of Math.* (2) 44, 315–329. 1943.

A. *Errera 2, Sur la crise contemporaine des mathématiques. *L'Ens. Math.* 34, 12–17. 1935. (Cf. M. Barzin: *ibid.*, 5–11; Errera: *ibid.*, 103–111; *Congr. Oslo 1936*, II, 270–271, 1937.)

— 3, Sur le principe du tiers exclu. *Mathematica* (Cluj) 9, 73–79. 1935.

M. *Euwe 1 = Euwe 1929.

S. *Faedo 1, Il principio di Zermelo per gli spazi astratti. *Annali della Scuola Norm. Super. Pisa* (2) 9, 263–276. 1940.

M. *Farber 1, Theses concerning the foundations of logic. *Philos. Review* 38, 219–231. 1929.

— 3, Logical systems and the principles of logic. *Philos. of Sc.* 9, 40–54. 1942.

Paulette *Février 3 (Destouches–Février), Logique adaptée aux théorie quantiques. *C.R. Paris* 221, 287–288. 1945.

J. *Findlay 1, Goedelian sentences: a non-numerical approach. *Mind*, N.S. 51, 259–265. 1942.

P. *Finsler 2, Formale Beweise und die Entscheidbarkeit. *Math. Z.* 25, 676–682. 1926.

— 5, Die Existenz der Zahlenreihe und des Kontinuums. *Commentarii Math. Helvet.* 5, 88–94. 1933. (Cf. *L'Ens. Math.* 31, 118–119, 1933.)

— 6, À propos de la discussion sur les fondements des mathématiques. *Les Entretiens de Zurich*, pp. 162–180. 1941.

— 7, Gibt es unentscheidbare Sätze? *Commentarii Math. Helvet.* 16, 310–320. 1944.

F. B. *Fitch 1, A system of formal logic without an analogue to the Curry *W* operator. *J.S.L.* 1, 92–100. 1936.

— 4, The consistency of the ramified *Principia*. *Ibid.* 3, 140–149. 1938.

— 8, A basic logic. *Ibid.* 7, 105–114. 1942. (Cf. *ibid* 13, 95–106; 14, 9–15, 209–218; 15, 17–24; J. R. Myhill: *ibid.* 15, 185–196; 1948–50.)

— 9, Representations of calculi. *Ibid.* 9, 57–62. 1944.

— 11, Self-reference in philosophy. *Mind*, N.S. 55, 64–73. 1946.

E. *Foradori 1, Grundbegriffe einer allgemeinen Teiltheorie. *Monatsh. Math. Ph.* 39, 439–454. 1932.

— 2, Stetigkeit und Kontinuität als Teilbarkeitseigenschaften. *Ibid.* 40, 161–180. 1933. (Cf. *ibid.* 41, 133–173, 1934.)

— 4, Grundgedanken der Teiltheorie. Leipzig, 1937. 79 pp.

A. L. *Foster 1, Formal logic in finite terms. *Annals of Math.* (2) 32, 407–430. 1931.

A. (A.) *Fraenkel 4, Axiomatische Begründung der transfiniten Kardinalzahlen. I. *Math. Z.* 13, 153–188. 1922.

— 13, Die heutigen Gegensätze in der Grundlegung der Mathematik. *Erkenntnis* 1, 286–302. 1930.

— 16, Sur la notion d'existence dans les mathématiques. *L'Ens. Math.* 34, 18–32. 1935.

— **18** = Fraenkel 1935.
— **20**, Discontinu et continu. *Act. Sc. Ind.* **535**, 193–200. 1937.
A. (A.) *Fraenkel and Y. Bar-Hillel **1**, Le problème des antinomies et ses développements récents. *R.M.M.* **51**, 225–242. 1939.
H. *Freudenthal **1**, Qualität in der Mathematik. *Euclides* **8**, 89–98. 1932.
— **2**, (Review of Heyting 1930 and 1930a) *Jahrb. über die Fortschritte der Mathematik* **56**ɪɪ, 823–824. 1935.
B. *von Freytag **1**, Die ontologischen Grundlagen der Mathematik. Eine Untersuchung über die "Mathematische Existenz". Thesis. Halle a.S., 1937. 49 pp. (Cf. M. Steck: Zum Problem der mathematischen Existenz, *Deutsche Math.* **3**, 467–473, 1938; B. von Freytag: *ibid.* **4**, 238–240, 1939.)
O. *Frink Jr. **3**, New algebras of logic. *Am. Math. Monthly* **45**, 210–219. 1938.

D. *García **2**, Assaigs moderns per a la fonamentació de les matemàtiques. *Soc. Catalana de Ci. Fis. etc., Public.* **1**, 225–275. 1933.
G. *Giorgi **1**, Riflessioni sui fondamenti primi della teoria degli insiemi. *Pontif. Ac. Sc., Acta* **5**, 35–40. 1941.
F. *Gonseth **4**, La vérité mathématique et la réalité. *L'Enseign. Math.* **31**, 96–114. 1933. (Cf. *Verhandl. der Schweiz. Naturforsch. Gesellsch.* **113**, 220–241, 1932; *Scientia* **56**, 313–325, 1934.)
— **5**, Les mathématiques et la réalité. Essai sur la méthode axiomatique. Paris, 1936. 386 pp. (Cf. *Semaine Intern. Synthèse* **5**, 9–44, 1934; *Revue Néo-Scolast. de Philos.* **39**, 169–183, 1936.)
— **6**, Qu'est-ce que la logique? *Act. Sc. Ind.* **524**, Paris, 1937. 89 pp. (Cf. *ibid.* **393**, 1–23. 1936.)
T. *Greenwood **2**, Invention and description in mathematics. *Proc. Arist. Soc.*, N.S. **30**, 79–90. 1930.
K. *Grelling **1** = Grelling 1910.
— **2**, Mengenlehre. Leipzig & Berlin, 1924. 49 pp.
— **6**, Identitas indiscernibilium. Erkenntnis **6**, 252–259. 1937.
E. R. *Guthrie **1**, The paradoxes of Mr. Russell with a brief account of their history. (Thesis, Univ. of Pennsylvania, 1914.) Lancaster Pa., 1915. 23 pp.
A. *Gutzmer **1**, Leopold Kronecker. *Naturw. Wochenschrift* **8**, 591–593. 1893.

Haalmeijer-Schogt **1** = Haalmeijer-Schogt 1926.
J. *Hadamard **4**, An essay on the psychology of invention in the mathematical field. Princeton, 1945. 143 pp. Revised ed. 1949.
K. G. *Hagström **1**, Om mängdteoriens paradoxier. *N. Tidsskrift f. Mat.* B **25**, 1–19. 1914.
— **2**, Note sur l'antinomie Burali-Forti. *Arkiv f. Mat. etc.* **10**, No. 2, 1914/15. 4 pp.
H. *Hahn **7**, Überflüssige Wesenheiten. (Occams Rasiermesser.) Wien, 1930. 24 pp.
— **9**, Logik, Mathematik und Naturerkennen. (*Einheitswissenschaft*, No. **2**.) Wien, 1933. (French edition by E. Vouillemin with an introduction by M. Boll: *Act. Sc. Ind.* **226**. Paris, 1935. 51 pp.)
— **10**, Gibt es Unendliches? *Alte Probleme—neue Lösungen in den exakten Wissenschaften* (*Fünf Wiener Vorträge*), 2. Zyklus, pp. 93–116. Leipzig & Wien, 1934.
*(Hahn–Neurath–Carnap) **1**, Wissenschaftliche Weltauffassung. Der Wiener Kreis. Wien, 1929. 59 pp.
P. *Hall **1**, On representatives of subsets. *J. London Math. Soc.* **10**, 26–30. 1934.
G. H. *Hardy **1**, A theorem concerning the infinite cardinal numbers. *Quarterly J. of p. and appl. Math.* **35**, 87–94. 1904.

— 2, The continuum and the second number class. *Proc. London Math. Soc.* (2) 4, 10–17. 1907.

H. *Härlen 1, Sur la paradoxie logique dans la théorie des ensembles. *C.R. Paris* 184, 367–369. 1927.

— 2, Über Vollständigkeit und Entscheidbarkeit. *Jahresb. D.M.V.* 37, 226–228. 1928. (Cf. *ibid.*, 229–230.)

— 6, Bemerkungen... (zu Behmann 1931). *Ibid.* 40, 156–159. 1931.

E. *Hartmann 1, Der Satz vom ausgeschlossenen Dritten in der Mathematik. *Philos. Jahrb. der Görresges.* 40, 127–128. 1927.

*Hasse-Scholz 1 = Hasse-Scholz 1928.

O. *Haupt 2, Existenzbeweise in der elementaren und höheren Mathematik. *Unterrichtsblätter f. Math. und Naturwiss.* 36, 224–226. 1930.

F. *Hausdorff 2 = Hausdorff 1906–07.

— 3 = Hausdorff 1908.

E. R. *Hedrick 1, Tendencies in the logic of mathematics. *Science*, N.S. 77, 335–343. 1933.

F. H. *Heinemann 1, The meaning of negation. *Proc. Ar. Soc.*, N.S. 44, 127–152. 1944.

R. *Heiss 1, Der Mechanismus der Paradoxien und das Gesetz der Paradoxienbildung. *Philos. Anzeiger* 2, 403–433. 1928.

P. *Henle 3, A note on the validity of Aristotelian logic. *Philos. of Sc.* 2, 111–113. 1935.

J. *Herbrand 5, Les bases de la logique hilbertienne. *R.M.M.* 37, 243–255. 1930.

G. *Hessenberg 10, Mengenlehre. *Taschenbuch f. Math. und Physiker* 3, 69–81. 1913.

A. *Heyting 1, Intuitionistische axiomatiek der projectieve meetkunde. Thesis Amsterdam. Groningen, 1925. 95 pp.

— 3, Zur intuitionistischen Axiomatik der projektiven Geometrie. *Math. Annalen* 98, 491–538.

— 4, De telbaarheidspraedicaten van Prof. Brouwer. *N. Archief v. Wiskunde* (2) 16, 47–58. 1929.

— 8, Die intuitionistische Grundlegung der Mathematik. *Erkenntnis* 2, 106–115. 1931. (Cf. the discussion of H. Hahn, R. Carnap, J. von Neumann, H. Scholz, A. Heyting, K. Gödel, K. Reidemeister: *ibid.*, 135–151.)

— 9, Anwendung der intuitionistischen Logik auf die Definition der Vollständigkeit eines Kalküls. *Kongr. Zürich 1932*, II, 344–345. 1933.

— 10, À propos d'un article de MM. Barzin et Errera. *L'Ens. Math.* 31, 121–122. 1933. (Cf. *ibid.*, 271–272, 274–275.)

— 12, Intuitionistische wiskunde. *Mathematica* (Leiden), B 4, 72–83, 123–136; 5, 62–80, 105–112. 1935/36.

— 13, Ruimteleer en axiomatiek. Groningen & Batavia, 1937. 16 pp.

— 14, Intuitionistische wiskunde. *Mathematica*, B 7, 129–142. 1939.

— 15, Les fondements des mathématiques du point de vue intuitionniste. *Act. Sc. Ind. 837*, 73–75. 1939.

— 17, On weakened quantification. *J.S.L.* 11, 119–121. 1946. (Cf. F. B. Fitch: *Portugaliae Math.* 7, 113–118, 1949.)

D. *Hilbert 3, Über den Zahlbegriff. *Jahresb. D.M.V.* 8, 180–184. 1900.

— 4, Mathematische Probleme. *Nachr. Göttingen*, 1900, pp. 253–297. (Reprinted with some additions in *Archiv der Math. und Ph.* (3) 1, 44–63, 213–237, 1901. In English: *Bull. A.M.S.* 8, 437–479, 1902. In French: *C.R. du 2me Congr. Intern. des Math....* Paris 1900, pp. 58–114, 1902.)

— 5, Über die Grundlagen der Logik und Arithmetik. *Kongr. Heidelberg 1904*, pp. 174–185. 1905. (In English: *The Monist* 15, 338–352, 1905. In French: *L'Ens. Math.* 7, 89–103, 1905.)

E. W. *Hobson 1, On the general theory of transfinite numbers and order types. *Proc. London Math. Soc.* (2) **3**, 170–188. 1905.

— 2, The theory of functions of a real variable and the theory of Fourier's series. Cambridge; vol. I (3rd ed.) 1927, vol. II (2nd ed.) 1926.

F. *Hoensbroech 2, On Russell's paradox. *Mind*, N.S. **48**, 355–358. 1939.

O. *Hölder 3, Die mathematische Methode. Berlin, 1924. 563 pp.

— 4, Der angebliche circulus vitiosus und die sogenannte Grundlagenkrise in der Analysis. *Ber. Leipzig* **78**, 243–250. 1926.

— 7, Axiome, empirische Gesetze und mathematische Konstruktion. *Scientia* **49**, 317–326. 1931.

J. M. *Horák 1, Sur les antinomies de la théorie des ensembles. *Bull. Intern. de l'Acad. des Sc. de Bohême* **26**, 38–44. 1926. (Cf. *Časopis* **57**, 256–259, 1928.)

C. E. *van Horn 2, A system of relative existential propositions connected with the relation of class membership. *Univ. of Chicago, Abstracts of Theses, Sc. Ser.* **1**, 31–37. 1925.

E. V. *Huntington 6, A new set of postulates for betweenness with proof of complete independence. *Tr. A.M.S.* **26**, 257–282. 1924.

— 9, The postulational method in mathematics. *Am. Math. Monthly* **41**, 84–92. 1934. (Cf. *Philos. of Sc.* **4**, 482–495, 1937; *Scr. Math.* **5**, 149–157, 233–238, 1939.)

— 10, Independent postulates for the "informal" part of *Principia Mathematica*. *Bull. A.M.S.* **40**, 127–136. 1934. (Cf. *ibid.*, 137–143.)

— 11, Independent postulates related to C. I. Lewis's theory of strict implication. *Mind*, N.S. **43**, 181–198. 1934. (Cf. *Fund. Math.* **25**, 147–156, 1935.)

E. *Husserl 1, Logische Untersuchungen. Vol. I (4th ed.), II 1 (4th ed.), II 2 (3rd ed.). Halle a.S., 1928 & 1921.

M. H. *Ingraham 1, Certain limitations of the value of the complete independence of a set of postulates. *Bull. A.M.S.* **29**, 199–200. 1923.

B. *Janowski 1, Les bornes de la mathématique grecque et ses fondements spéculatifs. *Act. Sc. Ind.* **395**, 9–19. 1936.

S. *Jaśkowski 1, On the rules of suppositions in formal logic. *Studia Logica* **1**, 5–32. 1934.

J. *Jørgensen 1, A treatise of formal logic. 3 vols. Copenhagen & London, 1931. 266 + 273 + 321 pp.

— 3, Remarques sur les principales implications métaphysiques des théories et des idées récentes de la physique. *R.M.M.* **39**, 323–351. 1932.

— 5, Traek af deduktionsteoriens udvikling i den nyere tid. Copenhagen, 1937. 117 pp.

— 6, Intervention. *Les Entretiens de Zurich*, pp. 181–184. 1941.

P. E. B. *Jourdain 1 = Jourdain 1905.

— 1a, On the transfinite cardinal number of well-ordered aggregates. *Philos. Mag.* (6) **7**, 61–75. 1904.

— 3, De infinito in mathematica. *Revista de Mat.* **8**, 121–136. 1906. (Cf. *Proc. London Math. Soc.* (2) **4**, 266–283, 1907; *The Monist* **20**, 93–118, 1910; *Quarterly J. of p. and appl. Math.* **41**, 324–352, 1910; **43**, 219–314, 1912; **44**, 113–128, 1913; *Scientia* **21**, 1–12, 1917.)

— 6, The philosophy of Mr. B*rtr*nd R*ss*ll, with an appendix of leading passages from certain other works. London, 1918. 96 pp.

— 10 = Jourdain 1922.

E. *Kaila 2, Probleme der Deduktion. *Annales Univ. Fennicae Aboensis*, B4, No. 2. 1928. 86 pp.

L. *Kalmar 5, Über einen Löwenheimschen Satz. *Acta Szeged* 7, 112–121. 1935.
— 7, Zurückführung des Entscheidungsproblems auf den Fall von Formeln mit einer einzigen, binären, Funktionsvariablen. *Compositio Math.* 4, 137–144. 1936. (Cf. *Kongr. Zürich 1932*, II, 337–338, 1933.)
E. *Kamke 2, Zur Definition der affinen Abbildung. *Jahresb. D.M.V.* 36, 145–156. 1927.
— 3 = Kamke 1928.
L. *Kattsoff 1, Concerning the validity of Aristotelian logic. *Philos. of Sc.* 1, 149–162. 1934. (Cf. P. Henle 3.)
— 4, Modality and probability. *Philos. Review* 46, 78–85. 1937.
F. *Kaufmann 2, Bemerkungen zum Grundlagenstreit in Logik und Mathematik. *Erkenntnis* 2, 262–290. 1931.
— 4, Über den Begriff des Formalen in Logik und Mathematik. *Act. Sc. Ind.* 535, 128–135. 1937.
F. *Kaulbach 1, Zur Logik und Kategorienlehre der mathematischen Gegenstände. Thesis Erlangen. 1937. 162 pp.
A. J. *Kempner 2, Remarks on "unsolvable problems". *Am. Math. Monthly* 43, 467–473. 1936.
B. *Knaster and C. Kuratowski 1, Sur les ensembles connexes. *F.M.* 2, 206–255. 1921.
M. Kondô 1, Sur l'hypothèse de M. B. Knaster dans la théorie des ensembles de points. *J. Fac. of Sc. Hokkaido Univ.*, Ser. I 6, 1–20. 1937.
J. *König 2, see J. König 1905.
A. *Korselt 2, Über mathematische Erkenntnis. *Jahresb. D.M.V.* 20, 364–380. 1911. (Cf. *ibid.* 12, 402–407, 1903; 17, 98–124, 1908; *Archiv. der Math. und Ph.* (3) 21, 371–373, 1913.)
— 4, Auflösung einiger Paradoxien. *Ibid.* 25, 132–138. 1917.
A. *Korzybski 1, Science and sanity. Lancaster Pa., 1933. 798 pp. 3rd ed., 1948.
A. *Koyré 1, The liar. *Philosophy and Phenomen. Research* 6, 344–362. 1946.
A. *Koźniewski and A. Lindenbaum 1, Sur les opérations d'addition et de multiplication dans les classes d'ensembles. *F.M.* 15, 342–355. 1930.
W. *Krull 1, Algebraische Theorie der Ringe. I. *Math. Annalen* 88, 80–122. 1923.
G. *Kurepa 2 = Kurepa 1935.

L. J. *Lafleur 1, Mathematical antinomies. *The Monist* 40, 526–534. 1930.
A. *Lamouche 1, Essai sur la méthode des sciences. *Revue Philosophique* 108, 48–104. 1929.
Susanne K. *Langer 1, Confusion of symbols and confusion of logical types. *Mind*, N.S. 35, 222–229. 1926.
C. H. *Langford 3 = Langford 1927.
— 9, Concerning logical principles. *Bull. A.M.S.* 34, 573–582. 1928.
E. H. *Larguier, S.J., 1, Brouwerian philosophy of mathematics. *Scr. Math.* 7, 69–78. 1940.
A. *Lautman 4, Nouvelles recherches sur la structure dialectique des mathématiques. (*Acta Sc. Ind.* 804.) Paris, 1939. 32 pp.
H. *Lebesgue 2 = Lebesgue 1904.
— 4, Sur certaines démonstrations d'existence *Bull. Soc. Math. de France* 45, 132–144. 1917. (Cf. *F.M.* 2, 259–260, 1921; *Bull. des Sc. Math.* (2) 46, 1re Partie, p. 48, 1922.)
— 5, Remarques sur les théories de la mesure et de l'intégration. *Annales Scientif. de l'École Normale Sup.* (3) 35, 191–250. 1918.
Beppo *Levi 1, Intorno alla teoria degli aggregati. *R. Istituto Lombardo di Sc. e Lettere, Rendiconti* (2) 35, 863–868. 1902. (Cf. F. Bernstein: *Nachr. Göttingen*, 1904, 557–560.)

— **2**, Antinomie logiche? *Annali di Mat. p. ed appl.* (3) **15**, 187–216. 1908.
— **6**, Nota di logica matematica. *R. Ist. Lomb. di Sc. e Lettere, Rendic* (2) **66**, 239–252. 1933. (Cf. Considerazioni sulle esigenze logiche della nozione del reale e sul principio delle infinite scelte. *Atti dell' VIII Congr. di Filos., Roma 1933.* 1934. 11 pp.)
— **7**, La nozione di "dominio deduttivo" e la sua importanza in taluni argomenti relativi ai fondamenti dell'analisi. *F.M.* **23**, 63–74. 1934. (Cf. S. Minetti: *Kongr. Zürich 1932*, II, 68–69. 1933.)
— **8**, A proposito del infinito e delle sue antinomie. *Atti della Soc. Ital. per il Progr. delle Sc.*, Riun. XXIV, vol. V, 363–367. 1936.

P. *Lévy, **1**, Sur le principe du tiers exclu et sur les théorèmes non susceptibles de démonstration. *R.M.M.* **33**, 253–258. 1926.
— **2**, Critique de la logique empirique. Réponse à M. R. Wavre. *Ibid.*, 545–551.
— **4**, Le raisonnement et l'expérience dans les fondements des mathématiques. *Scientia* **47**, 325–334. 1930.
— **5**, Les paradoxes de la théorie des ensembles infinis. *Recherches Philos.* **6**, 204–219. 1937.

L. *Lichtenstein **1** = Lichtenstein 1932.

W. *Lietzmann **2**, Formalismus und Intuitionismus in der Mathematik. *Ztschr. f. math. und naturwiss. Unterricht* **56**, 355–358. 1925.

H. *Lipps **2**, Bemerkungen zu der Paradoxie des "Lügners". *Kant-Studien* **28**, 335–339. 1923.
— **4**, Untersuchungen zur Phänomenologie der Erkenntnis. 2. Teil. Bonn, 1928.

J. E. *Littlewood **1** = Littlewood 1926.
— **2**, Mathematical notes. I: On transfinite cardinals. *J. London Math. Soc.* **1**, 193–194. 1926.

L. *Locher **1**, Die Finslerschen Arbeiten zur Grundlegung der Mathematik. *Commentarii Math. Helv.* **10**, 206–207. 1938.

B. *de Loor **1**, Die hoofstelling van die algebra van intuïsionistise standpunt. Thesis Amsterdam. Amsterdam, s.a. (1925). 63 pp.

H. *Löwy **1**, Die Krisis in der Mathematik und ihre philosophische Bedeutung. *Naturwissenschaften* **14**, 706–708. 1926.

J. *Łukasiewicz **3**, Philosophische Bemerkungen zu mehrwertigen Systemen des Aussagenkalküls. *C.R. Varsovie* **23**, 51–77. 1930. (Cf. already the notes written in Polish: *Ruch Filoz.* [Lwów] **5**, 169–171, 1920, and *Przegl. Fil.* **23**, 189–205, 1921.)

J. *Łukasiewicz and A. Tarski **1**, Untersuchungen über den Aussagenkalkül. *C.R. Varsovie* **23**, 30–50. 1930.

N. *Lusin **4**, Analogie entre les ensembles mesurables *B* et les ensembles analytiques. *F.M.* **16**, 48–76. 1930.
— **5**, Leçons sur les ensembles analytiques et leurs applications. (*Collection Borel.*) Paris, 1930. 328 pp.
— **7**, Sur les classes des constituantes des complémentaires analytiques. *Annali della Scuola Norm. Sup. Pisa* (2) **2**, 269–282. 1933.
— **8**, Sur les suites stationnaires. (*Act. Sc. Ind.* **149**.) Paris, 1934.
— **9**, Sur un raisonnement nouveau dans la théorie des fonctions descriptive. *C.R. Paris* **201**, 638–640. 1935.
— **10** = Lusin 1935.
— **11**, Sur les parties de la suite naturelle des nombres entiers. *C.R. de l'Acad. des Sc. U.R.S.S.*, N.S. **40**, 175–178. 1943. (Cf. *Izvest. Ak. Nauk S.S.S.R.*, Ser. Mat. **11**, 403–410, 1947.)

J. C. C. *McKinsey **13**, On the number of complete extensions of the Lewis systems of sentential calculus. *J.S.L.* **9**, 42–45. 1944.

A. M. *MacIver 1, More about some old logical puzzles. *Analysis* 6, 63–68. 1939.

P. *Mahlo 1 = Mahlo 1911.

— 2, Zur Theorie und Anwendung der ϱ_0-Zahlen. *Ber. Leipzig* 64, 108–112; 65, 268–282. 1912/13.

B. *Manià 2, Il pensiero scientifico di fronte al problema del infinito. *Atti della Soc. Ital. per il Progr. delle Sc.*, Riun. XXIV, vol. V, 352–361. 1936. (Cf. *Act. Sc. Ind.* 393, 51–57, 1936.)

G. *Mannoury 1, Methodologisches und Philosophisches zur Elementarmathematik. Haarlem, 1909. 276 pp.

— 3, Woord en gedachte. Een inleiding tot de signifika, inzonderheid met het oog op het onderwijs in de wiskunde. Groningen, 1931. —Also in *Euclides* 7, 1–61. 1931.

— 5, De "Wiener Kreis" en de signifische begrippenanalyse. *Algem. Nederl. Tijdschrift v. Wijsbegeerte en Psychol.* 29, 81–91. 1935.

— 6, La question vitale "*A ou B*". *N. Archief v. Wiskunde* (2) 21, 161–167. 1943.

T. *Matsumoto 1, On paradoxes and definitions. *Memoirs of the College of Sc.*, *Kyoto Imp. Univ.*, A 11, 367–373. 1928.

K. *Menger 1, Bericht über die Dimensionstheorie. *Jahresb. D.M.V.* 35, 113–150. 1926. (Cf. *ibid.* 36, 8–12 ital., 1927.)

— 9, Die neue Logik. *Krise und Neuaufbau in den exakten Wiss.* (Leipzig & Wien, 1933), 93–122. In English: *Philos. of Sc.* 4, 299–336. 1937.

J. *Meyer 1, Over de geldigheid van het beginsel van het uitgesloten derde. *Alg. Ned. Tijdschr. v. Wijsbegeerte etc.* 21, 1–29. 1927.

E. H. *Moore 1, Introduction to a form of general analysis. New Haven, 1910. 150 pp.

R. L. *Moore 1, Foundations of point set theory. (*A.M.S. Coll. Public.* 13.) New York, 1932. 486 pp.

C. W. *Morris 1 = Morris 1929.

— 3, Foundations of the theory of signs. (*Int. Enc. Unif. Sc.* I, No. 2.) Chicago, 1938. 59 pp.

E. *Nagel 6, Logic without ontology. *Naturalism and the Human Spirit* (New York, 1944), pp. 210–241.

J. *von Neumann 5, Ein System algebraisch unabhängiger Zahlen. *Math. Annalen* 99, 134–141. 1928.

C. *Nink 1, Der Satz vom ausgeschlossenen Dritten. Ein philosophischer Beitrag zur Grundlagenkrise der Mathematik. *Scholastik* 12, 552–558. 1937.

Emmy *Noether 1, Die allgemeinsten Bereiche aus ganzen transzendenten Zahlen. *Math. Annalen* 77, 103–128. 1916.

— 2, Die Funktionalgleichungen der isomorphen Abbildung. *Ibid.*, 536–545.

E. P. *Northrop 1, Riddles in mathematics. A book of paradoxes. New York, 1944. 262 pp. —London, 1945. 242 pp.

A. *Oikonomou (*ΑΡΙΣΤΟΤΕΛΗΣ ΟΙΚΟΝΟΜΟΥ*) 1, Ai ἀντινομίαι εἰς τὰ νεώτερα μαθηματικά. *Bull. de la Soc. Math. de Grèce* 7, 67–80. 1926. (Cf. S. Muller-Oikonomou: *ibid* 21, 67–103. 1941.)

J. *Orloff 1, Sur la théorie de la compatibilité des propositions. (Russian with French abstract) *Mat. Sbornik* 35, 263–286. 1928.

C. H. *van Os 1, De crisis der logica. *Synthese* 3, 314–336. 1938.

A. *Ostrowski 1, Über einige Fragen der allgemeinen Körpertheorie. *J. f. Math.* 143, 255–284. 1913.

A. *Padoa 1, Un nouveau système irréductible de postulats pour l'algèbre. *C.R. du 2me Congr. Intern. des Math.*, *Paris 1900*, 249–256. 1902.

S. *Pankajam 3, On the formal structure of the propositional calculus. *J. Indian Math. Soc.*, N.S. 5, 49–61; 6, 51–62, 102. 1941/42.

M. *Pasch 1 = Pasch 1882.
—   3, Die axiomatische Methode in der neueren Mathematik. *Ann. der Philos. und philos. Kritik* 5, 241–274. 1926.
—   4, Mathematik am Ursprung. Gesammelte Abhandlungen über Grundfragen der Mathematik. Leipzig. 1927. 149 pp. (Contains also 3.)
—   5, Der Ursprung des Zahlbegriffs. New edition: Berlin, 1930. 50 pp.

G. *Peano 2, Démonstration de l'intégrabilité des équations differentielles ordinaires. *Math. Annalen* 37, 182–228. 1890. (Cf. D. van Dantzig: *Proc. Amsterdam* 45, 367–373, 1942.)
—   5, Les définitions mathématiques. *Bibliothòque du Congrès Intern. de Philosophie, Paris 1900*, III (Paris, 1903), pp. 279–288. (Cf. *Bolletino della "Mathesis"*, N.S. 7, 106–120, 1915; *Periodico di Mat.* (4) 1, 175–189, 1921; W. Wilkosz: *Ann. de la Soc. Polon. de Math.* 16, 176–178, 1938.)

C. S. *Peirce 2 = Peirce 1933 (vols. II and V).

C. *Perelman 3, L'équivalence, la définition et la solution du paradoxe de Russell. *L'Ens. Math.* 36, 350–356. 1938.

H. *Pichler 1, Vom Wesen der Erkenntnis. Erfurt, 1926.

J. *Pierpont 2, Mathematical rigor, past and present. *Bull. A.M.S.* 34, 23–53. 1928.

H. *Poincaré 2, La science et l'hypothèse. Paris (1903). 40me mille (*Biblioth. de Philos. Scient.*), 1925. English ed. 1905. German ed. (*Wissenschaft und Hypothese* 1), 2nd ed., Leipzig, 1906.
—   3, Réflexions sur les deux notes précédentes. *Acta Math.* 32, 195–200. 1909.
—   4 = Poincaré 1910.

E. L. *Post 1, Introduction to a general theory of elementary propositions. *Am. J. of Math.* 43, 163–185. 1921.

M. *Presburger 1, Über die Vollständigkeit eines gewissen Systems der Arithmetik ganzer Zahlen, in welchem die Addition als einzige Operation hervortritt. *C.R. du I Congr. des Math. des Pays Slaves, Warszawa 1929*, pp. 92–101, 395. 1930.

H. *Prüfer 1, Theorie der Abelschen Gruppen. I. *Math. Z.* 20, 165–187. 1924.

W. V. O. *Quine 12, Truth by convention. *Philos. Essays for A.N. Whitehead* (New York, 1936), pp. 90–124.
—   16 = Quine 1937.
—   17, Logic based on inclusion and abstraction. *J.S.L.* 2, 145–152. 1937.
—   23, Russell's paradox and others. *Technology Review* 44, 16–17. 1941.
—   29, On ordered pairs. *J.S.L.* 10, 95–96. 1945. (Cf. *ibid.* 11, 71–72, 1946.)

R. *Rado 1, Bemerkungen zur Kombinatorik im Anschluss an Untersuchungen von Herrn D. König. *Sitz. der Berliner Math. Gesellschaft* 32, 60–75. 1933. (Cf. *ibid.*, 589–596; *Proc. London M.S.* (2) 48, 122–160, 1943.)

F. P. *Ramsey 3, Mathematical logic. *Math. Gazette* 13, 185–194. 1927. (Cf. *The Encycl. Britannica*, 13th ed., vol. 2 of the suppl. vols. [London & New York, 1926], pp. 830–832; *ibid.*, 14th ed. [London & New York, 1929], vol. 15, 82–84, and vol. 19, 678–679.)
—   5, The foundations of mathematics and other logical essays. Ed. by R. B. Braithwaite. New York & London, 1931.

G. *Rebec 1, Zu den Antinomien zurück. *Logos* 21, 195–219. 1932.

O. L. *Reiser 1, Non-Aristotelian logics. *The Monist* 45, 100–117. 1935.
—   2, Modern science and non-Aristotelian logic. *Ibid.* 46, 299–317. 1936. (Cf. *Scientia* 61, 137–150, 1937; *Philos. Review* 49, 662–672, 1940.)

Antoinette *Reymond 1, Points de contact entre la logique stoïcienne et la logique Russellienne. *Act. Sc. Ind.* **395**, 20–23. 1936.

A(rnold) *Reymond 2, L'axiomatique logique et le principe du tiers exclu. (Discussion de L. Brunschvicg, R. Lenoir, P. Lévy.) *Bull. de la Soc. Française de Philos.* **27**, 1–23. 1927. (Cf. *Revue de Théol. et de Philos.*, N.S. **15**, 309–312, 1927.)

— 4, Les principes de la logique et la critique contemporaine. (*Biblioth. de la Revue des Cours et Conférences.*) Paris, 1932. 277 pp.

— 5, La négation et le principe du tiers exclu. *Act. Sc. Ind.* **393**, 62–68. 1936. (Cf. Antoinette Virieux-Reymond: *Revue de Théol. et de Philos.*, N.S. **28**, 134–136, 1940.)

J. *Richard 2, Sur un paradoxe de la théorie des ensembles et sur l'axiome de Zermelo. *L'Ens. Math.* **9**, 94–98. 1907. (Cf. *ibid.*, 39–44.)

— 4, Sur l'axiome de Zermelo. *Bull. des Sc. Math.* (2) **53**, 106–109. 1929.

W. *Rivier 1, À propos du principe du tiers exclu. Empirisme et idéalisme dans les mathématiques. *Revue de Théol. et de Philos.*, N.S. **13**, 215–221. 1925. (Cf. J. Larguier des Bancels: *ibid.* **14**, 120–124, 1926.)

J. B. *Rosser 2, A mathematical logic without variables. II. *Duke Math. J.* **1**, 328–355. 1935. (Cf. *Annals of Math.* (2) **36**, 127–150, 1935.)

— 12, The Burali-Forti paradox. *J.S.L.* **7**, 1–17. 1942.

L. *Rougier 2, La philosophie géométrique de Henri Poincaré. (*Bibl. de Philos. Contemp.*) Paris, 1920.

B. *Russell 10, (Review of Ramsey 5) *Mind*, N.S. **40**, 476–482. 1931. (Cf. *Philosophy* **7**, 84–86, 1932.)

— 12, The limits of empirism. *Proc. Arist. Soc.*, N.S. **36**, 131–150. 1936.

U. *Saarnio 2, Zur heterologischen Paradoxie. *Theoria* **3**, 38–56. 1937. (Cf. W. V. O. Quine: *J.S.L.* **2**, 138. 1937.)

O. *Samuel 1, Über diskursive Sophismen. *Z. f. Philos. u. philos. Kritik* **147**, 185–222. 1912.

F. C. S. *Schiller 1, The infinite regress of proof. *Mind*, N.S. **37**, 353–354. 1928.

M. *Schlick 2, Erleben, Erkennen, Metaphysik. *Kantstudien* **31**, 146–158. 1926.

A. *Schmidt 2, Über deduktive Theorien mit mehreren Sorten von Grunddingen. *Math. Annalen* **115**, 485–506. 1938.

E. *Schmidt 1, Über Gewissheit in der Mathematik. Berlin, 1930. 14 pp.

A. *Schoenflies 1 = Schoenflies 1900–1907.

— 2, Über die logischen Paradoxien der Mengenlehre. *Jahresb. D.M.V.* **15**, 19–25. 1906. (Cf. *Math. Annalen* **60**, 181–186. 1905.)

— 5, Über eine vermeintliche Antinomie der Mengenlehre. *Acta Math.* **32**, 177–184. 1909.

— 6, Über die Stellung der Definition in der Axiomatik. *Jahresb. D.M.V.* **20**, 222–255. 1911.

— 7, Zur Grundlegung der Mengenlehre. *Math. Annalen* **72**, 551–561. 1912.

— 8 = Schoenflies 1913.

— 10, Bemerkung zur Axiomatik der Grössen und Mengen. *Math. Annalen* **85**, 60–64. 1922.

H. *Scholz 2, (Review of Becker 2) *Deutsche Literaturzeitung* **49**, 679–690. 1928.

— 3, Warum haben die Griechen die Irrationalzahlen nicht aufgebaut? *Kantstudien* **33**, 35–72. 1928. (Cf. Hasse–Scholz 1; B. L. van der Waerden: *Math. Annalen* **120**, 127–153, 676–700, 1949.)

— 12, Der Gottesgedanke in der Mathematik. *Blätter f. Deutsche Philosophie* **8**, 318–338. 1934.

M *Schönfinkel 1, Über die Bausteine der mathematischen Logik. *Math. Annalen* **92**, 305–316. 1924.

G. *Scorza Dragoni 1, Sul principio di approssimazione nella teoria degli insiemi e sulla quasi continuità delle funzioni misurabili. *Rendic. Semin. Mat. Roma* (4) 1, 53–58. 1936.

V. *von Seckendorff 1, Beweis des Induktionsschlusses der natürlichen Zahlen aus der Dedekindschen Definition endlicher Mengen. *Sitz. der Berliner Math. Gesellschaft* 36, 16–24. 1937.

I. *Segelberg 1, Bemerkungen zu einigen logischen Paradoxien. *Theoria* 9, 157–162. 1943.

H. M. *Sheffer 1, A set of five independent postulates for Boolean algebras, with application to logical constants. *Tr. A.M.S.* 14, 481–488. 1913. (Cf. *Am. Math. Monthly* 27, p. 310 footnote. 1920.)

— 2, Mutually prime postulates. (Abstract) *Bull. A.M.S.* 22, 287. 1916.

W. H. *Sheldon 1, Science, philosophy and certainty. *Philos. Review* 39, 243–257. 1930.

W. *Sierpiński 4 = Sierpiński 1922.

— 7 = Sierpiński 1928a.

— 13, Sur un théorème de recouvrement dans la théorie générale des ensembles. *F.M.* 20, 214–220. 1933.

— 15, Un exemple effectif d'un ensemble dénombrable de nombres réels qui n'est pas effectivement énumérable. *Ibid.* 21, 46–47. 1933.

— 17, Sur les ensembles partout de deuxième catégorie. *Ibid.* 22, 1–3. 1934.

— 26, Sur une proposition équivalente à l'axiome du choix. *Actas de la Acad. Nac. de Ci. exactas etc. de Lima* 11, 111–112. 1946. (Cf. *Rendic. Lincei* (8) 3, 216–217. 1947.)

— 29 = Sierpiński 1946–47a.

T. *Skolem 1 = Skolem 1919.

— 5, Ein Verfahren zu beliebig angenäherter Bestimmung einer Wurzel einer beliebigen algebraischen Gleichung. *Norsk Mat. Forenings Skrifter* (1) 15, 1924. 14 pp.

— 9, Über die Grundlagendiskussionen in der Mathematik. *C.R. du 7me Congrès des Mathématiciens Scandin., Oslo 1929*, pp. 3–21. 1930.

— 10, Über einige Satzfunktionen in der Arithmetik. *Skr. Norske Vid.-Akad. i Oslo*, I, 1930, No. 7, 1–28. 1931.

— 15, Ein Satz über Zählausdrücke. *Acta Szeged* 7, 193–199. 1935.

H. B. *Smith 2, On the construction of a non-Aristotelian logic. *The Monist* 28, 465–471. 1918. (Cf. *J. of Philos. etc.* 15, 453–458, 1918; 16, 379–383, 522–523, 1919; 21, 631–633. 1924; *Am. J. of Psychol.* 29, 431–434, 1918; *The Monist* 31, 304–309, 1921.)

— 3, Non-Aristotelian logic. Philadelphia, 1919. 40 pp.

— 7, The theory of multiple implication and its application to the generalized problem of Epimenides. *Bull. A.M.S.* 35, 60–66. 1929. (Cf. *J. of Philos.* 26, 182–185, and 28, 296–297, 1929/31; P. Henle: *Philos. of Sc.* 2, 111–113, and H. B. Smith, *ibid.*, 113–114, 1935.)

M. *Souslin 1, Sur un corps dénombrable de nombres réels. (Rédigé... par C. Kuratowski.) *F.M.* 4, 311–315. 1923.

H. *Stadie 1, (Review of Kaufmann 1930) *Göttinger Gelehrte Anzeigen* 193, 376–388. 1931.

J. *Stenzel 1, Zahl und Gestalt bei Platon und Aristoteles. 2nd ed. Leipzig & Berlin, 1933. 188 pp.

M. H. *Stone 4, The theory of representations for Boolean algebras. *Tr. A.M.S.* 40, 37–111. 1936. (Cf. *F.M.* 29, 223–303, 1937; N. H. McCoy and D. Montgomery: *Duke Math. J.* 3, 455–459, 1937; H. Cartan: *C.R. Paris* 205, 595–598, 1937.)

— 8, The representation of Boolean algebras. *Bull. A.M.S.* 44, 807–816. 1938.

M. Strauss **1**, Zur Begründung der statistischen Transformationstheorie der Quanten-
physik. *Sitz. Berlin* 1936, 382–398.

E. *Study **3**, Die angeblichen Antinomien der Mengenlehre. *Sitz. Berlin* 1929, 255–267.

R. *Tambs Lyche **1**, Sur l'équation fonctionelle d'Abel. *F.M.* **5**, 331–333. 1924. (Cf.
Rendic. Palermo **51**, 262, 1927.)

A. *Tarski **3** = Tarski 1924.
— **5** = Tarski 1925b.
— **6** = Tarski 1925a.
— **7**, Remarque concernant l'arithmétique des nombres cardinaux. (Abstract)
Ann. de la Soc. Pol. de Math. **5**, 101. 1927. (Cf. *C.R. Varsovie* **19**, 307, 1926;
W. Sierpiński: *F.M.* **34**, 113–118, 119–126, 1946.)
— **29**, Eine äquivalente Formulierung des Auswahlaxioms. *F.M.* **30**, 197–201. 1938.
— **32** = Tarski 1939.

A. E. *Taylor **1**, Forms and numbers: a study in Platonic metaphysics. *Mind*, N.S. **35**,
419–440; **36**, 12–33. 1926–27.

Tseng *Ting-Ho **1**, La philosophie mathématique et la théorie des ensembles. Thesis
Paris. 1938. 166 pp.

O. *Toeplitz **1**, Der Algebraiker Hilbert. *Naturwissenschaften* **10**, 73–77. 1922.
— **2**, Das Verhältnis von Mathematik und Ideenlehre bei Platon. *Quellen und
Studien zur Geschichte der Math.*, B **1**, 3–33. 1929.

E. *Toms **1**, The law of excluded middle. *Philos. of Sc.* **8**, 33–38. 1941.

L. *Tonelli **1**, Fondamenti di calcolo delle variazioni. **2** vols. Bologna, 1922/23. 466 +
661 pp.

F. I. *Toranzos **1**, Introducción a la epistemologia y fundamentación de la matemática.
Preface and appendix by J. Rey Pastor. Buenos Aires & Mexico City, 1943. 238 pp.

T. *Tsao-Chen **3**, Algebraic postulates and a geometric interpretation for the Lewis
calculus of strict implication. *Bull. A.M.S.* **44**, 737–744. 1938.

J. W. *Tukey **1** = Tukey 1940.

S. *Ulam **2**, Zur Masstheorie in der allgemeinen Mengenlehre. *F.M.* **16**, 140–150. 1930.
— **3**, Über gewisse Zerlegungen von Mengen. *Ibid.* **20**, 221–223. 1933. (Cf. W.
Sierpiński: *ibid.* **23**, 125–134, 1934.)

B. *Urbach **1**, Über das Wesen der logischen Paradoxa. *Z. f. Philos. und philos. Kritik*
140, 81–108. 1910. (Cf. *Annalen der Philos. u. phil. Kritik* **6**, 161–176, 265–273, 1928.)

A. *Ushenko **9**, Undecidable statements and metalanguage. *Philos. Review* **53**, 258–
262. 1944.
— **14**, Power and events. An essay on dynamics in philosophy. Princeton, 1946.
301 pp.

M. *Uta **1**, La crise de la théorie du savoir. Paris, 1928.

N. A. *Vasiliev **1**, Imaginary (non-Aristotelian) logic. *Atti del V Congr. Intern. di
Filos.*, *Napoli 1924*, pp. 107–109. 1925.

O. *Veblen **1**, A system of axioms for geometry. *Tr. A.M.S.* **5**, 343–384. 1904. (Cf.
also in J. W. A. Young, Monographs on topics of modern mathematics, pp. 1–51,
New York, 1911.)

H. *Vieler **1**, Untersuchungen über Unabhängigkeit und Tragweite der Axiome der
Mengenlehre in der Axiomatik Zermelos und Fraenkels. Thesis Marburg (Lahn).
1926. 40 pp.

T. *Viola **1**, Riflessioni intorno ad alcune applicazioni del postulato della scelta di
E. Zermelo e del principio di approssimazione di B. Levi nella teoria degli aggregati. *Boll. dell'Unione Mat. Ital.* **10**, 287–294. 1931.

— **2,** Sul principio di approssimazione di B. Levi nella teoria della misura degli aggregati e in quella dell'integrale di Lebesgue. *Ibid.* **11,** 74–78. 1932. (Cf. B. Levi and T. Viola: *Ibid.* **12,** 197–203, 1933.)

— **3,** Ricerche assiomatiche sulle teorie delle funzioni d'insieme e dell'integrale di Lebesgue. *Fund. Math.* **23,** 75–101. 1934.

D. H. T. *Vollenhoven **1,** De wijsbegeerte der wiskunde van theïstisch standpunt. Thesis Amsterdam. 1918.

— **2,** De noodzakelijkheid eener christelijke logica. Amsterdam, 1932.

P. G. J. *Vredenduin **1,** Axiomatische opbouw der verzamelingenleer, in het bijzonder der getallentheorie. Thesis Utrecht, s.a. (1931). 42 pp.

— **4,** De paradoxen. *Alg. Nederl. Tijdschr. v. Wijsbeg. en Psychol.* **31,** 191–200. 1938.

B. L. *van der Waerden **2** = van der Waerden 1950.

F. *Warrain **3,** Examen philosophique du transfini. Paris, 1935. 142 pp.

R. Wavre **2,** Logique formelle et logique empiriste. *R.M.M.* **33,** 65–75. 1926.

— **3,** Sur le principe du tiers exclu. *Ibid.,* 425–430.

— **4,** Sur les propositions indémontrables. *L'Ens. Math.* **27,** 321–323. 1928.

— **5,** Mathématique et philosophie. *Archives de la Soc. Belge de Philos.* **5,** No. 1, 1–16. 1933.

J. R. *Weinberg **2,** The possible solution of the heterological paradox. *Philos. Review* **46,** 657–659. 1937. (Cf. A. Church: *J.S.L.* **3,** 46, 1938.)

H. *Weyl **8,** Consistency in mathematics. *The Rice Institute Pamphlet* **16,** 245–265. 1929.

— **9** = Weyl 1931.

— **10,** Topologie und abstrakte Algebra als zwei Wege mathematischen Verständnisses. *Unterrichtsblätter f. Math. und Naturwiss.* **38,** 177–188. 1932.

— **11** = Weyl 1932.

— **12,** The mathematical way of thinking. *Science* **92,** 437–446. 1940. (Also in: *Studies in the History of Science* [Philadelphia, 1941].)

A. N. *Whitehead **5,** Indication, classes, numbers, validation. *Mind,* N.S. **43,** 281–297, 543. 1934.

T. *Whittaker **1,** The new algebras and their significance for physics and philosophy. *The London, Edinburgh & Dublin Philos. Magazine and J. of Sc.* (7) **35,** 1–15. 1944. (Also in *Yearbook of the R. Soc. of Edinburgh,* 1944, pp. 5–14.)

N. *Wiener **1,** A simplification of the logic of relations. *Proc. of the Cambridge Philos. Soc.* **17,** 387–390. 1914. (Cf. *ibid.,* 441–449; **18,** 14–28, 1916.)

R. L. *Wilder **1,** The nature of mathematical proof. *Am. Math. Monthly* **51,** 309–323. 1944.

M. *Winants **1,** À propos d'un catalogue paradoxal. *L'Ens. Math.* **31,** 268. 1933. (Cf. F. Gonseth: *Ibid.,* 269–271.)

J. *Wolff **1,** Over het subjectieve in de wiskunde. *Jaarboek der Rijksuniv. te Utrecht,* 1922–23, pp. 3–22.

Dorothy M. *Wrinch **5,** On mediate cardinals. *Am. J. of Math.* **45,** 87–92. 1923.

S. *Zaremba **2,** La logique des mathématiques. (*Mémorial des Sc. Math.* **15.**) Paris, 1926. 52 pp.

Z. (S.) *Zawirski **1,** Les logiques nouvelles et le champ de leur application. *R.M.M.* **39,** 503–519. 1932. (Cf. *Act. Sc. Ind.* **535,** 82–87, 1937.)

E. *Zermelo **4** = Zermelo 1909.

— **6,** Über ganze transzendente Zahlen. *Math. Annalen* **75,** 434–442. 1914. (Cf. E. Noether **1.**)

— **10,** Grundlagen einer allgemeinen Theorie der mathematischen Satzsysteme. I. *F.M.* **25,** 136–146. 1935.

M. *Zorn **2** = Zorn 1944.

INDEX OF AUTHORS

(Numbers refer to pages)

Ackermann, W. (c. 1900–1963) 205
Alexandroff, P. 104
Alexandroff, P. S. 153
Altwegg, M. 131
Archimedes (287–212 B.C.) 122 f., 156
Aristotle (384–322 B. C.) 2, 10, 61, 159
Aronszain, N. 143
Artin, E. (1898–1963) 123
Aubert, K. E. 33

Bachmann, F. 62
Bachmann, H. 11, 188, 205, 208, 212, 214, 229
Baer, R. 62, 121, 123, 229
Bagemihl, F. 229, 235
Baire, R. (1874–1932) 2, 11, 183
Banach, S. (1892–1945) 76, 77
Banaschewski, B. 224
Bar-Hillel, Y. 10, 237
Bays, S. 81
Bell, E. T. (1883–1960) 179
Bendixson, I. (1861–1935) 2
Bennett, A. A. 179
Bentley, A. F. 55
Berkeley, E. C. 107
Bernays, P. 180, 224
Bernoulli, John (1667–1748) 121
Bernstein, F. (1878–1956) 77, 98, 147, 229, 238
Beth, E. W. (1908–1964) 11, 173, 180
Birkhoff, Garrett 107, 128, 131f., 151, 179
Birkhoff, G. D. (1884–1944) 238
Blumberg, H. (1886–c. 1950) 131, 179
Bocheński, I. M. 2
Bodewig, E. 2
Boehm, C. (1873–1958) 38
du Bois-Reymond, P. (1831–1889) 123, 237
Bolzano, B. (1781–1848) 2, 29, 30, 80, 104, 164, 236 f.
Boole, G. (1815–1864) 107
Borel, É. (1871–1956) 2, 72, 75, 77, 238
Bouligand, G. 238

Bourbaki, N. (*pseudonym*) 11, 239
Bridgman, P. W. 55
Broderick, T. S. 107
Brouwer, L. E. J. 104
Bruns, G. 76, 229
Burali-Forti, C. (1861–1931) 202

Cantor, G. (1845–1918) *passim*
Carathéodory, C. (1873–1950) 238
Carmichael, P. A. 17
Carnap, R. 59, 129
Carruth, P. W. 214
Cassirer, E. (1874–1945) 61, 127
Cauchy, A.-L. (1789–1857) 37, 101, 146, 164
Cavaillès, J. (1903–1944) 2, 193
Chajoth, Z. (1896–1955) 154, 234
Church, A. VI, 180, 216
Cipolla, M. 17
Cohen, H. (1842–1918) 121
Cohen, Paul, J. VI, 229
Cohn, J. (1869–c. 1935) 2
Courant, R. 156
Couturat, L. (1868–1914) 2
Crescas, Chasdai (c. 1340–1412) 2
Cuesta, D. N. 11, 147, 156, 174

Dantzig, T. (1884–1956) 24
Davis, A. C. 163
Day, M. M. 128
Dedekind, R. (1831–1916) 1, 10, 29, 70, 72, 77, 103, 132, 156 f., 165 f., 180, 193 f., 230, 239
Denjoy, A. 166, 187, 216
Descartes, R. (1596–1650) 2, 58, 193
Devidé, V. 173
Dubislav, W. (1895–1937) 80
Dubreil, P. & M.-L. 61
Duren, W. L. Jr. 179
Dushnik, B. 135, 190

Eneström, G. (1852–1923) 80
Erdös, P. 166, 174, 188
Ésénin-Vol'pin, A. S. 166

Euclid (c. 300 B. C.) 55, 122, 159, 179, 211
Eudoxos (c. 410–c. 356 B.C.) 122, 156
Euwe, M. 239
Eyraud, H. 147

Faber, G. (1877–c. 1950) 38
Felscher, W. 180
Fermat, P. de (1601–1665) 15, 206
Foradori, E. 157
Fraenkel, A. A. 1, 10, 55, 224, 231
Fraïssé, R. 33, 90, 140, 160
Franklin, P. (1899–1965) 163
Frege, G. (1848–1925) 14, 61 f., 193
Freudenthal, H. 179

Galileo, G. (1564–1642) 29
Gauss, C. F. (1777–1855) 1, 2, 122
Gelfond, A. 57
Gersonides (Levi ben Gershon) (1288–1344) 179
Gillman, L. 174
Ginsburg, S. 140, 174, 195, 210
Gleyzal, A. 153
Gödel, K. 229 f.
Godfrey, E. W. 38
Goldbach, C. (1690–1764) 206
Goodstein, R. L. 191
Graves, L. M. 157
Grelling, K. (1886–c. 1941) 194
Grünbaum, A. 7
Gutberlet, C. (1837–1928) 2

Haalmeijer, B. P. 11
Haar, A. (1885–1933) 168
Habermann, E. 238
Haenzel, G. (1898–1944) 207
Hahn, H. (1879–1934) 104, 123, 238
Halmos, P. R. 11
Hanani, H. 38
Hankel, H. (1839–1873) 80, 237
Hardy, G. H. (1877–1947) 123, 237
Harnack, A. (1851–1888) 237
Hartogs, F. (1874–1943) 228
Hasse, H. 7
Hausdorff, F. (1868–1942) 11, 61, 84, 120, 131, 147, 153, 168 f., 180, 183, 192, 204 f., 208, 211, 219, 228, 230, 235
Heine, E. (1821–1881) 237
Hermes, H. 81, 132
Hermite, C. (1822–1901) 1

Hessenberg, G. (1874–1925) 2, 70, 81, 132, 183, 190, 204, 214, 219, 230
Hilbert, D. (1862–1943) 104, 122, 156, 180, 229, 239 f.
Hölder, O. (1859–1937) 117
Hudekoff, N. 131
Hume, D. (1711–1776) 58
Huntington, E. V. (1874–1952) 166
Hurewicz, W. (1904–1956) 104
Hurwitz, A. (1859–1919) 2

Isenkrahe, K. 2
Itô, M. 33

Jacobsthal, E. 188, 205, 214
Jašek, M. 237
Johnston, L. S. 38
Jourdain, P. E. B. (1879–1919) 2, 98, 120, 222, 237
Kalmár, L. 180, 239
Kaluza, T. (1885–1954) 121
Kaluza, T. Jr. 212
Kamiya, H. 104
Kamke, E. (1890–1961) 11
Kapuano, I. 229
Kasner, E. (1878–1955) 123
Keene, G. B. 11
Keyser, C. J. (1862–1947) 2, 29
Khintchine, A. 179
Klaua, D. 11
Kleene, S. C. 19, 70, 180, 216
Klein, F. (1849–1925) 2
Kolmogoroff, A. 238
König, Dénes (1884–?) 77, 168, 239
König, Julius (1849–1913) 77, 79, 98, 116, 119, 221, 223
Koopman, B. O. 107
Korselt, A. (1864–?) 77
Kreisel, G. 55
Kronecker, L. (1823–1891) 1, 2, 81, 103
Kummer, E. E. (1810–1893) 6
Kuratowski, C. 11, 77, 104, 108, 132, 155, 166, 172, 204
Kurepa, G. 77, 118, 131, 153 f., 166, 192, 216, 221
Kurosch, A. 131

Landau, E. (1877–1938) 180
Langford, C. H. 156
Lasswitz, K. (1848–1910) 61
Laugwitz, D. 125
Lebesgue, H. (1875–1941) 192, 238

Leibniz, G. W. (1646–1716) 13, 61, 103, 121
Levi, Beppo (1875–c. 1950) 224
Levi-Civita, T. (1873–1941) 122
Lévy, Azriel 28
Lewis, C. I. 156
Lichtenstein, L. (1878–1933) 61
Lindenbaum, A. (1904–1941) 77, 98, 131, 153 f., 199, 219
Liouville, J. (1809–1882) 57
Lorenzen, P. 180
Löwenheim, L. (1878–c. 1940) 191
Lucretius, Titus L. C. (98–55 B.C.) 2
Lüroth, L. (1844–1910) 103
Lusin, N. 121, 229
Luxemburg, W. A. J. 125

MacLane, S. 107
MacNeille, H. N. 131
Mahlo, P. (b. 1883) 153
Maximoff, J. 156
Mendelson, E. 174
Menger, K. 104, 238
Méray, H. C. (1835–1911) 157
Meyerson, É. (1859–1933) 61
Miller, E. W. 135, 190
Mittag-Leffler, G. (1846–1927) 1, 2
Montague, R. 204
de Morgan, A. (1806–1878) 106 f.
Morris, C. W. 7
Mostowski, A. 11, 107, 204

Nagel, E. 61
Natorp, P. (1854–1924) 121
von Neumann, J. (1903–1957) 32, 62 f., 107, 127, 180, 199, 201, 238
Neumer, W. 205, 216, 229
Newton, I. (1642–1727) 123
Nicod, J. G. P. (1893–1924) 62

Obreanu, F. 120
Occam, W. (c. 1280–1347) 12, 106
Oglobin, N. 38

Ohkuma, T. 173
Olmsted, J. M. H. 96
Ore, O. 61
Otchan, G. 77

Padoa, A. (1868–1937) 33
Pascal, B. (1623–1662) 179
Pasch, M. (1858–1932) 14, 33, 77, 104, 173, 180

Peirce, C. S. (1839–1914) 29, 121, 132, 193
Perron, O. 157, 179
Piccard, S. 124
Plato (c. 429–c. 348 B. C.) 159
Plessner, A. 183
Poincaré, H. (1854–1913) 1, 2, 52
Popruzenko, J. 229

Quine, W. V. O. 11, 70, 131, 199

Rabin, M. 118
Rado, R. 166, 174, 188
Reichbach, M. 77
Riemann, B. (1826–1866) 120, 238
Riesz, F. (1880–1956) 131
Robbins, H. 156
Robinson, A. 33, 79, 125
Rolle, M. (1652–1917) 122
Rosenfeld, L. 77
Rosenthal, A. (1887–1959) 238
Rosser, J. B. 16, 180
Russell, B. 2, 7, 12, 17, 24, 28, 61 f., 71, 90 f., 127 f., 164, 193, 202, 224
Rust, W. M. Jr. 55

Scheeffer, L. (1859–1885) 2
Schlick, M. (1882–1936) 61
Schmidt, Erhard (1876–1959) 224
Schmidt, F. K. 118
Schmidt, Jürgen 76, 132, 151, 176, 179 f., 229 f.
Schneider, T. 57
Schoenflies, A. (1853–1928) 1, 2, 11, 72, 80, 120, 180, 238
Schogt, J. H. 11
Scholz, H. (1884–1956) 7, 33, 62, 237
Schreier, O. (1901–1929) 123
Schröder, E. (1841–1902) 77, 127
Schrödinger, E. 107
Schumacher, H. C. (1780–1850) 1
Schütte, K. 205
Schwarz, G. 131
Schwarz, H. 131
Schweitzer, H. 33, 62
Shannon, C. E. 107
Shepherdson, J. C. 174
Shiraishi, S. 7
Sieczka, F. 112
Siegel, C. L. 57
Sierpiński, W. 11, 75, 77, 104 f., 108, 115, 140, 147, 163, 174, 188, 204, 206, 208, 210, 212, 228 f., 234

Sikorski, R. 76, 214
Skolem, T. (1887–1962) 11, 156, 160, 208
Słupecki, J. 174
Smart, H. R. 62
Smith, H. J. S. (1826–1883) 171, 237
Souslin (Suslin), M. (1894–1919) 166
Specker, E. 15
Spector, C. 216
Spinoza, B. (1632–1677) 2
Stäckel, P. (1862–1919) 2, 103, 237
Stebbing, L. S. (1885–1943) 12
Steckel, S. 192
Stein, S. K. 199
Steiner, J. (1796–1863) 234
Steinitz, E. (1871–1928) 239
Stöhr, A. 131
Stone, M. H. 107, 124
Sudan, G. 205, 208
Suppes, P. 11
Szpilrain, E. 155
Szymański, P. 120

Tarski, A. 28, 77, 97 f., 107 f., 115, 125,
    132, 135, 140, 153 f., 156, 193 f., 199,
    219, 224, 228, 230, 235
Ternus, J. 1, 2
Theodoros (c. 400 B.C.) 159
Thomas, I. 29
Tsuchikura, T. 229
Tukey, J. W. 179

Ulam, S. 77

Vaihinger, H. (1852–1933) 12
de la Vallée Poussin, C. (1866–1962) 113
Vandiver, H. S. 36

Vaught, R. L. 160
Vehlen, O. (1880–1960) 166, 205, 216
Veress, P. 236
Veronese, G. (1854–1917) 122
Vitali, G. (1875–1932) 238
Voltaire, F. M. (1694–1778) 123
Volterra, V. (1860–1940) 237
de Vries, H. 229

van der Waerden, B. L. 239
Wallman, H. 104
Wang, H. 180, 194
Webber, W. J. 166
Weierstrass, K. (1819–1897) 1, 103, 157,
    164
Weiss, P. 7
Wernick, G. 107
Weyl, H. (1885–1955) 2, 27, 59, 61, 121
Whitehead, A. N. (1861–1947) 62, 128,
    240
Whitney, H. 124
Whittacker, J. M. 77
Wiener, N. (1895–1964) 122
Wolfson, H. 2
Wrinch, D. M. 153, 204

Young, G. C. 2, 183
Young, W. H. (1863–1942) 2, 183

Zakon, E. 188, 211 f.
Zenon (c. 450 B.C.) 7
Zermelo, E. (1871–1953) 1, 17, 32, 63,
    70, 77, 90 f., 98, 113, 190, 194, 223 f.,
    230, 239
Zorn, M. 179, 219, 228, 230

INDEX OF TERMS

(Numbers refer to pages)

Abstraction, principle of — 62
accumulation point 169
addition, see union, sum
aggregate, see set
aleph 60, 215–218
algebra of logic 108
algebraic number 8, 39–42
antinomies 71, 98, 202, 218
Archimedean axiom 122
associative 21, 79
asymmetrical 14, 129
axiom of choice 44/5, 82, 90, 224
— — extensionality 14
— — infinity 32
— — pairing 18
— — power-set 72
— — subsets 16
— — substitution (replacement) 199
— — sum-set 20

Base 110
between 133
biunique 23, 24
Boolean algebra 107–108

Cantor's theorem 70
cardinal (number) 59–63, 139, 218
Cartesian, see product
chain 232
characteristic function 113, 124
class 11
closed interval 158
closed set 170, 234
commutative 21, 79
comparability of sets or cardinals 68,
     78, 216, 227/8
— — well-ordered sets or ordinals
     183, 200
complex 89
condensation point 169
condition on — 16
confinal 133
conjunction 18
connexity 68, 129

consecutive 133
contains 12
continuous (cut, set) 157
— (function) 119, 206
continuum 49/50, 56, 61, 164–166
continuum problem, hypothesis 69,
     228–230
— —, generalized 113, 229
correspondence 23, 24, 134
countable, see denumerable
cut 157

Decimal (terminating, infinite) 51
definite 16
dense 156
dense-in-itself 169
denumerable 33, 139
denumerably many 34
derivation, derived set 169
determined by — (section) 134
diagonal method of Cantor 54
— — of Cauchy 37
difference of ordinals 209
— of sets 22
different 13, 60, 130
dimension 103ff.
discontinuum of Cantor 171
disjoint 14
—, almost 14, 125
disjointed 14
disjunction 18
distributive 22, 79
division, divisible (of ordinals) 210–212
duality 106

Effectively (equivalent, denumerable)
     75
element, see member
empty 17
ends 133
enumerated 33
epsilon number 208
equality of sets 13–15
— of cardinals 60

equality of ordered sets 130
— of order-types 138
equipollent 24
equivalence theorem 73
equivalent 24, 27, 135
exponent 110
exponentiation, see power

Factor 87
finite number (cardinal, type, ordinal) 60, 139, 193
finite set 28–32, 192–194
first 133
fixed point 140
formal laws 21, 79, 113, 206
Foundations 10
function 23, 63, 112

Gap 157
greater than 67, 196

Image 25
implies 14
impossibility proof 55
included 13
indirect proof 29, 191/2
induction, mathematical 28, 179, 183
—, transfinite 179–183
inductive (set, number) 28, 193
inequalities 97ff., 208/9
infinite 6, 28–32, 121
infinitesimals 120–123
initial (set) 133
initial number (regular, singular) 216, 218/9
insertion-set 112
intersection 19, 20, 105
interval 157/8
irreflexive 14, 129
isolated (ordinal) 197
— (point) 169

Jump 157

Kind (first, second) of ordinals 197

Last 133
lattice (point) 37, 132
less than 66, 78, 195
(anti-)lexicographic order 151
limit-number 197, 201
line of numbers 8, 155/6

linear 155ff.

Mapping (one-to-one) onto-, into- 24, 67
—, homeomorphic 108
—, identical 25
—, similar 134
member 12
membership relation 12
monotone (set) 174, 231
multiplication, see product
multiplicative principle (axiom), see axiom of choice

Natural number (= positive integer) 5
neighbor 133
neighborhood 169
non-Archimedean magnitudes 122f.
normal form of ordinals 212
normal function 205
nowhere-dense 171
null-set 17
number-class 216

One-to-one 23, 24
open interval 157
open set 133
order of cardinals 66
— of ordinals 195
order-relation 129, 132
order-type 138
ordinal (number) 187, 198/9
—, prime 212
—, rational 211

Pair 18
—, ordered 130
perfect 170
permanence, principle of 80
power (= cardinal) of a set 60, 68, 222, 238
— of the continuum 60, 222
power of cardinals 110, 112
— of order-types 152–153
— of ordinals 203–204
power-set 70, 112
precedes, predecessor 129, 133
predicate 16, 25
principle of —, see axiom
product, Cartesian 87, 89
product of cardinals 92
— of ordered sets 152

product of order-types 149–154
— of ordinals 188, 203, 204
property 25

Rational (reduced) number, point 36,
    39, 160
real number 7, 155/6
recursive (rule, property) 181
reflexive relation 13, 25, 33
— set (cardinal) 29, 193
relation (dyadic, etc.) 12, 25, 33
relation-type 140
remainder (set) 133
— (ordinal) 210
representative 83

Section 134
sequence 19, 34
sequent 133
series of alephs 218
— of ordinals 207
set (finite, infinite) 9, 11, 12, 13, 28–32,
    127, 192–194
—, abstract 12
— of points 12, 155ff.
—, ordered 129/130
—, partly ordered 131
—, doubly (n-tuply) ordered 131
—, well-ordered 175–178

similar 134
single-valued 23
subset 13, 16, 129
—, proper 13
substitutivity 67, 129
subtraction, see difference
succeeds, successor 129, 133
sum, natural 214/5
—, ordered 141, 144
— of cardinals 82–83
— of order-types 141, 144
sum-set, see union
symmetrical 13, 25

Transcendental number 9
transfinite cardinal 60
— order-type 138
— ordinal 187
— rational 96
transitive 13, 26, 129
type, see order-type

Union 19, 20, 27, 81
unique 23
unit-set 18
universal set 106

Well-ordering theorem 222

SYMBOLS

C	70	{ }	15	
f	64	( )	19, 126, 157	
O	17	$\langle\,\rangle$	104, 158	
P	89	$\cup, \mathsf{U}$	19, 20, 81	
T (c)	140	$\cap, \mathsf{\cap}$	19, 20, 105	
V	106	$\subset, \subseteq$	13	
W (a)	197	$<, >$	66, 67, 195/6	
Z (c)	216	$\leqslant, \geqslant$	67	
$\epsilon, \notin$	12	$\prec, \succ$	129	
$\varepsilon_0, \varepsilon$	208	$\sim$	24	
η	160	$\simeq$	134	
λ	165	$+$	82, 83, 141	
$\prod$	89, 92	$-$	22, 197, 209	
$\sum$	83, 144	$\times$	87, 89	
ω	139	$=, \neq$	13	
ω_α	216	$\overline{S}$	138	
$\mathfrak{S}$	215	$\overline{\overline{S}}$	60	
lim	197	$(S\,|\,T)$	112	
$\aleph$	60, 61, 215	$\overline{\sigma}$	139	
$\aleph_0$	60, 61	$^*\sigma$	139	
$\aleph_n, \aleph_\alpha$	60, 218